Lives of

BOULTON
& WATT

James Watt, F.R.S.
Engraved by W. Holt, after the portrait by Sir W. Beechy, R.A.

Lives of
BOULTON
& WATT

SAMUEL SMILES

NONSUCH

First published 1865
This edition published 2007

Copyright © in this edition Nonsuch Publishing, 2007

Nonsuch Publishing Limited
Cirencester Road, Chalford, Stroud, Gloucestershire, GL6 8PE, UK
www.nonsuch-publishing.com

Nonsuch Publishing is an imprint of NPI Media Group

British Library Cataloguing in Publication Data
A catalogue record for this book is available from the British Library

ISBN 978-1-84588-371-3

Typesetting and origination by NPI Media Group
Printed and bound in Great Britain by Oaklands Book Services

Contents

Introduction to the Modern Edition

The steam engine may well be one of the most significant technological advances since Johannes Gutenberg invented moveable-type printing in the mid-fifteenth century. Without the steam engine the Industrial Revolution would never have happened; the 'first world' countries would still be agricultural economies in which the majority of the population were peasants who had never travelled much further than the next village. It enabled rapid and fundamental changes to take place in mining, manufacturing and shipping, as well as, of course, being essential to the development of the railway as a practical mode of travel. Essentially a large kettle connected to a piston, even nuclear power is effectively generated on the same principles as the basic steam engine.

The idea of steam as a motive force is almost two thousand years old, its invention having been ascribed to Hero of Alexandria, whose *aeolipile* ('ball of Aeolus,' the Greek god of wind) used a vessel of boiling water to generate steam, which passed into an air-tight (spherical or cylindrical) chamber and out through pipes, exploiting Newton's Third Law of Motion (to every action there is an equal and opposite reaction) to cause the sphere/cylinder to revolve in the direction opposite to that of the steam's exit. Although people did try to harness the power of steam in the interim, it was not until more than a millennium and a half later that the next significant development occurred, when Denis Papin, assisted by Gottfried Leibnitz, created the 'steam digester,' the forerunner of the pressure cooker. Watching the steam-release (safety) valve move up and down gave Papin the idea for utilising a piston and cylinder propelled by steam, and it was from his designs that Thomas Savery built the first functioning 'fire engine,' as it was then called, in 1698.

It was the ironmonger and Baptist lay preacher Thomas Newcomen, however, who developed Savery's 'fire engine' into a steam engine that could be used for practical purposes. Newcomen, a resident of Dartmouth in Devon, was aware that flooding was a major problem for the nearby tin mines of Cornwall, and so he devised an 'atmospheric' steam engine to pump the water out. Newcomen's engine used steam to lower the air pressure in the cylinder, so that atmospheric pressure would force the piston down; the piston was attached to one end of a beam, with the pumping gear being attached to the other; when the piston reached the bottom of its stroke, the weight of the pump would cause it to return to the top and the cycle would begin again. While Newcomen's engine was the first to do useful work, and was successful in its objective of pumping out tin mines, it was very expensive to operate because of its inefficient consumption of coal: the steam was created by injecting cold water into a heated cylinder, which therefore had to be reheated at the beginning of each stroke.

James Watt (1736–1819), a mathematical instrument-maker working at the University of Glasgow, hit on the idea of a separate condenser when he was repairing a Newcomen engine belonging to the university. He realised that by condensing the steam in a separate vessel, it would be possible to keep the cylinder heated with a much lower consumption of coal, thus making the engine more efficient and, potentially, more powerful and able to be used in more ways. He created a working model in 1765, but had great difficulties, especially of a financial nature, in patenting his design, constructing full-scale engines and persuading mine-owners to replace their inefficient but functional Newcomen engines with more efficient but essentially untried 'improved' versions.

His saviour, and that of his new steam engine, was Matthew Boulton (1728–1809), a Birmingham manufacturer of metal buttons who was a good engineer as well as a good businessmen. Acquiring two-thirds of the patent right in Watt's design, the two men went into partnership in 1775 and began making the new engines at their foundry in Soho, near Birmingham. When fully developed, Watt's engine used about a quarter of the fuel of Newcomen's and was four times as powerful, but it took a great deal of effort and an extremely large amount of money to turn Boulton & Watt into a profitable concern. Once persuaded, however, all agreed that the engines produced by Boulton & Watt were much better than those of Newcomen's design. The payment they received for their engines was based on a percentage of the fuel saved over that of a Newcomen engine, and their patent granted them a monopoly on producing Watt's design until 1799.

The Cornish mine-owners, however, were very suspicious and tried hard to avoid paying them or to lower the amount they owed by claiming they would go out of business; other engineers tried to copy Watt's design despite the patent, saying that a machine of such great importance should be readily available to all. Boulton and Watt, however, remained determined that the patent should be maintained and enforced in order to recompense them for all that they had put into making the design work.

Having perfected the pumping engine, Boulton and Watt, ably assisted by William Murdoch, one of their most trusted employees and a skilled inventor and engineer in his own right, went on to apply the steam engine to producing rotary motion, enabling it to be employed to drive machinery; Richard Arkwright pioneered its use in his cotton mills and by 1824 Boulton & Watt had produced 1,124 steam engines. Although neither James Watt nor Matthew Boulton actually invented the steam engine, nor were they the first to make practical use of it (the credit for that must still go to Thomas Newcomen), they were the people responsible for actually turning it into the machine that would change the world. Watt was undoubtedly the mechanical genius, but without Boulton's business skills and financial support it would have remained a brilliant idea and nothing more. Thanks to their partnership, factories, ships and trains powered by steam became possible and because of those factories, ships and trains the modern world took shape. So much that is taken for granted today owes its existence to Matthew Boulton and James Watt.

Preface

The present volume concludes the author's 'Lives of the Engineers.' Its preparation was begun many years since. The favourable reception given to the 'Life of George Stephenson,' the principal improver and introducer of the locomotive engine, encouraged the author to follow it by a Life of James Watt, the principal inventor and introducer of the condensing engine. On making inquiries, however, he found that the subject had already been taken in hand by J. P. Muirhead, Esq., the literary executor of the late Mr. Watt, of Aston Hall, near Birmingham. As Mr. Muirhead was in all respects entitled to precedence, and was, moreover, in possession of the best sources of information, the author's contemplated Life of Watt was abandoned, and he satisfied himself with embodying the substance of the materials he had collected, in a review of Mr. Muirhead's work, which appeared in the 'Quarterly Review' for July, 1858.

Having recently, however, through the kindness of M. P. W. Boulton, Esq., of Tew Park, Oxon, been enabled to examine the extensive collection of documents brought from Soho, including the original correspondence between Watt and Small, between Watt and Boulton, and between the latter and his numerous intimate friends and business correspondents, it has appeared to the author that, notwithstanding the valuable publications of Mr. Muirhead, the story of the life of Watt is one that will well bear to be told again, in connexion with the life and labours of Matthew Boulton of Soho. The two men were so intimately related during the most important period of their lives, and their biographies so closely intermingle, that it is almost impossible to separate them. They are therefore treated conjointly in the present volume, under the title of 'Boulton and Watt,' the name of the old Soho firm which so long enjoyed a world-wide reputation. But though the name of Boulton takes priority in the title, that of Watt will be found in many respects the most prominent in the narrative.

The MS. papers which have been consulted for the purposes of the present volume are of an unusually complete and varied character. They consist of several thousand documents selected from the tons of business books and correspondence which had accumulated at Soho. The most important were selected and arranged by the late M. Robinson Boulton, Esq., who entertained the highest regard for his father's memory; and from the character of the collection, the author inclines to the opinion that it must have been made with a view to the preparation and publication of a Life of Matthew Boulton, – which has not, however, until now been undertaken. Thus, among sundry papers endorsed "M. Boulton – Biographical Memoirs," is found a MS. memoir in the handwriting of James Watt, entitled "Memorandum concerning Mr. Boulton, commencing with my first acquaintance with him," and another of a similar character, by Mr. James Keir – both written shortly after Mr. Boulton's death. Another collection, endorsed "Familiarum Epistolæ et Selectæ, 1755 to 1808," contains letters received from various distinguished personages in the course of Mr. Boulton's long and interesting career. The number of original documents is indeed so large, that, but for a rigid exclusion of non-essential matter, these Lives must have expanded into several volumes, instead of being compressed into one. But the author believes labour to be well bestowed in practising the art of condensation, and that the interest of biography gains much by judicious rejection. What Watt said to Murdock as to the production of a machine, holds equally true as to the production of a book, – "It is a great thing," said Watt, "to know what to do without."

Besides the memoirs of Boulton and Watt, which occupy the principal places in the following volume, it will also be found to contain memoirs of the other inventors who have at various times laboured at the invention and application of the steam-engine – of the Marquis of Worcester, Dionysius Papin, Thomas Savery, and Thomas Newcomen. The author has also been enabled to gather from the Boulton papers a memoir of William Murdock, which probably contains all that is likely to be collected respecting that excellent and most ingenious mechanic.

In addition to the essential assistance received from M. P. W. Boulton, Esq., in preparing the present book, without which it would not have been undertaken, the author desires to record his acknowledgments to J. W. Gibson Watt, Esq., for information relative to James Watt; to Charles Savery, Esq., Clifton, J.T. Savery, Esq., Modbury, Lieutenant-Colonel Yolland, R.E., and

Quartermaster Connolly, R.E., for various facts as to the family history and professional career of Thomas Savery, inventor of the "Fire Engine;" and to Thomas Pemberton, Esq., Heathfield; W.C. Aitkin, Esq., Coventry; George Williamson, Esq., Greenock; the late J. Myrdock, Esq., Handsworth; and the late Mr. William Buckle, of the Royal Mint, formerly of Soho, for various information as to the lives and labours of Boulton and Watt.

In his treatment of the subject, it will be observed that the author has endeavoured, as much as possible, to avoid introducing technical details relating to the steam-engine. Those who desire further information on such points, are referred to the works of Farey, Tedgold, Bourne, Scott Russell, Muirhead ('Mechanical Inventions of James Watt'), and other technical treatises on the subject, where they will find detailed particulars of the various inventions which are only incidentally referred to in the following pages.

London, October, 1865

Beginnings of the Steam-engine

The Early Inventors

Edward, second Marquis of
Worcester
(by T.D. Scott, after Vandyck)

Ancient Greek Æolipile

I

Dawnings of Steam Power – The Marquis of Worcester

When Matthew Boulton entered into partnership with James Watt, he gave up the ormolu of business in which he had been principally engaged. He had been accustomed to supply George III with articles of this manufacture, but ceased to wait upon the King for orders after embarking in his new enterprise. Some time after, he appeared at the Royal Levee and was at once recognized by the King. "Ha! Boulton," said he, "it is long since we have seen you at Court. Pray, what business are you now engaged in?" "I am engaged, your Majesty, in the production of a commodity which is the desire of kings." "And what is that? what is that?" asked the king. "POWER, your Majesty," replied Boulton, who proceeded to give a description of the great uses to which the steam-engine was capable of being applied.

If the theory of James Mill[1] be true, that government is founded on the desire which exists among men to secure and enjoy the products of labour, by whatsoever means produced, probably the answer of Boulton to George III was not far from correct. In the infancy of nations this desire manifested itself in the enforcement of labour by one class upon another, in the various forms of slavery and serfdom. To evade the more onerous and exhausting kinds of bodily toil, men were impelled to exercise their ingenuity in improving old tools and inventing new ones, – while, to increase production, they called the powers of nature to their aid. They tamed the horse, and made him their servant; they caught the winds as they blew, and the waters as they fell, and applied their powers to the driving of mills and machines of various kinds.

But there was a power greater by far than that of horses, wind, or water, – a power of which poets and philosophers had long dreamt, – capable of being applied alike to the turning of mills, the raising of water the rowing of ships, the driving of wheel-carriages, and the performance of labour in its severest forms. As early as the thirteenth century, Roger Bacon described this great new power in terms which, interpreted by the light of the present day, could only apply to the power of Steam. He anticipated that "chariots may be made so as to be moved with incalculable force, without any beast drawing them," and that "engines of navigation might be made without oarsmen, so that the greatest river and sea ships, with only one man to steer them, may sail swifter than if they were fully manned." But Bacon was a seer rather than an expounder, a philosophic poet rather than an inventor; and it was left to men of future times to find out the practical methods of applying the wonderful power which he had imagined and foretold.

The enormous power latent in water exposed to heat had long been known. Its discovery must have been almost contemporaneous with that of fire. The expansive force of steam would be obvious on setting the first partially-closed pipkin upon the fire. If closed, the lid would be blown off; and even if the vessel were of iron, it would soon burst with appalling force. Was it possible to render so furious and apparently unmanageable an agent docile and tractable? Even in modern times, the explosive force of steam could only be compared to that of gunpowder; and it is a curious fact, that both De Hautefeuille and Papin proposed to employ gunpowder in preference to steam in driving a piston in a cylinder, considering it to be the more manageable power of the two.

Although it appears from the writings of the Greek physician, Hero, who flourished at Alexandria more than a century before Christ, that steam was well known to the ancients, it was employed by them merely as a toy, or as a means of exciting the wonder of the credulous. In his treatise on Pneumatics, Hero gives descriptions of various methods of employing steam or heated air for the purpose of producing apparently magical effects; from which we infer that the agency of heat was employed by the heathen priests in the performance of their rites. By one of the devices which he describes, water was apparently changed into wine; by another, the temple doors were opened by fire placed on the sacrificial altar; while by a third, the sacrificial vessel was so contrived as to flow only when the money of the votary was cast into it. Another ingenious device consisted in the method employed to pour out libations.

Upon the altar-fire being kindled, the air in the interior became expanded and, pressing upon the surface of the liquid which it contained, forced it up a connecting-pipe, and so out of the sacrificial cup. The libation was made, and the people cried, "A miracle!" But Hero knew the trick, and explained the arrangement by which it was accomplished: it forms the subject of his eleventh theorem.

The most interesting of the other devices described by Hero is the whirling Æolipile, or ball of Æolus, which, though but a toy, possessed the properties of a true steam-engine, and was most probably the first ever invented. As Hero's book professes to be, for the most part, but a collection of the devices handed down by former writers, and as he does not lay claim to its invention, it is probable the Æolipile may have been known long before his time. The machine consisted of a hollow globe of metal, moving on its axis, and communicating with a caldron of water placed underneath. The globe was provided with one or more tubes projecting from it, closed at the ends, but open on one side. When a fire was lit under the caldron, and the steam was raised, it filled the globe, and, projecting itself against the air through the openings in the tubes, the reactive force thus produced caused the globe to spin round upon its axis "as if it were animated from within by a living spirit."[2]

The mechanical means by which these various objects were accomplished, as explained by Hero, show that the ancients were acquainted with the ordinary expedients for communicating motion, such as the wheel and axle, spur-wheels, toothed pinions and sectors, the lever-beam, and other well-known expedients; while they also knew of the cylinder and piston, the three-way cock, slide-valves and valve-clacks,[3] and many other ingenious mechanical details which have been reinvented in modern times.

Hero's book lay hidden in manuscript and buried in libraries, until the revival of learning in Italy in the sixteenth century, when a translation of it appeared at Bologna in 1547. By that time printing had been invented; and the multiplication of copies being thereby rendered easy, the book was soon brought under the notice of inquiring men throughout Europe. The work must, indeed, have excited an extraordinary degree of interest; in proof of which it may be mentioned that eight different editions, in different languages, were published within a century. The minds of the curious and the scientific were thus directed to the subject of steam as a motive power. But for a long time they never got beyond the idea of Hero's Æolipile, though they endeavoured to apply the rotary motion produced by it in different ways. Thus, a German writer suggested that it should be used to turn spits, instead of turn-spit dogs; and Branca, the Italian architect, used the steam jet projected from a brazen head to drive an apparatus contrived by him for pounding drugs. The jet forced round the vanes of a wheel, so as to produce a rotary motion, and this, being communicated to other wheels, set in motion a rod and stamper, after the manner shown in the following cut.

Solomon de Caus was another of the speculative inquirers whose attention was drawn to the subject of steam by the publication of Hero's book. De Caus

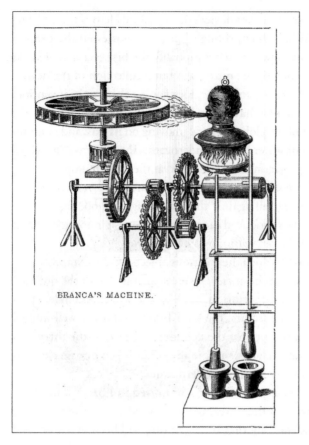

BRANCA'S MACHINE.

Branca's Machine

was a native of Normandy, and for some time studied the profession of an architect in Italy; from whence he returned to France early in the seventeenth century. Religious persecution was then raging, and, being a Protestant, he was glad to take refuge from it in England. He entered the service of the Prince of Wales, by whom he was for a time employed in designing grottoes, fountains, and hydraulic ornaments for the Palace Gardens at Richmond. While occupied in that capacity he gave lessons in design to the Princess Elizabeth; and on her marriage to the Elector Palatine he accompanied her to Heidelberg, to take charge of the Castle gardens there. It was while residing at Heidelberg that De Caus wrote his well-known book on hydraulics, which was published at Frankfort in 1615.[4]

One of De Caus's expedients for raising water consisted of an apparatus in which he proposed to employ the expansive power of steam for the purpose. In Hero's book it is shown how a column of water may be thrown up by means of

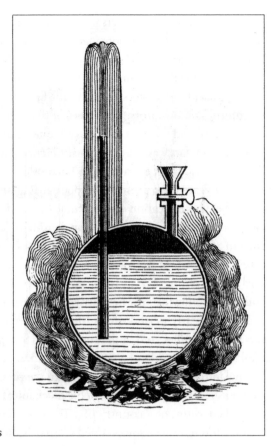

De Caus's Steam Apparatus

compressed air; and De Caus merely proposed to employ steam instead of air. His apparatus was very simple. It consisted of a spherical vessel fitted with two pipes, one of them provided with a cock and funnel; the other, which reached down to near the bottom of the vessel, being open at the top to the external air. When the vessel was filled with water and a fire lit underneath, the water was forced up the open tube in a jet, greater or less in proportion to the elasticity of the steam. When both tubes were tightly closed, so that neither steam nor water could escape, the heat, says De Caus, would shortly cause a compression from within so violent that "the ball will burst in pieces, with a noise like a petard."

It will be observed that there was little mechanical contrivance, and no practical use in this apparatus; it merely furnished an illustration of the extraordinary force of pent-up steam, and that was all. Though De Caus made many experiments with his steam-vessel, he never succeeded in making – if, indeed, he ever attempted to make – a working steam-engine of any kind. It is not improbable that he was dismayed, as others were, by the apparent violence of the imprisoned monster; and it needed a more ingenious head than his to contrive a method of rendering him docile, and making him go quietly in harness.[5]

It is probable that the first contriver of a working steam-engine was Edward, second Marquis of Worcester, one of the first and most illustrious of a long line of unfortunate inventors. The career of that nobleman – born though he was to high rank and great estate – was chequered and sad in no ordinary degree. Edward Somerset was the eldest son of Henry Lord Herbert, afterwards Earl of Worcester, and consequently heir to that title. He was born in London in 1601. His early years were principally spent at Raglan Castle, his father's country seat, where his education was carefully attended to. In the course of his pupil-age he made occasional visits to the continent, accompanied by his tutor, for the purpose of acquiring that degree of polish and culture considered neces-sary for a person of his social position. On the accession of his father to the Earldom of Worcester, in 1627, Edward became Lord Herbert by courtesy; and in the following year he married, and went to reside at Raglan Castle.

From an early period of his life Lord Herbert took especial pleasure in mechanical studies, and in the course of his foreign tours he visited and exam-ined the famous works of construction abroad; for as yet there were none such in England. On settling down at Raglan, he proceeded to set up a laboratory, or workshop wherein to indulge his mechanical tastes, and perhaps to while away the tedium of a country life. To assist him in his labours, he engaged a clever foreign mechanic, named Caspar Kaltoff, who remained in his ser-vice for many years, and materially helped him in his various contrivances. Among the works executed by Lord Herbert and his assistant at Raglan, was the hydraulic apparatus by means of which the castle was supplied with water. From an incidental reference to the "water-works" by a contemporary writer, we learn that they consisted of a series of engines and wheels, by means of which water was raised through pipes to a cistern placed on the summit of the central tower.[6] It is probable that the planning and construction of these works induced Lord Herbert to prosecute the study of hydraulics, and to enter upon that series of experiments as to the power of steam which eventu-ally led to the contrivance of his "Water-commanding Engine."

In pursuits and studies such as these, Lord Herbert spent about seven years at Raglan Castle. But his wife dying in 1635, the place became connected in his mind with too painful associations, and he shortly after left it to reside in London. On his arrival there, he proceeded to put to the practical test a plan of perpetual motion which he had long studied, and now thought he had brought to perfection. He accordingly had his self-moving wheel[7] set up in the Tower; but though it moved, its motion did not prove perpetual, and it shortly dropped out of sight, to be no more heard of.

After the lapse of four years, Lord Herbert again married, taking to wife the Lady Margaret, second daughter of the Earl of Thomond. In the year after his second marriage, the celebrated Long Parliament began its sittings. Questions of great public import were agitating the minds of thinking men, and the nation was gradually becoming divided into two hostile parties, soon to be arrayed against each other in deadly strife. A Royalist and a Roman Catholic like his father, Lord Herbert at once ranged himself on the side of the King. On the outbreak of the Civil War, we find both father and son actively employed in mustering forces, and preparing to hold the western counties against the Parliament. Raglan Castle was strongly garrisoned, and fortifications were thrown up around it, so as to render it secure against assault. The Earl, now Marquis of Worcester, was appointed Generalissimo of the Western Forces, while his son, Lord Herbert, was made General of South Wales. From this office he was shortly after called by the King, who, creating him Earl of Glamorgan, despatched him on a mission to Ireland, with the object of stirring up the loyalists of that kingdom, and inducing them to come to his help. This delicate office he is said to have performed with more zeal than discretion. Indeed, the studious habits of his early life must in a measure have unfitted him for the conduct of so important an affair; and the bungle he made of it was such that the King felt himself under the necessity of repudiating the acts which the Earl had done in his name.

It is unnecessary that we should follow the fortunes of the house of Raglan in the course of the civil war. Suffice it to say that the King's cause was utterly lost; that Raglan Castle was besieged, taken, and dismantled; that the Marquis of Worcester, having advanced to the King at different times as much as 122,500*l.*, had completely impoverished himself, and that when the Earl succeeded to his father's title; and became second Marquis of Worcester, in 1646, he inherited an exhausted exchequer, a confiscated estate, and a ruined home. The services he had rendered to the King were remembered against him; and to escape the vengeance of his political enemies he took refuge in France. There he lived in poverty and in exile for a period of about five years. At length, drawn to England by the powerful attractions of wife and family, and probably also commissioned to perform a service for the exiled Charles II, the Marquis secretly visited London in 1655, where he was shortly after detected, apprehended, and imprisoned in the Tower. He sought and found solace, during his confinement, in study and contemplation, reverting to his early experiments in mechanics; and he occupied the long and weary hours in committing to paper descriptions of his many ingenious devices, which he afterwards published in his 'Century of Inventions.' The Marquis's old and skilled mechanic, Caspar Kaltoff, continued faithful to him in his adversity, and was permitted to hold free communication with him; from which we infer that his imprisonment was not of a very rigid character.

After lying in the Tower for about two years, the Marquis was liberated on bail, in October, 1654, when he proceeded to take steps to erect his long-contemplated Water-commanding Engine. Even while a prisoner, we find him negotiating with the then owner of Vauxhall for its purchase, with a view to the establishment there of a school of skilled industry; thus anticipating by nearly two centuries the School of Mines and Manufactures at South Kensington. In the month preceding his enlargement we find Hartlib writing to the Hon. Robert Boyle, "The Earl of Worcester is buying Fauxhall from Mr. Trenchard, to bestow the use of that house upon Caspar Calchoff and his son as long as they shall live, for he intends to make it a College of Artizans."[8] His main difficulty, however, consisted in raising the necessary means for carrying his excellent project into effect. He was, indeed, so reduced in his circumstances as to be under the necessity of petitioning his political enemies for the bare means of living; and we find Cromwell, in the course of the year following his liberation from prison, issuing a warrant for the payment to him of three pounds a week "for his better maintenance." The Marquis also tried the experiment of levying contributions from his friends; but they were, for the most part, as poor as himself. He next tried the wealthy men of the Parliamentary party, and succeeded in obtaining several advances of money from Colonel Copley, who took an active interest in the prosecution of various industrial undertakings.[9] The following letter from the Marquis to Copley shows the straits to which he was reduced:

Dear Friend, – I know not with what face to desire a curtesie from you, since I have not yet payed you the five powndes, and the mayne businesse soe long protracted, whereby my reality and kindnesse should with thankfullnesse appeare, though the least I intende you is to make up the somme already promised to a thousand powndes yearly, or a share ammounting to four more, which, to nominate before the perfection of the woorke, were but an *individuum vagam*, and, therefore, I deferre it, and upon noe other score. Yet in this interim, my disappointments are soe great, as that I am forced to begge, if you could possible, eyther to helpe me with tenne powndes to this bearer, or to make use of the coache, and to goe to Mr. Clerke, and if he could this day help me to fifty powndes, then to paye your selfe the five powndes I owe you out of them. The

Alderman has taken three days' time to consider of it. Pardon the great trouble
I give you, which I doubt not but in time to deserve, by really appearing
Your most thankfull friend,
Worcester
28th March, 1656.
To my honoured friend, Collonel Christopher Coppley, these.

The original of this letter is endorsed "My Lord of Worcester's letter about my
share in his engine," from which it would appear that the Marquis induced
his friends to advance him money on the promise of a certain proportion of
shares in the undertaking. He also pressed his invention upon the notice of
Government, representing that he was in a position to do his Highness the
Protector "more service than any one subject of his three nations." But neither the Protector nor his Ministers took any further notice of the Marquis
or his project. It is probable that they regarded him as a bore, and his water-
commanding engine as the mere dream of a projector.

The Marquis himself continued to be as confident as ever of the ultimate
success of his scheme. He believed that it would yet realise him an immense
fortune. Writing of the engine to the Earl of Lotherdale, he described it as
"the greatest invention for profit that I ever yet heard of vouchsafed to a man,
especially so unworthy and ignorant as I am." But the Marquis was not so
humble as he affected to be, believing in his heart that he had invented, without exception, the most wonderful machine of the age. Still it remained a mere
project. Without the means of erecting an engine, it promised to remain such;
and all his efforts to raise the necessary funds had thus far proved unavailing.

The Restoration of Charles II, in 1660, revived his hopes. Now that the
King enjoyed his own again, the Marquis believed that he, too, would come
into possession of the means for carrying out his project. For thirteen years
he had lived in exile, in prison, and in poverty: but brighter days had dawned
at last; and he indulged in the hope that compensation would at length be
made to him for his sufferings in the cause of the Stuarts, and that he would
now bask in the sunshine of Royal favour. He made all haste to represent his
case to the king, and to claim restitution for his heavy losses in the late war.
But there were thousands of like suppliants all over the kingdom, and redress
came slowly. The Marquis was, however, shortly put in possession of such
parts of his estates as had not been sold by the Protector; but he found
them for the most part cleared of their timber, and comparatively valueless.
The castle at Raglan was in ruins. He himself was heavily burdened with debt,
and his creditors were becoming increasingly importunate for money. It was

thus long before he could shake himself clear of his embarrassments, and devote himself to the great object of his life, the prosecution of his water-commanding engine.

One of his first cares, on the partial recovery of his property, was to obtain a legal protection for his inventions; and in the year following the Restoration we find him taking out a patent for four of his schemes, – a watch or clock, guns or pistols, an engine to give security to a coach, and a boat to sail against wind and tide. In the session of Parliament, 1662–3, he obtained an Act securing to himself the profits of the water-commanding engine. About the same time he gave to the world his famous 'Century,'[10] which contains his own account of his various inventions. In the second dedication of the book to the members of both Houses of Parliament he states that he had already expended the large sum of 10,000*l*. on experiments; but he professed that he esteemed himself sufficiently rewarded by the passing of "the Act of the Water-commanding Engine," and, his debts once paid, he intended to devote the rest of his life to the service of his King and country. The 'Century' is a mere summary of things alleged to have been tried and perfected, conveyed in vague and mysterious language, and calculated rather to excite wonder than to furnish information. The descriptions were unaccompanied by plans or drawings, so that we can only surmise the means by which he proposed to carry his schemes into effect. It is possible that he purposely left the descriptions of his inventions vague, in order that he might not be anticipated in their application; for it is certain that at the time the book was written the Marquis had not taken out his first patent, nor obtained the Act securing to him the profits of his engine.

There can, however, be no doubt that, vague and mysterious though the 'Scantlings' be, they indicate a knowledge of mechanical principles considerably in advance of the age, as well as a high degree of mechanical ingenuity. The hundred Articles into which the book is divided contain suggestions, in shorthand descriptions, of things so various as ship-destroying machines, telegraphs, combination and escutcheon locks,[11] improvements in fire-arms, universal alphabets, seals and watches, various kinds of cipher, a boat rowing against wind and tide, automata, and mechanical appliances of different kinds, including the "stupendious and semi-omnipotent" engine. Some of them read like descriptions of conjuring tricks, such as the artificial bird, the hour water-ball, the flying man, the brazen head, the dicing-box, and various automata. Others are full of prophetic insight, and contain anticipations of mechanical marvels, which, however wonderful they may at that time have appeared, have since been fully realised. The style in which the treatise was written, however, presented so remarkable a contrast to the contemporary writings of Newton, Boyle, Pascal, Guericke, and others, that it is not improbable it had the effect of prejudicing the minds of scientific men against the writer, and led them to regard his schemes as those of a wild projector, and hence to treat his propositions with neglect, if not with contumely.

So soon as the Marquis had become possessed of the requisite funds, he proceeded to erect an engine at Vauxhall to illustrate the uses of his principal invention. He was assisted, as before, by his old workman, Caspar Kaltoff. It is probable that the engine was erected by the beginning of 1663; for in the course of that year M. Sorbière paid his visit to England, and found the Marquis's "hydraulic machine" at work. He describes it as capable of raising, by the strength of one man only, within a minute of time, four large buckets of water to a height of forty feet, through a pipe eight inches in diameter. He proceeds to compare it with another machine at Somerset House, worked by one or two horses, which he considers the more effective machine of the two.[12] This account of the Marquis's invention is confirmed by another brief description of it, which occurs in the narrative of the travels of Cosmo, Grand Duke of Tuscany, in England, some years later. Count Magalotti, the narrator, says, "It raises water more than forty geometrical feet, by the power of one man only; and in a very short space of time will draw up four vessels of water through a tube or channel not more than a span in width, on which account it is considered to be of greater service to the public than the other machine at Somerset House." It will thus be observed that the Duke's secretary entertained a different opinion from that expressed by M. Sorbière as to the comparative merits of the two engines spoken of.

It is worthy of remark that the incidental accounts of these two foreigners contain almost the only contemporary information we possess as to the character of the Marquis's invention. English writers of the time are almost entirely silent about it; and when Dr. Hooke, the learned Secretary of the Royal Society, refers to the contrivance, it is in a tone of ridicule rather than of praise. Writing to Mr. Boyle, in 1667, he characterises the definition or description of the water-commanding engine as "so purely romantic that it would serve one rarely to fill up half a dozen pages in the 'History of Fortunatus his Wishing Cap' ... "I was," he adds, "since my return to London to see this engine, when I found Caltrop [Kaltoff], his chief engineer, to laugh at it; and as far as I was able to see it, it seemed one of the perpetual-motion fallacies; of which kind Caltrop himself, and two or three others that I know, are labouring at this time in vain to make, but after several ways; and nothing but costly experience will make them desist."[13]

It is difficult to gather from the statements of Sorbière and Cosmo de Medici what was the precise nature of the Marquis's hydraulic apparatus. There is no mention whatever of steam, either in their accounts or in that of Dr. Hooke; but the latter does not seem to have been allowed to examine the details of the machine. From the mention by Sorbière of the "four large buckets of water," and by Cosmo's secretary, of "four vessels of water," it might possibly have been only an improved hydraulic apparatus, worked by a man instead of a horse. In order, therefore, to obtain a clue to the real nature of the machine we find it necessary to resort to the Marquis's 'Scantlings' for his own account of its action, and we find it in article No. 68, which runs as follows:

68. An admirable and most forcible way to drive up water by fire, not by drawing or sucking it upwards, for that must be as the Philosopher calleth it, *Intra sphœram activitatis*, which is but at such a distance. But this way hath no Bounder, if the Vessels be strong enough; for I have taken a piece of a whole Cannon, whereof the end was burst, and filled it three-quarters full of water, stopping and scruing up the broken end; as also the Touch-hole; and making a constant fire under it, within twenty-four hours it burst and made a great crack: So that having a way to make my Vessels, so that they are strengthened by the force within them, and the one to fill after the other, I have seen the water run like a constant Fountaine-stream forty foot high; one Vessel of water rarified by fire driveth up forty of cold water. And a man that tends the work is but to turn two Cocks, that one Vessel of water being consumed, another begins to force and refill with cold water, and so successively, the fire being tended and kept constant, which the self-same Person may likewise abundantly perform in the interim between the necessity of turning the said Cocks.

From this account we gather that the Marquis had contrived a plan for raising water by the expansive force of steam, after the manner of De Caus, but with important modifications and improvements. It had obviously occurred to him, that by generating the steam in a separate vessel, and conveying it by means of a suitable pipe to a second closed vessel, he could thereby make it expel the water which the latter contained by pressing upon its surface, as in De Caus's apparatus. The admission of the steam could easily be regulated by the turning of two cocks; one to admit the steam from the boiler, and the other to allow the exit of the water. On the expulsion of the water, and the production of a vacuum by the condensation of the contained steam, the empty vessel would at once be refilled by the action of the atmospheric pressure on the surface of the water to be raised. It is probable that this engine was – in the absence of a feed-pump, of which there is no mention – provided with two boilers as well as with the two cisterns in which the "forcing and refilling" went on, so as to maintain the "constant fountain-stream" which the Marquis describes. But the precise arrangement of parts by which he accomplished this object must ever remain a matter of mere conjecture.

We have other distinct indications of a steam-engine in the Marquis's 98th, 99th, and 100th Articles, which ought to be read in connection with the 68th Article: they run as follows:

98. An Engine so contrived, that working the *Primum mobile* forward or backward, upward or downward, circularly or cornerwise, to and fro, streight, upright or downright, yet the pretended Operation continueth, and advanceth none of the motions abovementioned, hindering, much less stopping the other; but unanimously, and with harmony agreeing they all augment and contribute strength unto the intended work and operation: And therefore I call this *A Semi-omnipotent Engine*, and do intend that a Model thereof be buried with me.

99. How to make one pound weight to raise an hundred as high as one pound falleth, and yet the hundred pound descending doth what nothing less than one hundred pound can effect.

100. Upon so potent a help as these two last-mentioned Inventions a Waterwork is by many years experience and labour so advantageously by me contrived, that a Child's force bringeth up an hundred foot high an incredible quantity of water, even two foot Diameter, so naturally, that the work will not be heard even into the next Room; and with so great ease and Geometrical Symmetry, that though it work day and night from one end of the year to the other, it will not require forty shillings reparation to the whole Engine, nor hinder ones day-work. And I may boldly call it *The most stupendious Work in the whole world*: not onely with little charge to drein all sorts of Mines, and furnish Cities with water, though never so high seated, as well to keep them sweet, running through several streets, and so performing the work of Scavengers, as well as furnishing the Inhabitants with sufficient water for their private occasions; but likewise supplying Rivers with sufficient to maintaine and make them portable from Towne to Towne, and for the bettering of Lands all the way it runs; with many more advantageous, and yet greater effects of Profit, Admiration, and Consequence. So that deservedly I deem this Invention to crown my Labours, to reward my Expences, and make my Thoughts acquiesce in way of further Inventions: This making up the whole Century, and pre-

venting any further trouble to the Reader for the present, meaning to leave to
Posterity a Book, wherein under each of these Heads the means to put in execution and visible trial all and every of these Inventions, with the shape and form
of all things belonging to them, shall be Printed by Brass-plates.

The promised book was never written, and we are accordingly left in
uncertainty as to the precise character of the Marquis's inventions. That he
had a full conviction of the great powers of steam, as well as of its manageabil-
ity and extensive practical uses, is sufficiently clear; but that he ever erected
any engines after the plans thus summarily described is matter of considerable doubt. It is remarkable that, notwithstanding the number and variety of
his suggested inventions, not a single model or machine constructed by the
Marquis or his skilled workmen has been preserved. Mr. Dircks, who has collected and published all that is likely to be brought to light relative to the life
and works of the Marquis, and has laboured at his task with a rare love and
enthusiasm for his subject, naturally expresses surprise that "none of the many
cabinets of the curious seem to have possessed any model or work of his production; not even the indefatigable Tradescant, although his museum was at
Lambeth."[14] But it is probable, as we have already observed, that the Marquis's
'Scantlings,' notwithstanding his statement that he had "tried and perfected"
the inventions of which he speaks, were rather the foreshadowings of things
to come than the descriptions of things that had actually been executed. Thus,
no one pretends that the Marquis ever constructed a steamboat, and yet his
description of a vessel "to work itself against wind and tide, yea, both, without the help of man or beast," can apply to nothing else.[15] "This engine," said
he, "is applicable to any vessel or boat whatsoever, without being therefore
made on purpose, and worketh these effects: it roweth, it draweth, it driveth,
(if need be) to pass London Bridge against the stream at low-water, and a
boat laying at anchor, the engine may be used for loading or unloading." But
it would not be possible for any one to make an engine after the description
given in the 'Scantlings;' and to a generation unacquainted with the powers
of steam, his suggestions would be altogether without meaning.

The strongest evidence which could be adduced of the ambiguity of the
Marquis's 'Articles' is to be found in the fact that the various ingenious writers
who have given plans of his supposed engine have represented it in widely
different forms. Farey assumes that it worked by the expansive force of steam;
Bourne, that it worked by condensation and atmospheric pressure; Dircks
infers that it included such ingenious expedients as valves and even a four-
way cock, worked by a lever-handle; Stuart, that it contained a cylinder and

piston, and was, in fact, a complete high-pressure lever-engine. Again, the drawings of the various writers on engineering who have attempted to reproduce the engine – of Stuart, Galloway, Millington, and Dircks – differ in essential respects.

When Watt was on one occasion asked for his opinion as to the precise nature of the Marquis's contrivance, his answer was, that the descriptions given were too obscure to enable any definite opinion to be formed on the subject; but he thought that the expansive power of steam was the principle on which the engine worked. He added, that no one could possibly erect an engine after the Marquis's 'Scantlings,' and that any inventor desirous of constructing a steam-engine would have to begin again at the beginning. But though the Marquis did not leave the steam-engine in such a state as to be taken up and adopted as a practicable working power, he at least advanced it several important steps. In this world, it is not given to man to finish; to persevere, to improve, and to advance, are all that can be hoped for; and these are enough for the real philosopher.

Little remains to be told of the unfortunate Marquis's history. His water-commanding engine proved of no service to him. It only increased his embarrassments by involving him in further debts. The Restoration, though it gave him back his estates, did not mend his fortunes, and he continued to importune his friends for loans. He sought access to the King by petition; but it became more and more difficult to approach him. On one occasion he tried to accomplish his purpose through the influence of his Majesty's mistress, Lady Castlemaine. Provided she could persuade the king to grant his request, he offered to present to her "a thousand pieces to buy her a little jewel, which she deserves to wear every day of the week. And if it please God I live but two years," he added, "I will, out of the profits of my water-commanding engine, appropriate four hundred pounds yearly, for ever, to her Grace's disposal … all which, as I am a gentleman and a Christian, shall be faithfully and most thankfully performed; though the benefit I pretend to by my petition will not amount to what my gratitude obliges, yet the satisfaction which it will be to my mind, and my credit therein at stake, I value at ten times as much. And this will enable me to place my Water-commanding Engine, when I am certained of an hundred pounds a day profit, without further troubling the king or anybody."[16]

All his piteous importunity proved of no avail. His friends turned aside from his petitionings, and the king would give him no help. He came to be regarded as a crack-brained enthusiast, and a wild projector of impracticable things. He could not find any one to believe in his water-commanding

Ruins of Raglan Castle (by Percival Skelton)

engine, though he himself regarded it as of greater worth than either his titles or his estates. It had been his own creation – the child of his brain – the product of studies and experiments extending over nearly forty years. But what signified all this if no one would make use of the invention?

His difficulties and embarrassments grew from day to day; and his projects met with increased contumely and even contempt. None valued them, because none understood them. It was even proposed to appropriate to other purposes the premises at Vauxhall, on which he so much plumed himself, but which he had been unable to purchase. To prevent this, he again petitioned the king in 1666, representing that he had expended 9000*l*. in building the house he occupied there as "an operatory for engineers and artists to makepublic works in," and "above 50,000*l*. trying conclusions of arts in that operatory which may be useful to his Majesty and his kingdom;" and he concluded by praying that Vauxhall might be granted to him at a fee-farm rent. The Marchioness, his wife, at the same time petitioned the House of Lords, representing the state of poverty to which her husband had been reduced, and that, in consequence of an execution having been put in at Worcester House, through a debt of 6000*l*. which the Marquis had incurred in 1642 to pay the garrison of Monmouth, then in a state of mutiny, he was actually threatened to be turned out of house and home. It is not known what came of this petition; but shortly after its presentation the poor Marquis was beyond all worldly help. Broken in health, harassed, embarrassed, and disappointed, he died in April, 1667, in the sixty-sixth year of his age, and his remains were conveyed to Raglan for interment in the family vault.

It will be remembered that the Marquis concluded the 98th article of his 'Century' with the words, "I call this a semi-omnipotent engine, and do intend that a model thereof be buried with me." A diligent search for the model has recently been made in the vault under Raglan church, under the direction of Mr. Bennet Woodcroft, whose enthusiasm as a collector of primitive engines and machines is so well known; but the search proved unsuccessful, and no traces of the Marquis's model could be found.

NOTES

1   Article "Government," in 'Encyclopædia Britannica.'
2   The principle of the Æolipile is the same as that embodied in Avery and Ruthven's engines for the production of rotary motion. "These engines," says Bourne, "are more expensive in steam than ordinary engines, and travel at an inconvenient speed; but in other respects they are quite as effectual, and their construction is extremely simple and inexpensive."
3   See Bennet Woodcroft's 'Pneumatics of Hero of Alexandria,' from the original Greek. London, 1851.
4   Les Raisons des Forces Mouvantes, avec diverses machines tant utiles que plaisantes, &c., par Solomon de Caus, Ingénieur et Architects du Roy. Frankfort, 1615.
5   De Caus eventually returned to France, and was appointed engineer to the King. During the later years of his life he was employed in carrying out plans for the better supply of Paris with water. The story so often told of De Caus having been shut up in the Bicêtre turns out to be a fiction. Though a Huguenot, he was not persecuted by Richelieu, but was, on the contrary, employed by him; and in 1624 he dedicated to that prelate his treatise entitled 'Horologes Solitaires.' Mr. Charles Read, editor of several interesting memoirs of early French Protestants, has recently brought to light and published in the 'Gazette des Tribunaux' the proofs of the patronage of De Caus by Richelieu, and reproduced the original documents, which he discovered slumbering in the dust of the State Records at Paris. In 1621 De Caus is found proposing to Louis XIII to adopt measures for cleansing Paris and the faubourgs of dirt and uncleanness, by a system of reservoirs

established at elevated points, and by fountains at various places which
he indicated. The king and his council sent the propositions to the chief
magistrate of Paris, and Mr. Read transcribes the deliberation which took
place on the subject at the City Council, as handed down in the records
deposited in the Imperial Archives. De Caus died at Paris, and was buried in
the church of La Trinité in February, 1626.

6   'Dr. Bayly, in his 'Apothegms' (1682), p. 87, describes the fright given to
    some Puritan visitors on the occasion of their searching Raglan Castle
    for arms, the Marquis of Worcester being a known Papist. "Having
    carried them up and down the castle, his lordship at length brought
    them over a high bridge that arched over the moat between the castle
    and the great tower, wherein the Lord Herbert had lately contrived
    certain water-works, which, when the several engines and wheels were
    set agoing, much quantity of water through the hollow conveyances of
    the aqueducts was to be let down from the top of an high tower." When
    all was ready for the surprise, the water was let in, and it made such a
    hideous and fearful noise by reason of the hollowness of the tower, and
    the neighbouring echoes of the castle, that the men steed amazed and
    terror-struck. At this point up came a man staring and running, who
    exclaimed, "Look to yourselves, my masters, for the lions are got loose."
    whereupon the Puritans fled down the narrow staircase in such haste
    that they lost footing and fell, tumbling one over the other, and never
    halted until they had got the castle out of sight. Mr. Dircks, in his able
    and exhaustive 'Life, Times, and Scientific Labours of the Marquis of
    Worcester,' London, 1865, says that this hydraulic apparatus "probably
    depended for its operation on the influence of heat from burning fuel
    acting on a suitably constructed boiler, and so arranged as to be able
    to apply the expansive force of steam to the driving of water through
    vertical pipes to a considerable elevation." But it does not seem to us that
    the facts stated are sufficient to warrant this assumption.

7   Mr. Dircks says "it was a machine consisting of a wheel 14 feet in
    diameter, carrying forty weights of forty pounds each, and is supposed to
    have rotated on an axle supported on two pillars or upright frames," as
    indicated in the 'Century of Inventions,' Art. 56.

8   'Weld's Royal Society,' i.53

9   'Industrial Biography,' p.57.

10 'A Century of the Names and Scantlings of such Inventions as at present
    I can call to mind to have tried and perfected, which (my former Notes
    being lost) I have, at the instance of a powerful Friend, endeavoured

now, in the year 1655, to set these down in such a way as may sufficiently instruct me to put any of them in practice.' London, 1663.

11 The writer of the elaborate article "Lock," in the supplement to the 'Penny Cyclopedia' (ii. 217), in describing the combination lock, says: "The Marquis of Worcester, in whose 'Century of Inventions' several different kinds of lock, which lay claim to the most marvelous properties, are enumerated, would appear, from his 72nd article, to have devised an improvement on this apparatus; as he refers to 'an escutcheon to be placed before any of these locks,' one of the properties of which he described as being 'the owner, though a woman, may, with her delicate hand, vary the ways of coming to open the lock ten millions of times beyond the knowledge of the smith that made it, or of me who invented it.' The details of this invention are not given; but in the third volume of the 'Transactions of the society of Arts,' pp. 160-5, is an eschutcheon of similar character, invented by the Society in 1784. The details of this ingenious contrivance are fully given in the volume referred to."

12 His words are these: "One of the most curious things that I wished to see was an hydraulic machine which the Marquis of Worcester has invented, and of which he is making trial. I went with all speed to Fox-hall, on the other side of the Thames, a little below Lambeth, which is the Palace of the Archbishop of Canterbury, in sight of London. This machine will raise to the height of forty feet, by the strength of one man only, and in a minute of time, four large buckets of water through a pipe of eight inches. But what will be the most powerful help to the wants of the public is the work which is performed by another ingeniously-constructed machine, which can be seen raised on a wooden tower on the top of Somerset House, which supplies that part of the town with water, but with some difficulty, and a smaller quantity than could be desired. It is somewhat like our Samaritane water-work on the Pont Neuf; and on the raising-pump they have added an impulsion which increases the force; but for what we obtain by the power of the Seine, they employ one or two horses, which incessantly turn the machine, as the river changes its course twice a day, and the spring or wheels are used for the ebbing tide would not do for the flow." – Sorbiere, 'Relation d'un Voyage en Angleterre.'

13 The Works of the Hon. Robert Boyle, v. 532.

14 Dircks's 'Life and Times,' &c., 356.

15 Mr. Woodcroft is, however, of opinion that the Marquis's contrivance was but a boat with paddle-wheels, with an axis across it, which axis was turned by the action of the stream on the paddles, and thus wound up a

rope and dragged the boat onward to the other end of the rope fixed by an anchor; certainly a more clumsy and less notable contrivance than that of a steamboat.

16 Letter to some person unknown, quoted by Mr. Dircks from the Badminton MSS. – Dircks's 'Life, Times,' &c., 276.

II

Sir Samuel Morland – Dr. Dionysius Papin

After the death of the Marquis of Worcester, the Marchioness, his widow, made various efforts to turn his inventions to account. Sceptical though the world was as to their utility, she fully believed in them; and now that he was gone, it would have been dishonouring to his memory to entertain a doubt as to his engine being able to do all that he had promised. The Marchioness had not only to maintain the fame of her dear husband, but to endeavour, if possible, to pay the debts he had contracted in prosecuting his inventions. She accordingly sought to interest persons of authority and influence in the water-commanding engine, and seized every opportunity of bringing it into notice.

To such an extent did the Marchioness carry her zeal, that her friends began to fear lest her mind was becoming disordered; and her father-confessor was requested to expostulate with her as to the impropriety of her conduct. He accordingly implored her to desist from her vain endeavours to get "great sums of money from the King to pay her deceased lord's debts, enriching herself by the great machine, and the like." He added that he feared "the devil, to make his suggestions the more prevalent, doth make use of some motives that seem plausible, as of paying your lord's debts, of founding monasteries, and the like; pointing out that the end did not justify the means, and that such undertakings were improper for her ladyship, and by no means likely to be attended with success. It is not improbable that these representations had their effect; the more especially as the Marchioness was no more successful in inducing the public to adopt the invention than the Marquis himself had been. Accordingly, the water-commanding engine very shortly dropped out of sight, and in the course of a few years was almost entirely forgotten.

The steam-engine project, however, did not die; it only slept. It had been the fruit thus far of noble effort, of persevering self-denial, and unquestionable skill. What was good in it would yet live, and reappear perhaps in other forms, to vindicate the sagacity and foresight of its inventor. Even during the Marquis's lifetime other minds besides his were diligently pursuing the same subject. Indeed, his enthusiasm was of a kind especially calculated to inflame other minds; and the success he had achieved with his engine, imperfect though it might be, was of so novel and original a character that it could not fail to excite a warm interest amongst men of like mechanical genius.

One of the most distinguished of these was Sir Samuel Morland, appointed Master of Mechanics to Charles II immediately after the Restoration. He had been for some time previously in the employment of the Protectorate. He formed one of the embassy to Sweden, with Whitlocke, in 1653. Some years later he took an active part in the relief of the sufferings of the persecuted Protestants of Piedmont – whose history he afterwards wrote, – having been appointed Commissioner Extraordinary for the distribution of the collected moneys. For some time he officiated as assistant to Thurloe, Cromwell's secretary; and it was while acting in this capacity that he became cognisant of a plot against the life of Charles II, then in exile. Morland divulged the plot to the king's friends, and thereby perhaps saved his life. For this service, Charles, on his Restoration, presented him with a medal, as a badge of his signal loyalty, and also appointed him Master of Mechanics.

From that time until the close of his life, Morland devoted himself entirely to mechanical studies. Among his various inventions may be mentioned the speaking-trumpet;[1] two arithmetical machines, of which he published an illustrated description; the capstan to heave ships' anchors; and various kinds of pumps and water engines. His pumps were of a very powerful and effective kind. One of them, worked by eight men, forced water from the Thames at Blackmoor Park, near Winkfield, to the top of Windsor Castle. He also devoted himself to the improvement of the fire-engine, in which he employed a cylinder and piston, as well as a stuffing-box. Towards the later years of his life, he applied himself more particularly to the study of the powers and uses of steam.[2] In 1677, we find him taking a lease of Vauxhall, most probably the identical house occupied by the Marquis of Worcester, where he conducted a series of experiments as to the power requisite to raise water by cylinders of different dimensions.[3] It is not, however, known that he ever erected a steam-engine. If he did, no account of its performances has been preserved.

Morland's inventions proved of no greater advantage to him than those of the Marquis of Worcester had done. His later years were spent in poverty

Dionysius Papin,
M.D., F.R.S.

and blindness, and he must have perished but for the charitable kindness of Archbishop Tenison and a few other friends. Evelyn gives the following interesting account of a visit to him in October, 1695, two months before his death: – "The Archbishop and myself went to Hammersmith to visit Sir Samuel Morland, who was entirely blind; a very mortifying sight. He showed me his invention of writing, which was very ingenious; also his wooden calendar, which instructed him all by feeling, and other pretty and useful inventions of mills, pumps, &c., and the pump he had erected that serves water to his garden, and to passengers, with an inscription, and brings from a filthy part of the Thames now near it, a most perfect and pure water. He had newly buried 200*l.* worth of music books, being, as he said, love songs and vanity. He plays himself psalms and religious hymns on the theorbo." The inscription to which Evelyn refers was on a stone tablet fixed on the wall of his house, still preserved, which runs thus: – "SIR SAMUEL MORLAND'S WELL, the use of which he freely gives to all persons: hoping that none who shall come after him, will adventure to incur God's displeasure, by denying a cup of cold water (provided at another's cost and not their own) to either neighbour, stranger, passenger, or poor thirsty beggar. July 8, 1695."

The next prominent experimenter on the powers of steam was Dr. Dionysius Papin. He was born at Blois about the middle of the seventeenth century, and educated to the profession of medicine. After taking his degree at Paris, he turned his attention more particularly to the study of physics, which soon occupied his whole attention; and under the celebrated Huyghens, then resident in that city, he made rapid progress. He would, doubtless, have risen to great distinction in his own country, but for the circumstance of his being a Protestant. To escape the persecutions to which all members of that persuasion were then subject, Papin fled from France in 1681, together with thousands of his countrymen, a few years before the Revocation of the Edict of Nantes. He took refuge in London, where he was welcomed by men of science, and more especially by the celebrated Boyle, under whose auspices he was introduced to the Royal Society, of which he was appointed Curator at an annual salary.

It formed part of Papin's duty, in connection with his new office, to produce an experiment at each meeting of the Society. He was thus induced to prosecute the study of physical science; and in order to stimulate the interest of the members, he sought to introduce new subjects from time to time to their notice. One of the greatest novelties of his "entertainments" was the production of his well-known Digester, which excited a considerable degree of interest; and on one occasion a philosophical supper, cooked by the Digester, was served up to the Fellows, of which Evelyn gives an amusing account in his Diary.

He was led to the invention of the Digester by certain experiments which he made for Boyle. He discovered that if the vapour of boiling water could be prevented escaping, the temperature of the water would be raised much above the boiling point; and it occurred to him to employ this increased heat in more effectually extracting nutritious matter from the bones of animals, until then thrown away as useless. The great strength required for his Digester, and the means he was obliged to adopt for the purpose of securely confining the cover, must have early shown him what a powerful agent he was experimenting on. To prevent the bursting of the vessel from the internal pressure, he was led to the invention of the safety-valve, which consisted of a small moveable plate, or cylinder, fitted into an opening in the cover of the boiler, and kept shut by a lever loaded with a weight, capable of sliding along it in the manner of a steel yard. The pressure of the weight upon the valve could thus be regulated at pleasure. When the pressure became so great as to endanger the safety of the boiler, the valve was forced up, and so permitted the steam to escape. Although Papin was thus the inventor of the safety-valve, it is a curious fact that he did not apply it to the steam-machine which he subsequently invented, but adopted another expedient.

The reputation of Papin having extended to Germany, he was, in 1687, invited to fill the office of Professor of Mathematics in the University of Marburg, and accepted the appointment. He continued, however, to maintain a friendly correspondence with his scientific friends in England, and communicated to the Royal Society the results of the experiments in physics which he continued to pursue. In the same year in which he settled at Marburg, he submitted to the Society an important paper, which indicated the direction in which his thoughts were then running. It had occurred to him, as it had before done to Hautefeuille, that the explosion of gunpowder presented a ready means of producing a power to elevate a piston in a tube or cylinder, and that, when so raised, a vacuum could be formed under the piston by condensing the vapour, and so ensuring its return by the pressure of the atmosphere. He thought that he might thus be enabled to secure an efficient moving force. But it was found in practice, that the proposed power was too violent as well as uncertain, and it was shortly given up as impracticable.

Papin next inquired whether his proposed elastic force and subsequent vacuum might not better be produced by means of steam. He accordingly entered upon a series of experiments, which gradually led him to the important conclusions published in his celebrated paper on "A New Method of Obtaining very Great Moving Powers at Small Cost," which appeared in the 'Acta Eruditorum' of Leipsic, in 1790. "I felt confident," he there observes, "that machines might be constructed wherein water, by means of no very intense heat, and at small cost, might produce that perfect vacuum which had failed to be obtained by means of gunpowder." He accordingly contrived a machine to illustrate this idea, but it was very imperfect and slow in its action, as may well be imagined from the circumstance that to produce the condensation he did not apply cold, but merely took away the fire! Still he was successfully working out, step by step, the important problem of steam power. He clearly perceived that a piston might be raised in a cylinder by the elastic force of steam, and that on the production of a vacuum by its condensation, the piston might be driven home again by the pressure of the atmosphere. The question was, how was this idea to be realised in a practicable working machine? After many experiments, Papin had the courage to make the attempt to pump water by atmospheric pressure on a large scale. He was employed to erect machines after his principle, for the purpose of draining mines in Auvergne and Westphalia; but from the difficulty he experienced in procuring and preserving a vacuum, and the tediousness of process, his enterprise proved abortive.

The truth is, that fertile though Papin was in conception, he laboured under the greatest possible disadvantage in not being a mechanic. The eyes and hands of others are not to be relied on in the execution of new and untried machines. Unless eyes and hands be disciplined by experience in skilled work, and inspired by intelligence, they are comparatively useless. The chances of success are vastly greater when mind, eyes, and hands, are combined in one person. Hence the unquestionable fact that though the motive power of steam had long been the subject of ingenious speculation and elaborate experiment amongst scientific men, it failed to be adopted as a practicable working power until it was taken in hand by mechanics – by such men as Newcomen, the blacksmith; Potter, the engine-driver; Brindley, the millwright; and, above all, by James Watt, the mathematical instrument maker.

The sagacious foresight of Papin as to the extensive applicability of steam-power as a motive agent, is strikingly shown by the following passage in the paper above referred to: – "If any one," says he, "will consider the magnitude of the forces to be obtained in this way (i. e. by the atmospheric high-pressure engine he was suggesting), and the trifling expense at which a sufficient quantity of fuel can be procured, he will certainly admit that this very method is far preferable to the use of gunpowder above spoken of, especially as in this way a perfect vacuum is obtained, and so the inconveniences above recounted are avoided. In what manner that power can be applied to draw water or ore from mines, to discharge iron bullets to a great distance, to propel ships against the wind, and to a multitude of other similar purposes, it would be too long here to detail; but each individual, according to the particular occasion, must select the construction of machinery appropriate to his purpose." This last was, however, the real difficulty to be overcome. Steam, doubtless, contained a power to do all these things; but as for the machine that would work quietly, docilely, and effectively, in pumping water, discharging bullets, or propelling ships, the mechanic had not yet appeared that was able to make one.

Papin was, however, a man of great perseverance; and, strong in his faith as to the power of steam to propel ships, he gradually worked his way to the contrivance of a model steamboat. When in London, he had seen an experiment tried by the Prince Palatine Rupert on the Thames, in which a boat fitted with revolving paddles attached to the two ends of an axle which received its motion from a trundle working on a wheel turned round by horses, went with such rapidity as to leave the king's barge, manned by sixteen rowers, far behind in the race. The idea which occurred to Papin was to apply a steam machine to drive the paddles, and thus ensure a ship's motion independent of wind or tide. For this purpose, it was necessary to convert the alternate

Ancient Paddle-
Boat

motion of the piston-rod into a continuous rotary one; and this he proposed
to effect "by having the rods of the pistons fitted with teeth, which would
force round small wheels, toothed in like manner, fastened to the axis of the
paddles."

The use of paddle-wheels in propelling boats had long been known. The
Harleian MSS. contain an Italian book of sketches, attributed to the fifteenth
century, in which there appears the annexed sketch of a paddle-boat. This
boat was evidently intended to be worked by two men turning the crank
by which the paddles were made to revolve. There were many other early
schemes of paddle-boats, some of which were proposed to be worked by
horse power. The name of Blasco Garay has often been mentioned as the first
who applied the power of steam to the driving of paddle-boats; but for this
there is not the slightest foundation. M. Bergenroth informs us that he has
carefully examined all the documents relating to the trials of Blasco Garay
in the archives at Simancas, but has found no reference whatever to steam as
the power employed in causing the paddles to revolve.[4] The experiments were
made at Malaga and Barcelona respectively, in the years 1540 and 1543: in one
the vessel was propelled by a paddle-wheel on each side worked by twenty-
five men, and in the other by a paddle-wheel worked by forty men.

It appears probable that although others before Papin had speculated as to
the possibility of constructing a boat to be driven by the power of steam, he
was the first to test the theory by actual experiment; the first to construct a

model steamboat. His first experiments were doubtless failures. The engine contrived by himself was found inapplicable to the driving of ships, as it had been to the pumping of mines; and it was not until he saw the model of Savery's engine exhibited to the Royal Society of London, in 1698, and witnessed the trial of the same inventor's paddle-wheel boat on the Thames in the course of the same year that it occurred to him to combine the two contrivances in one, and apply Savery's engine to drive Savery's paddle-wheels. Returning to Marburg, he proceeded with his experiments, and informed Liebnitz that he had employed both suction and pressure by steam; that he had made a model of a carriage propelled by this force, which succeeded; and he hoped that the same power would answer for boats. Papin prosecuted his idea with great zeal, trying many expedients, encountering many difficulties, and meeting with many disappointments. At length, after about fifteen years' labour, he succeeded in constructing a model engine, fitted in a boat – "une petite machine d'un vaisseau à roues" – which worked to his satisfaction. His next object was to get his model transported to London, to exhibit it on the Thames. "It is important," he writes to Liebnitz (7th July, 1707), "that my new construction of vessel should be put to the proof in a seaport like London, where there is depth enough to apply the new invention, which, by means of fire, will render one or two men capable of producing more effect than some hundreds of rowers." Papin had considerable difficulty in obtaining the requisite permission from the authorities to enable his model to pass from the Fulda to the Weser; but at length he succeeded, and the little vessel reached Münden, when, to Papin's great grief, it was seized by the boatmen of the river, and barbarously destroyed.

The year after this calamity befel Papin's machine he wrote an urgent letter to his old friends of the Royal Society at London, asking them to advance him sufficient money to construct another engine "and to fit it so that it might be applied for the rowing of ships." The Society, however, did not see their way to assisting Papin in the manner proposed, most likely because of the expense as well as uncertainty of the experiment. Two years later, worn out by work and anxiety, the illustrious exile died; and it was left for other labourers to realise the great ideas he had formed as to locomotion by steam-power.

The apparently resultless labours of these men will serve to show what a long, anxious, and toilsome process the invention of the steam-engine has been. The early inventors had not the gratification of seeing their toils rewarded by even the faintest glimmering of practical success. One after another, they took up the subject, spent days and nights of study over it, and, laying down their lives, there left it. To many the study brought nothing but anxiety, toil, distress, and sometimes ruin; while some fairly broke their hearts over it. But it was never abandoned. Disregarding the fate of their predecessors, one labourer after another resumed the investigation, advancing it by further stages, until at length the practicable working steam-engine was invented, presenting, perhaps, the most remarkable illustration of the power of human skill and perseverance to be found in the whole history of civilisation.

NOTES

1 We are informed that Morland's Tuba Stentorphornica, or speaking-trumpet, is still to be seen at Trinity College, Cambridge. Butler, in his 'Hudibras,' alludes to the invention: –
"I heard a formidable voice
Loud as the stentophornic noise."

2 His first idea seems to have been to employ gunpowder for the production of motive power, for in the 'Calendar of State Papers' (Dom) we find the following entry: – "Decr. 11th, 1691. – Warrant for a grant to Sir Samuel Morland of the sole use for 14 years of his invention for raising water out of the pits, &c., to a reasonable height, by the force of powder and air conjointly." – ('Entry Book,' V., p.85) In vol. XLVI., p.49, we find this entry under the same date: – "Warrant for a grant to Sir S. Morland of the sole making of an engine invented by him for raising water in mines or pits, draining marshes, or supplying buildings with water."

3 The 'Harleian Miscellany' (Brit. Mus.), No. 5771, contains the following brief tract in French, written by Morland in 1682. It is on vellum, and entitled 'Les Principles de la Nouvelle Force de Feu:' – "L'eau estant évaporée par la force de feu, ces vapeurs demandent incontinent une plus grand'espace [environ deux mille fois] que l'eau n'occupoiet auparavant, et plus tost que d'etre toujours emprisonnés, feroient crever une piece de canon. Mais estant bien gouvernées selon les regles de la mesure au poids, et à la balance, alors elles portent paisiblement leurs fardeaux [comme des bons cheveaus] et ainsy seroient elles du grand usage au gendre humain, particulièrement pour l'evelation des eaux, selon la table suivante que marque les nombres des livres qui pourrant ester levés 1800 fois par heure, a 6 pouces de levée, par de cylinders à moitie d'eau, ausi bien que les divers diameters et profundeurs des dit cylinders." Tables are then given, showing the power requisite to raise given quantities of water to certain heights by cylinders of different dimensions.

4   M. Bergenroth says the documents at Simancas consist of – 1. A holograph
     letter of Blasco Garay to the Emperor, dated Malaga, 10th Sept., 1540,
     containing his report on the trial trip of one of his paddle-wheel ships; 2.
     The report of the Captain Antonio Destigsrura on the same trial trip; 3.
     The report of the Provcedores of Malaga concerning the same trip, dated
     27th July, 1540; 4. The report of Blasco Garay to the Emperor, dated 6th
     July, 1543, concerning the trial trip of another of his paddle-wheel ships
     made at Barcelona in June, 1543 ; 5. A letter of Blasco Garay to Carrs,
     dated 20th June, 1543. In none of these is there to be found any reference
     to steam-power; but only to the power of men employed in driving the
     paddle-wheels. This is confirmed by the independent examination of
     the same documents by J. Macgregor, Esq., of the Temple, who gives
     the result in a Letter to Bennet Woodcroft, Esq., inserted as a note to
     the 'Abridgments of the Specifications relating to Steam Propulsion,' pp.
     105–7.

III

Captain Savery – His Fire-engine

The attempts hitherto made to invent a working steam-engine, it will be observed, had not been attended with much success. The most that could be said of them was, that, by demonstrating the impracticable, they were gradually leading other experimenters in the direction of the practicable. Although the progress made seemed but slow, the amount of net result was by no means inconsiderable. Men were becoming better acquainted with the elastic force of steam. The vacuum produced by its condensation in a closed vessel, and the consequent atmospheric pressure, had been illustrated by repeated experiments; and many separate and minor inventions, which afterwards proved of great value, had been made, such as the four-way cock, the safety-valve, and the piston moving in a cylinder. The principle of a true steam-engine had not only been demonstrated, but most of the separate parts of such an engine had been contrived by various inventors. It seemed as if all that was now wanting was a genius of more than ordinary power to combine them in a complete and effective whole.

To Thomas Savery is usually accorded the merit of having constructed the first actual working steam-engine. Little is known of his early history; and various surmises have been formed as to his origin and calling. Some writers have described him as the captain of a tin-mine; others as a naval captain; while a third says he was an immigrant Frenchman.[1] We are, however, enabled to state, from information communicated by his descendants, that he was the scion of a well-known Devonshire family. John Savery, of Halberton, or Harberton, afterwards of Great Totness, was a gentleman of considerable property in the reign of Henry VIII. In the sixteenth century the Saverys became connected by marriage with the Servingtons of Tavistock, another old county family, one of whom served as sheriff in the reign of Edward III.

Thomas Savery, F.R.S.

In 1588, Christopher Savery, the head of the family, resided in Totness Castle, of which he was the owner; and for a period of nearly forty years the town was represented in Parliament by members of the Savery family. Sir Charles served as Sheriff of Devon in 1619. Though the Saverys took the side of the Parliament, in resisting the despotic power assumed by Charles I, they nevertheless held a moderate course; for we find Colonel Savery, in 1643, attaching his name to the famous "round robin" presented to Parliament. Richard Savery, the youngest son of the Colonel, was father of Thomas Savery, the inventor of the "fire-engine." Other members of the Savery family, besides Thomas, were distinguished for their prosecution of physical science. Thus we find from the family MSS., Servington Savery corresponding with Dr. Jurin, Secretary to the Royal Society, respecting an improvement which he had made in the barometer, and communicating the results of some magnetic experiments of a novel kind, which he had recently performed.[2]

Thomas Savery was born at Shilston, near Modbury, in Devon, about the year 1650. Nothing is known of his early life, beyond that he was educated to the profession of a military engineer, and in course of time duly reached the rank of Trench-master. The corps of engineers was not, however, regarded as an essential part of the military force until the year 1787, when the officers ranked with those of the Royal Artillery. The pursuit of his profession, as well as his natural disposition, led Savery to the study of mechanics, and he became well accomplished in the physical knowledge of his time. He occupied much of his spare time in mechanical experiments, and in projecting and executing contrivances of various sorts. One of his early works was a clock, still preserved in the family,[3] which until lately kept very good time; and when last repaired by a watchmaker of Modbury was pronounced to be a piece of very good work, of a peculiar construction, displaying much ingenuity.

Another of Savery's early contrivances was a machine for polishing plate-glass, for which he obtained a patent. He was occupied about the same time with an invention for rowing ships in calms by the mechanical apparatus subsequently described in his treatise, entitled 'Navigation Improved.' He there relates how it troubled his thoughts and racked his brains to find out this invention, which he accomplished after many experiments, conducted "with great charge." He naturally set much value on the product of so much study and labour; and he was proportionately vexed on finding that others regarded it with indifference. He professed to have had "promises of a great reward from the Court, if the thing would answer the end for which he proposed it;" but instead of a reward, Savery received only contumely and scorn. He attributed his want of success to the ill-humour of the then Surveyor of the Navy, who reported against his engine, because, said he, "it's the nature of some men to decry all inventions that are not the product of their own brains." He only asked for a fair trial of his paddle-boat, believing in its efficiency and utility; declaring that it was not his "fondness for his own bratt that made him think so," but the favourable opinions of several very judicious persons in town, that encouraged him to urge his invention for public adoption.

The invention in question consisted of a boat mounted with two paddle-wheels, one on each side, worked by a capstan placed in the centre of the vessel. The following cut will show the nature of the arrangement, which probably did not differ much from the scheme of Blasco Garay, above referred to.

Savery says he was led to make the invention through the difficulty which had been experienced in getting ships in motion so as to place them alongside of the enemy in sea-fights, especially during calm weather. He thought that if our fighting-ships could be made to move independent of the winds, we should thereby possess an advantage of essential consequence to the public service. "The gentlemen," said he, "that were on the Brest expedition with

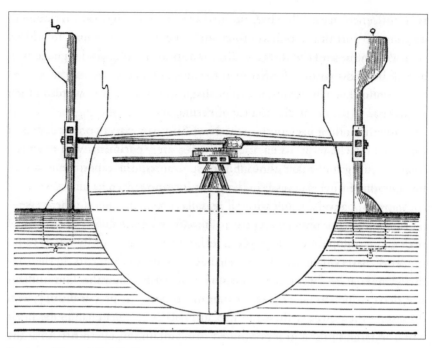

Section of Savery's Paddle-Boat

my Lord Caermarthen must know how useful this engine would have been; for had they had them there on board each ship, they might have moved themselves where they had pleased." He also urged the usefulness of the engine for packet-boats, bomb-vessels, and sloops, and especially for use in sea-fights, in bringing off disabled ships. When he had completed his invention, he took steps to bring it under the notice of Mr. Secretary Trenchard. The plan was shown to the King, who thought highly of it, and referred Savery to the Admiralty. When he went there he was told that he should have gone to the Navy Board. At the Navy Board he was told that certain objections to the adoption of his scheme had already been sent to the Admiralty.

Savery having ascertained that the Surveyor was himself the author of the objections, proceeded to discuss the matter with him. But the Surveyor was not a man to be argued out of his views by an inventor; and he shut up Savery with the remark: "What have interloping people, that have no concern with us, to do to pretend to contrive or invent things for us?" Savery was highly indignant at the official snub, and published the conversation in his Treatise. "Though one has found out," said he, "an improvement as great to shipping as turning to windward or the Compass, unless you can sit round the Green Table in Crutched Friars, your invention is damned, of course;" and the testy inventor concluded: "All I have now to add is, that whoever is an ry with the Truth for appearing in mean language may as well be angry with an honest man for his plain habit; for, indeed, it is as common for Lyes and Nonsense to be disguised by a jingle of words as for a Blockhead to be hid by abundance of Peruke."[4]

Notwithstanding his rebuff by the Navy Surveyor, Savery proceeded to fit up a small yacht with his engine, and tried an experiment with it on the Thames, in sight of many thousands of spectators. The experiment was, in his opinion, entirely successful. The yacht, manned by eight sailors working the capstan, passed a ketch with all its sails spread, as well as other vessels. "All people," said Savery, "seemed to like the demonstration of the use of my engine, the public newspapers speaking very largely of it, yet all to no purpose." Savery had already expended 200*l.* in his experiments on the pad-dle-wheel boat, and was not disposed to go any further, now that Government had decided not to take up the invention. Indeed, its practical utility was doubtful. The power of the wind was, after all, better than hand-labour for working large ships; and it continued to maintain its superiority until the steam-engine was brought to perfection.

It is curious that it should not have occurred to Savery, who invented both a paddle-wheel boat and a steam-engine, to combine the two in one machine; but he was probably sick of the former invention, which had given him so much vexation and annoyance, and gave it up in disgust, leaving it to Papin, who saw both his inventions at work, to hit upon the grand idea of combin-ing the two in a steam-vessel, – the only machine capable of effectually and satisfactorily rowing ships in a calm, or against wind and tide.

It is probable that Savery was led to enter upon his next and most impor-tant invention by the circumstance of his having been brought up in the neighbourhood of the mining districts, and being well aware of the great difficulty experienced by the miners in keeping their pits clear of water, to enable them to proceed with their underground operations. The early tin-mining of Cornwall was for the most part what was called "stream-work," being confined mainly to washing and collecting the diluvial deposits of the ore. Mines usually grew out of these stream-works; the ground was laid open at the back of the lodes, and the ore was dug out as from a quarry. Some of these old openings, called "coffins," are still to be met with in different parts of Cornwall. The miners did not venture much below the surface, for fear of the water, by which they were constantly liable to be drowned out. But as the upper strata became exhausted, they were tempted to go deeper in search of the richer ores. Shafts were sunk to the lodes, and they were followed underground. Then it was that the difficulty of water had to be encountered and overcome; for unless it could be got rid of the deeper ores of Cornwall were as so much buried treasure. When the mines were of no great depth, it was possible to bale out the water by hand-buckets. But this expedient was soon exhausted; and the power of horses was then employed to draw the buckets. Where the lodes ran along a bill-side, it was possible, by driving an adit from a lower point, to let off the water by natural drainage. But this was not often found practicable, and in most cases it had to be raised directly from the shafts by artificial methods. As the quantity increased, a whim or gin moving on a perpendicular axis was employed to draw the water.[5] An improvement on this was the rack and chain pump, consisting of an endless iron chain mounted with knobs of cloth stiffened with leather, inclosed in a wooden pump of from six to eight inches bore, the lower part of which rested in the well of the mine. The chain was turned round by a wheel two or three feet in diameter, usually worked by men, and the knobs with which it was mounted brought up a stream of water according to the dimensions of the pump. Another method, considered the most effectual of all, was known as "the water-wheel and bobs," consisting of a powerful pump, or series of pumps, worked by a water-wheel. But although there is no want of water underground in Cornwall, and no want of rain above ground, there are few or no great water-courses capable of driving machinery; besides, as the mines are for the most part situated on high ground, it will be obvious that water-power was available to only a very limited extent for this purpose.

It is also worthy of notice that the early mining of Cornwall was carried on by men of small capital, principally by working men, who were unable to expend any large amount of money in forming artificial reservoirs, or in erecting the powerful pumping machinery necessary for keeping the deeper mines clear of water. The Cornish miners, like the Whitstable oyster dredgers, worked upon the principle of co-operation. This doctrine, now taught as a modern one, was practised by them almost time out of mind. The owner of the land gave the use of his land, the adventurers gave their money, and the miners their labour; all sharing in the proceeds according to ancient custom. For the use of his land, and for the ore taken from the mine, the lord usually took a sixth part; but in consideration of draining the mine, and in order to encourage the adventure, he was often content with an eighth, or it might be only a tenth part of the produce. The miners, on their part, agreed to divide in the proportions in which they took part in the work. Their shares of the ore raised were measured by harrows, and parceled into heaps; "and it is surprising," says Borlase, "to see how ready and exact the reckoners are in dividing, though oftentimes they can neither write nor read. The parcels being laid forth, lots are cast, and then every parcel has a distinct mark laid on it with one, two, or three stones, and sometimes a bit of stick or turf stuck up in the middle or side of the pile; and when these marks are laid on, the parcels may continue there half a year or more unmolested."[6]

These were, however, the early and primitive days of mining, when the operations were carried on comparatively near the surface, and the capital invested in pumping-machinery was comparatively small in amount. As the miners went deeper and deeper into the ground, and the richer lodes were struck and followed, the character of mining became considerably changed. Larger capitals were required to sink the shafts and keep them clear of water until the ore was reached; and a new class of men, outside the mining districts, was induced to venture their money in the mines as a speculation. Yet the system above described, though greatly modified by altered circumstances, continues to this day; and the mining of Cornwall continues to be carried on mainly upon the co-operative or joint-stock system.

When the surface lodes became exhausted, the necessity of employing some more efficient method of pumping the water became more and more urgent. In one pit after another the miners were being drowned out, and the operations of an important branch of national industry were in danger of being brought to a complete standstill. It was under these circumstances that Captain Savery turned his attention to the contrivance of a more powerful engine for the raising of water; and after various experiments, he became persuaded that the most effective agency for the purpose was the power of steam. It is very probable that he was aware of the attempts that had been previously made in the same direction, and he may have gathered many useful and suggestive hints from the Marquis of Worcester's 'Century;' but as that book contained no plans nor precise definitions of the methods by which the Marquis had accomplished his objects, it could have helped him but little towards the contrivance of a practicable working engine.[7]

How Savery was led to the study of the power of steam has been differently stated. Desaguliers says his own account was this, – that having drunk a flask of Florence at a tavern, and thrown the empty flask on the fire, he called for a basin of water to wash his hands, and perceiving that the little wine left in the flask had changed to steam, he took the vessel by the neck and plunged its mouth into the water in the basin, when, the steam being condensed, the water was immediately driven up into the flask by the pressure of the atmosphere. Desaguliers disbelieved this account, but admits that

Savery made many experiments upon the powers of steam, and eventually succeeded in making several engines "which raised water very well." Switzer, who was on intimate terms with Savery, gives another account. He says the first hint from which he took the engine was from a tobacco-pipe, which he immersed in water to wash or cool it; when he discovered by the rarefaction of the air in the tube by the heat or steam, and the gravitation or pressure of the exterior air on the condensation of the latter, that the water was made to spring through the tube of the pipe in a most surprising manner;[8] and that this phenomenon induced him to search for the rationale, and to prosecute a series of experiments which issued in the invention of his fire-engine.

However Savery may have obtained his first idea of the expansion and condensation of steam, and of atmospheric pressure, it is certain that the subject occupied his attention for many years. He had the usual difficulties to encounter in dealing with a wholly new and untried power, in contriving the novel mechanism through which it was to work, and of getting his contrivances executed by the hands of mechanics necessarily unaccustomed to such kind of work. "Though I was obliged," he says, "to encounter the oddest and almost insuperable difficulties, I spared neither time, pains, nor money, till I had absolutely conquered them."

Having sufficiently matured his design, he had a model of his new "Fire Engine," as he termed it, made for exhibition before the King at Hampton Court in 1698. William III, who was himself of a mechanical turn, was highly pleased with the ingenuity displayed in Savery's engine, as well as with its efficient action, and he permitted the inventor to dedicate to him 'The Miner's Friend,' containing the first published description of his invention. The King also promoted Savery's application for a Patent, which was secured in July, 1698,[9] and an Act confirming it was passed in the following year.

Savery's next step was to bring his invention under the notice of the Royal Society, whose opinion on all matters of science was listened to with profound respect. He accordingly exhibited his model at a meeting held on the 14th of June, 1699, and it is recorded in the minutes of that date, that "Mr. Savery entertained the Society with showing his engine to raise water by the force of fire. He was thanked for showing the experiment, which succeeded according to expectation, and was approved of." The inventor presented the Society with a drawing of his engine, accompanied by a description, which was printed in the 'Transactions.'[10]

Savery next endeavoured to bring his invention into practical use, but this was a matter of much greater difficulty. So many schemes with a like object had been brought out and failed, that the mining interest came to regard new projects with increasing suspicion. To persuade them that he was no mere projector, but the inventor of a practicable working engine, Savery wrote and published his 'Miner's Friend.' "I am not very fond," he there said, 'of lying under the scandal of a bare projector, and therefore present you here with a draught of my machine, and lay before you the uses of it, and leave it to your consideration whether it be worth your while to make use of it or no."

Inventors before Savery's time were wont to make a great mystery of their inventions; but he proclaimed that there was no mystery whatever about his machine, and he believed that the more clearly it was understood, the better it would be appreciated. He acknowledged that there had been many pretenders to new inventions of the same sort, who had excited hopes which had never been fulfilled; but this invention which he had made was a thing the uses of which were capable of actual demonstration. He urged that the old methods of raising water could not be carried further; and that an entirely new power was needed to enable the miner to prosecute his underground labours. "I fear," said he, "that whoever by the old causes of motion pretends to improvements within the last century does betray his knowledge and judgment. For more than a hundred years since, men and horses would raise by engines then made as much water as they have ever done since, or I believe ever will, or, according to the law of nature, ever can do. And, though my thoughts have been long employed about water-works, I should never have pretended to any invention of that kind, had I not happily found out this new, but yet a much stronger and cheaper force or cause of motion than any before made use of." He proceeded to show how easy it was to work his engine, – boys of thirteen or fourteen years being able to attend and work it to perfection after a few days' teaching, – and how he had at length, after great difficulty, instructed handicraft artificers to construct the engine according to his design, so that, after much experience, said he, "they are become such masters of the thing that they oblige themselves to deliver what engines they make exactly tight and fit for service, and as such I dare warrant them to anybody that has occasion for them."[11]

Savery's engine, as described by himself, consisted of a series of boilers, condensing vessels, and tubes, the action of which will be readily understood with the help of the following drawing.[12]

Its principal features were two large cylindrical vessels, which were alternately filled with steam from an adjoining boiler and with cold water from the well or mine out of which the water had to be raised. When either of the hollow vessels was filled with steam, and then suddenly cooled by a dash of cold water, a vacuum was thereby created, and, the vessel being closed at the top and open at the bottom, the water was at once forced up into it from the

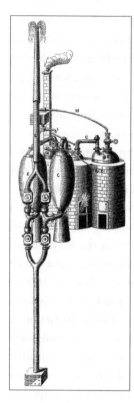

Savery's Fire-Engine

well by the pressure of the atmosphere. The steam, being then let into the vessel from the top, pressed upon the surface of the water, and forced it out at the bottom by another pipe (its return into the well being prevented by a clack), and so up the perpendicular pipe which opened into the outer air. The second vessel being treated in the same manner, the same result followed; and thus, by alternate filling and forcing, a continuous stream of water was poured out from the upper opening. The whole of the labour required to work the engine was capable of being performed by a single man, or even by a boy, after very little teaching.

Although Savery's plans and descriptions of the arrangement and working of his engines are clear and explicit, he does not give any information as to their proportions, – beyond stating that an engine employed in raising a column of water 3½ inches in diameter 60 feet high, requires a fireplace 20 inches deep. Speaking of their performances, he says, "I have known, in Cornwall, a work with three lifts of about 18 feet each, lift and carry a 3½-inch bore, that cost 42s. a day (reckoning 24 a day) for labour, besides the wear and tear of engines, each pump having four men working eight hours, at 14d. a man, and the men obliged to rest at least a third part of that time." He pointed out that at least one-third part of the then cost of raising water might be saved by the adoption of his invention, which on many mines would amount to "a brave estate" in the course of a year. In estimating the power of his engine, Savery was accustomed to compare it with the quantity of work that horses could perform, and hence he introduced the term "horse power," which is still in use.

Although, in the treatise referred to, Savery describes an engine with two furnaces, the drawing which he presented to the Royal Society showed only one; and it appears that in another of his designs he showed only one cylindrical vessel instead of two. In order to exhibit the working of his engine on a larger scale than in the model, he proceeded to erect one in a potter's house at Lambeth, where, Switzer says, though it was a small engine, the water struck up the tiles and forced its way through the roof in a manner that surprised all the spectators. Switzer mentions other engines erected after Savery's designs for the raising of water at Camden House and Sion House, which proved quite successful. The former, he says, was the plainest and best proportioned engine he had seen: it had only a single condensing vessel; and "though but a small one in comparison with many others of the kind that are made for coal-works, it is sufficient for any reasonable family and other uses required for it in watering middling gardens."[13] Four receivers full of water, or equal to 52 gallons, were raised every minute, or 3110 gallons in the hour; whilst, in the case of the larger engines with double receivers, 6240 gallons an hour might easily be raised. The cost of the smaller engine was about fifty pounds, and the consumption of coal about a bushel in the twenty-four hours, supposing it was kept constantly at work during that time.

The uses to which Savery proposed to apply his engine were various. One was to pump water into a reservoir, from which, by falling on a water-wheel, it might produce a continuous rotary motion. Another was to raise water into cisterns for the supply of gentlemen's houses, and for use in fountains and as an extinguisher in case of fire. A third was to raise water for the supply of towns, and a fourth to drain fens and marsh lands. But the most important, in the inventor's estimation, was its employment in clearing drowned mines and coal-pits of water. He showed how water might be raised from deep mines by using several engines, placed at different depths, one over the other. Thus by three lifts, each of 80 feet, water might be raised from a mine about 240 feet – then considered a very great depth. From Savery's own account, it is evident that several of his engines were erected in Cornwall; and it is said that 'the first was tried at Huel Vor, or "The Great Work in Breage," a

Huel Vor, with remains of the old works (by R.P. Leitch)

few miles from Helstone, then considered the richest tin mine in the county. The engine was found to be an improvement on the methods formerly employed for draining the mine, and sent the miners to considerably greater depths. But the great pressure of steam required to force up a high column of water was such as to strain to the utmost the imperfect boilers and receivers of those early days; and the frequent explosions which attended its use eventually led to its discontinuance in favour of the superior engine of Newcomen, which was shortly after invented.

Savery also endeavoured to introduce his engine in the coal-mining districts, but without success, and for the same reason. The demand for coal in connection with the iron manufacture having greatly increased in the county of Stafford, and the coal which lay nearest the surface having been for the most part "won," the mining interest became very desirous of obtaining some more efficient means of clearing the pits of water, in order to send the miners deeper into the ground. Windlass and buckets, wind-mills, horse-gins, rack-and-chain pumps, adits, and all sorts of contrivances had been tried, and the limit of their powers had been reached. The pits were fast becoming drowned out, and the ironmasters began to fear lest their manufacture should become lost through want of fuel. Under these circumstances they were ready to hail the invention of Captain Savery, which promised to relieve them of their difficulty. He was accordingly invited to erect one of his engines over a coal-mine at the Broadwaters, near Wednesbury. The influx of water, however, proved too much for the engine; the springs were so many and so strong, that all the means which Savery could employ failed to clear the mine of water. To increase the forcing power he increased the pressure of steam; but neither boiler nor receiver could endure it, and the steam "tore the engine to pieces; so that, after much time, labour, and expense, Mr. Savery gave up the undertaking, and the engine was laid aside as useless."[14]

He was no more successful with the engine which he erected at York-buildings to pump water from the Thames for the supply of the western parts of London. Bradley says that to increase its power he doubled every part, but "it was liable to so many disorders, if a single mistake happened in the working of it, that at length it was looked upon as a useless piece of work, and rejected."[15] Savery's later engines thus lost him much of the credit which he had gained by those of an earlier and simpler construction. It became clear that their application was very limited. They involved much waste of fuel through the condensation of the hot steam pressing upon the surface of the cold water, previous to the expulsion of the latter from the vessel; and eventually their use was confined to the pumping of water for fountains and the supply of gentlemen's houses, and in some cases to the raising of water for the purpose of working an overshot water-wheel. Various attempts were made to improve the engine by Bradley, by Papin, by Desaguliers, and others; but no great advance was made in its construction and method of working until it was taken in hand by Newcomen and Calley, whose conjoint invention marks an important epoch in the history of the steam-engine.

Not much is known of the later years of Savery's life. We find him a Captain of Military Engineers in 1702;[16] and in 1705, with the view of advancing knowledge in his special branch of military science, he gave to the world a translation, in folio, of Cohorn's celebrated work on fortification. The book was dedicated to Prince George of Denmark, to whom he was indebted, in the same year, for his appointment to the office of Treasurer of the Hospital for Sick and Wounded Seamen. Various letters and documents are still to be found in the Transport Office, Somerset House, addressed to him in that capacity.[17] In 1714 he was further indebted to Prince George for the appointment of Surveyor to the Waterworks at Hampton Court; but be did not live to enjoy it, as he died in the course of the following year. He is said to have accumulated considerable property, which lie bequeathed to his wife, together with all interest in his inventions. His will was executed on the day of his death, the 15th of May, 1715, and was proved four days after in the Prerogative Court of Canterbury. He there described himself as "of the parish of Saint Margaret, at Westminster, Esquire." His widow herself died before all his effects were administered. There was a considerable amount of unclaimed stock, which the Savery family were prevented from claiming, as it had passed to the widow; and it has since been transferred to the credit of the National Debt.

NOTES

1   Burn, 'History of Foreign Protestant Refugees,' 261

2   In a letter, dated Shilston, August 9th, 1727, he writes: – "The late Mr. Thomas Savery, inventor of the engines for rowing, and raising water by fire, was, I believe, well known to several of the Royal Scoiety, perhaps to the President; but as I am perfect stranger, do acquaint you that his father was the youngest brother to my grandfather. The late Servington Savery, M.D., of Marlborough, was one of my family, viz., a brother to my deceased father."

3   It is now in the possession of Capt. Lowe, of the 26th Regiment, whose grand-aunt was a Miss Savery of Shilston.

4   'Navigation Improved; or the Art of Rowing Ships of all rates in calms, with a more easy, swift and steady motion than oars can. Also, a description of the engine that performs it; and the Author's answer to all Mr. Drummer's objections that have been made against it. By Tho. Savory, Gent. London, 1698.'

5   Mr. Davies Gilbert says even this method was comparatively modern, as he remembered a carpenter who used to boast that he had assisted in making the first whim ever seen westward of Hayle. – Davies, 'Parochial History of Cornwall,' London, 1838, ii. 83.

6   Borlase, 'Natural History of Cornwall,' 175–6.

7   The absurd story is told by Dr. Desaguliers ('Experimental Philosophy,' ii. 465) that Savery, having read the Marquis's book, "was the first to put in practice the raising of water by fire, which he proposed for the draining of mines;" and having copied the Marquis's engine, "the better to conceal the matter, bought up all the Marquis of Worcester's books that he could purchase in Paternoster-row and elsewhere, and burned 'em in the presence of the gentleman, his friend, who told me this!" It need scarcely be said that it was very unlikely that Savery should have attempted thus to conceal an invention recorded in a printed book which had been in circulation for more than forty years.

8   Switzer, 'System of Hydrostaticks and Hydraulicks,' London, 1729.

9   The patent is dated the 25th July, 1698, and is entitled, "A grant to Thomas
     Savery, Gentl., of the sole exercise of a new invencon, by him invented,
     for raiseing of water, and occasioning mocon to all sort of mill works, by
     the impellant force of fire, which will be of great use for draining mines,
     serving towns with water, and for working of all sorts of mills when they
     have not the benefit of water nor constant winds; to hold for 14 years; with
     usual clauses."

10   'Philosophical Transactions,' No. 252. Weld's 'Royal Society,' i. 357

11   The Miner's Friend, or an Engine to Raise Water by Fire, described, and of
     the manner of fixing it in mines, with an account of the several uses it is
     applicable unto; and an answer to the objections made against it. By Tho.
     Savery, Gent.' London, 1702.

12   Two boilers, a large, A, A, and a smaller, B, were fixed in a furnace, and
     connected together at the top by a pipe, C. The larger boiler was filled
     two-thirds full, and the smaller quite full of water. When that in the larger
     one was raised to the boiling-point, the handle of the regulator, D, was
     thrust back as far as it would go, by which the steam forced itself through
     the pipe connected with the vessel E, expelling the air it contained through
     the clack at F. The handle of the regulator being then drawn towards you,
     the communication between the boiler and the vessel, E, was closed, and
     that between the boiler and the second vessel, G, was opened, which latter
     was also filled with steam, the air being in like manner discharged through
     the clack, H. Cold water was then poured from the water-cock, I, on to
     the vessel E, by which the steam was suddenly condensed, and a vacuum
     being thereby caused, the water to be raised was drawn up through the
     sucking-pipe, J, its return being prevented by a clack or valve at K. The
     handle of the regulator D being again thrust back, the steam was again
     admitted, and pressing upon the surface of the water in E, forced it out
     at the bottom of the vessel and up through the pipe L, from which it was
     driven into the open air. The handle of the regulator was then reversed, on
     which the steam was again admitted to G, and the water in like manner
     expelled from it, while E, being again dashed with cold water, was refilling
     from below. Then the cold water was turned upon G, and thus alternate
     filling and forcing went on, and a continuous stream of cold water kept
     flowing from the upper opening. The large boiler was replenished with the
     cold water by shutting off the connection of the small cold water pipe, M,
     which supplied it from above, on which the steam contained in the latter
     forced the water through the connecting pipe, C, into the large boiler, and

kept it running in a continuous stream until the surface of the water in the smaller boiler was depressed below the opening of the connecting pipe, which was indicated by the noise of the clack, when it was refilled from the cold water pipe, M, as before.

13   Switzer, 'Introduction to a General System of Hydrostaticks and Hydraulicks,' 237

14   Dr. Wilkes in 'Shaw's History of Staffordshire,' i. 85, 119

15   Bradley, 'Discourses on Earth and water, &c.' Westminster, 1727.

16   We are informed by Quartermaster Conolly, R.E., who has given much attention to the early history of the Royal Engineers, that the book of Warrants and Appointments, anno 1712, No. 172½, in the Tower Record-room, contains the following memorandum in pencil on the inside cover: – [Thomas] "Savery, Engineer officer, 1702–14."

17   A pamphlet published in 1712, entitled 'An Impartial Inquiry into the Management of the War in Spain,' contains the following reference to Savery: – "Sums allowed by Parliament for carrying on the war in Spain … for the year 1710. To Thomas Savery, Esq., for Thomas Cale, surgeon, for the care of disabled soldiers, 306*l*. 6*s*. 4*d*."

IV

Thomas Newcomen –
The Atmospheric Engine

The invention of the steam-engine had advanced thus far with halting steps. A new power had been discovered, but it was so dangerous and unmanageable that it was still doubtful whether it could be applied to any useful purpose. What was still wanting was an engine strong enough to resist the internal pressure of highly heated steam, and so constructed as to work safely, continuously, and economically. Many attempts had been made to contrive such a machine, but, as we have shown, the results were comparatively barren. Savery's small engine could raise water in moderate quantities to limited heights; but the pumping of deep mines was beyond its power. It could force water to a height of about sixteen fathoms; but as the depth of mines at that time was from fifty to a hundred yards, it was obviously incompetent for their drainage. It is true, Savery proposed to overcome the difficulty by erecting a series of engines, placed one over another in the shaft of the mine; but the expense of their attendants, the great consumption of fuel, the cost of wear and tear, the constant danger of explosion, and the risk of the works being stopped by any one of the engines becoming temporarily deranged, rendered it clear that the use of his engine for ordinary mining purposes was altogether impracticable.

Such was the state of affairs when Thomas Newcomen of Dartmouth took up the subject. Comparatively little is known of the personal history of this ingenious man. Mechanical inventors excited little notice in those days; they were looked upon as schemers, and oftener regarded as objects of suspicion than of respect. Thomas Newcomen was by trade an ironmonger and a blacksmith. The house in which he lived and worked stood, until quite recently, in Lower Street, Dartmouth. Like many of the ancient timber houses of that quaint old town, it was a building of singularly picturesque appearance.

Newcomen's House,
Dartmouth
(by R.P. Leitch)[1]

Lower Street is very narrow; the houses in it are tall and irregular, with over-hanging peaked gable-ends. A few years since, Newcomen's house began to show indications of decay; the timber supports were fast failing; and for safety's sake it was determined to pull it to the ground.

The Newcomen family have long since become extinct in Dartmouth. They are said to have left the place long ago, and gone northward; but we have been unable to trace them. The Newcomens appear to have occupied a respectable position in Dartmouth down to about the middle of the last century. Their burying-place was in the north-side chapel of the fine old parish church of the town, where several tablets are erected to their memory. Amongst others, there is one to William Newcomin, Attorney-at-Law, who died the 24th of August, 1745, aged 57, supposed to have been a brother, and another of the same name, who died in 1787, aged 65, supposed to have been a son of the ironmonger.

Thomas Newcomen was a man of strong religious feelings, and from an early period of his life occupied his leisure in voluntary religious teaching. He belonged to the sect of Baptists; and the place was standing until recently in which he regularly preached. When he afterwards went into distant parts of the country on engine business, he continued to devote his Sundays to the same work. How he first came to study the subject of steam is not known. Mr. Holdsworth says a story was current in Dartmouth in his younger days, and generally believed, that Newcomen conceived the idea of the motive power to be obtained from steam by watching the tea-kettle, the lid of which would frequently rise and fall when boiling; and, reasoning upon this fact, he contrived, by filling a cylinder with steam, to raise the piston, and by immediately injecting some cold water, to create a vacuum, which allowed the weight of the atmosphere to press the piston down, and so give motion to a pump by means of a beam and rods.[2]

It is probable that Newcomen was well aware of the experiments of Savery on steam while the latter was living at Modbury, about fifteen miles distant. It will be remembered that Savery was greatly hampered in his earlier contrivances by the want of skilled workmen; and as Newcomen had the reputation of being one of the cleverest blacksmiths in the county, it is supposed that he was employed to make some of the more intricate parts of Savery's engine. At all events, he could scarcely fail to hear from the men of his trade in the neighbourhood, what his speculative neighbour at Modbury was trying to compass in the invention of an engine for the purpose of raising water by fire. He was certainly occupied in studying the subject about the same time as Savery; and Switzer says he was well informed that "Mr. Newcomen was as early in his invention as Mr. Savery was in his, only the latter being nearer the Court, had obtained the patent before the other knew it; on which account Mr. Newcomen was glad to come in as a partner to it."[3]

Another account[4] states that a draft of Savery's engine having come under Newcomen's notice, he proceeded to make a model of it, which he fixed in his garden, and soon found out its imperfections. He entered into a correspondence on the subject with the learned and ingenious Dr. Hooke, then Secretary to the Royal Society, a man of remarkable ingenuity, and of great mechanical sagacity and insight. Newcomen had heard or read of Papin's proposed method of transmitting motive power to a distance by creating a vacuum under a piston in a cylinder, and transmitting the power through pipes to a second cylinder near the mine. Dr. Hooke dissuaded Newcomen from erecting a machine on this principle, as a waste of time and labour, but he added the pregnant suggestion, "could he (meaning Papin) make a speedy vacuum under your piston, your work were done."

The capital idea thus cursorily thrown out – of introducing a moveable dia-
phragm between the active power and the vacuum – set Newcomen at once
upon the right track. Though the suggestion was merely that of a thoughtful bystander it was a most important step in the history of the invention,
for it contained the very principle of the atmospheric engine. Savery created
his vacuum by the condensation of steam in a closed vessel, and Papin created his by exhausting the air in a cylinder fitted with a piston, by means
of an air-pump. It remained for Newcomen to combine the two expedients
– to secure a sudden vacuum by the condensation of steam; but, instead of
employing Savery's closed vessel, he made use of Papin's cylinder fitted with
a piston. After long scheming and many failures, he at length succeeded, in
the year 1705,[5] in contriving a model that worked with tolerable precision;
after which he sought for an opportunity of exhibiting its powers in a full-
sized working engine. It ought to be mentioned, that in the long course of
experiments conducted by Newcomen with the object of finding out the new
motive power, he was zealously assisted throughout by one John Calley, a
glazier of Dartmouth, of whom nothing further is known than that he was
Newcomen's intimate friend, of the same religious persuasion, and afterwards
his partner in the steam-engine enterprise.

Newcomen's engine may be thus briefly described: – The steam was generated in a separate boiler, as in Savery's engine, from which it was conveyed
into a vertical cylinder underneath a piston fitting it closely, but moveable
upwards and downwards through its whole length. The piston was fixed to a
rod, which was attached by a joint or a chain to the end of a lever vibrating
upon an axis, the other end being attached to a rod working a pump. When
the piston in the cylinder was raised, steam was let into the vacated space
through a tube fitted into the top of the boiler, and mounted with a stopcock.
The pump-rod at the further end of the lever being thus depressed, cold water
was applied to the sides of the cylinder, on which the steam within it was
condensed, a vacuum was produced, and the external air, pressing upon the
top of the piston, forced it down into the empty cylinder. The pump-rod was
thereby raised; and the operation of depressing and raising it being repeated, a
power was thus produced which kept the pump continuously at work. Such,
in a few words, was the construction and action of Newcomen's first engine.

It will thus be observed that this engine was essentially different in principle
from that of Savery. While the latter raised water partly by the force of steam
and partly by the pressure of the atmosphere, that of Newcomen worked
entirely by the pressure of the atmosphere, steam being only used as the most
expeditious method of producing a vacuum. The engine was, however, found

to be very imperfect. It was exceedingly slow in its motions; much time was occupied in condensing the contained steam by throwing cold water on the outside of the cylinder; and as the boiler was placed immediately under the cylinder, it was not easy to prevent the cold water from splashing it, and thus leading to a further loss of heat. To remedy these imperfections, Newcomen and Calley altered the arrangement; and, instead of throwing cold water on the outside of the cylinder, they surrounded it with cold water. But this expedient was also found inconvenient, as the surrounding water shortly became warm, and ceased to condense until replaced by colder water; but the colder it was the greater was the loss of heat by condensation, before the steam was enabled to fill the cylinder again on each ascent of the piston.

Clumsy and comparatively ineffective though the engine was in this form, it was, nevertheless, found of some use in pumping water from mines. In 1711 Newcomen and Calley made proposals to the owners of a colliery at Griff, in Warwickshire, to drain the water from their pits, which until then had been drained by the labour of horses; but, the owners not believing in the practicability of the scheme, their offer was declined. In the following year, however, they succeeded in obtaining a contract with Mr. Back, for drawing the water from a mine belonging to him near Wolverhampton. The place where the engine was to be erected being near to Birmingham, the ironwork, the pump-valves, clacks, and buckets, were for the most part made there, and removed to the mine, where they were fitted together. Newcomen had great difficulty at first in making the engine go; but after many laborious attempts he at last partially succeeded. It was found, however, that the new method of cooling the cylinder by surrounding it with cold water did not work so well in practice as had been expected. The vacuum produced was very imperfect, and the action of the engine was both very slow and very irregular.

While the engine was still in its trial state, a curious accident occurred which led to another change in the mode of condensation, and proved of essential importance in establishing Newcomen's engine as a practicable working power. The accident was this: in order to keep the cylinder as free from air as possible, great pains were taken to prevent it passing down by the side of the piston, which was carefully wrapped with cloth or leather; and, still further to keep the cylinder air-tight, a quantity of water was kept constantly laying on the upper side of the piston. At one of the early trials the inventors were surprised to see the engine make several strokes in unusually quick succession; and on searching for the cause, they found it to consist in *a hole in the piston*, which had let the cold water in a jet into the inside of the cylinder, and thereby produced a rapid vacuum by the condensation of the contained steam.

A new light suddenly broke upon Newcomen. The idea of condensing by injection of cold water directly into the cylinder, instead of applying it on the outside, at once occurred to him; and he proceeded to embody the expedient which had thus been accidentally suggested, as part of his machine. The result was the addition of the injection-pipe, through which, when the piston was raised and the cylinder was full of steam, a jet of cold water was thrown in, and the steam being suddenly condensed, the piston was at once driven down by the pressure of the atmosphere.

An accident of a different kind shortly after led to the improvement of Newcomen's engine in another respect. To keep it at work, one man was required to attend the fire, and another to turn alternately the two cocks, one admitting the steam into the cylinder, the other admitting the jet of cold water to condense it. The turning of these cocks was easy work, usually performed by a boy. It was, however, a very monotonous duty, though requiring constant attention. To escape the drudgery and obtain an interval for rest, or perhaps for play, a boy named Humphrey Potter, who turned the cocks, set himself to discover some method of evading his task. He must have been an ingenious boy, as is clear from the arrangement he contrived with this object. Observing the alternate ascent and descent of the beam above his head, he bethought him of applying the movement to the alternate raising and lowering of the levers which governed the cocks. The result was the contrivance of what he called the scoggan,[6] consisting of a catch worked by strings from the beam of the engine. This arrangement, when tried, was found to answer the purpose intended. The action of the engine was thus made automatic; and the arrangement, though rude, not only enabled Potter to enjoy his play, but it had the effect of improving the working power of the engine itself; the number of strokes which it made being increased from six or eight to fifteen or sixteen in the minute. This invention was afterwards greatly improved by Mr. Henry Beighton, of Newcastle-on-Tyne, who added the plug-rod and hand-gear. He did away with the catches and strings of the boy Potter's rude apparatus, and substituted a rod suspended from the beam, which alternately opened and shut the tappets attached to the steam and injection cocks.

Thus, step by step, Newcomen's engine grew in power and efficiency, and became more and more complete as a self-acting machine. It will be observed that, like all other inventions, it was not the product of any one man's ingenuity, but of many. One contributed one improvement, and another another. The essential features of the atmospheric engine were not new. The piston and cylinder had been known as long ago as the time of Hero.

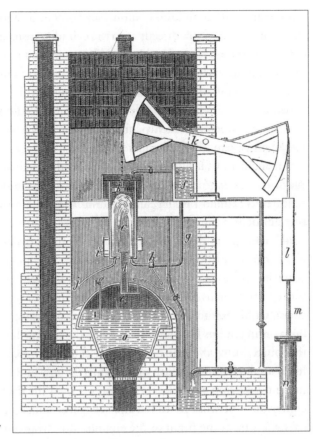

Newcomen's Engine[7]

The expansive force of steam and the creation of a vacuum by its condensation had been known to the Marquis of Worcester, Savery, Papin, and many more. Newcomen merely combined in his machine the result of their varied experience, and, assisted by the persons who worked with him, down to the engine-boy Potter, he advanced the invention several important stages; so that the steam-engine was no longer a toy or a scientific curiosity, but had become a powerful machine capable of doing useful work.

The comparative success which attended the working of Newcomen's first engine at the colliery near Wolverhampton, shortly induced other owners of coal-mines to adopt it. There were great complaints in the north, of the deeper mines having become unworkable. All the ordinary means of pumping them clear of water had failed. In their emergency, the colliery-owners called Newcomen and Calley to their aid. They were invited down to Newcastle-upon-Tyne, in the neighbourhood of which town they erected their second and third engines. They were next summoned to Leeds, and erected their fourth engine at Austhorpe, in 1714. It was the sight of this engine at work which first induced Smeaton, when a boy, to turn his attention to mechanics, and eventually led him to study the atmospheric-engine, with a view to its improvement. The cylinder of the engine erected at Austhorpe, like those which had preceded it, was about 23 inches in diameter, and made about fifteen strokes a minute. The pumps, which were in two lifts, and of 9 inches bore, drew the water from a depth of 37 yards. The patentees had 250*l.* a year for working and keeping the engine in order. Calley superintended its erection, and afterwards its working; but he did not long survive its completion, as he died at Austhorpe in 1717.

The next engines were erected by Newcomen in Cornwall, where there was as great a demand for increased pumping-power as in any of the collieries of the north. The first of Newcomen's construction in Cornwall was erected in 1720, at the Wheal Fortune tin mine, in the parish of Ludgvan, a few miles northeast of Penzance. The mine was conducted by Mr. William Lemon, the founder of the fortunes of the well-known Cornish family. He was born in a humble station in life, from which be honourably raised himself by his great industry, ability, and energy. He began his career as a mining-boy; was at an early age appointed one of the managers of a tin-smelting house at Chiandower, near Penzance; and after the experience gained by him in that capacity he engaged in the working of the Wheal Fortune mine. With the help of Newcomen's engine, the enterprise proved completely successful; and after realising a considerable sum he removed to Truro, and began working the great Gwennap mines on such a scale as had never before been known in Cornwall.[8]

The Wheal Fortune engine was on a larger scale than any that had yet been erected, the cylinder being 47 inches in diameter, making about fifteen strokes a minute. It drew about a hogshead of water at each stroke, from a pump 30 fathoms deep, through pit-barrels 15 inches in diameter, and its performances were on the whole regarded as very extraordinary. The principal objection to its use consisted in the very large quantity of coal that it consumed and the heavy cost of maintaining it in working order. There was a great waste, especially in boilers, the making of which was then ill understood. Smeaton relates that in the course of four years' working of the first Austhorpe engine, not fewer than four boilers were burnt out. The Wheal Fortune engine, however, answered its purpose. It kept down the water sufficiently to enable Mr. Lemon to draw up his tin, and on leaving the mine, he took with him to Truro a clear sum of ten thousand pounds. The engine-house is now in ruins, and presents a highly picturesque appearance, as seen from the heights of Trewal, reminding one of a Border Peel rather than of a mining engine-house.

Ruins of Wheal Fortune (by R.P. Leitch)

Another of Newcomen's engines was erected about the same time at the Wheal Rose mine, a few miles north of Redruth. The engineer appointed to superintend its erection was Joseph Hornblower, who came from Staffordshire for the purpose about the year 1725. Mr. Cyrus Redding, one of Hornblower's descendants, says, "how he became in any way connected with Newcomen must have arisen from the latter being at Bromsgrove, when he visited Mr. Potter, who got him to build one of his newly-invented engines at Wolverhampton in 1712."[9] Another engine was afterwards erected by Hornblower at Wheal Busy, or Chacewater, and a third at Polgooth – all rich and well-known mines in Cornwall.

Though the use of Newcomen's engine rapidly extended, nothing is known of the man himself during this time. All over the mining districts his name was identified with the means employed for pumping the mines clear of water, and thereby enabling an important branch of the national industry to be carried on; but of Newcomen's personal history, beyond what has been stated above, we can gather nothing. It is not known when or where he died, whether rich or poor. The probability is that, being a person of a modest and retiring disposition, without business energy, and having secured no protection for his invention, it was appropriated and made use of by others, without any profit to him, whilst he quietly subsided into private life.

Polgooth

It is supposed that he died at Dartmouth about the middle of last century; but no stone marks the place where he was laid. The only memorial of Newcomen to be found at his native place is the little steam-boat called by his name, which plies between Totness and Dartmouth.

During Newcomen's lifetime the proposal was revived of applying the steam-engine to the propelling of ships. Since Papin's time nothing had been accomplished in this direction. Now that the steam-engine was actively employed in pumping mines, it was natural enough that the idea should be revived of applying it to navigation. The most enthusiastic advocate of the new power was Jonathan Hulls, a native of Campden, in Gloucestershire, where he was born in 1699. He married a wife in 1719, before he was out of his teens; an act of indiscretion in which, however, he had the example of one no less distinguished than Shakespeare. Living as he did in an inland country place, it seems remarkable that he should have directed his attention to the subject of steam-navigation. We find him making experiments with models of boats on the river Avon, at Evesham, and in course of time he duly matured his ideas and embodied them in his patent of 1736.[10] He proposed to place a

Jonathan Hulls's Steam-boat

Newcomen engine on board a tow-boat, and by its means to work a paddle-wheel placed at the stern. His method of converting the rectilinear motion of his piston into a rotary one was ingenious, but, like Savery, he missed the crank on the paddle-shaft, and many years passed before this simple expedient was adopted.[11] "The work to be done by this machine," said he, "will be upon particular occasions, when all other means yet found out are wholly insufficient. How often does a merchant wish that his ship were on the ocean, when, if she were there, the wind would serve tolerably well to carry him on his intended voyage, but does not serve at the same time to carry him out of the river he happens to be in, which a few hours' work of the machine would do. Besides, I know engines that are driven by the same power as this is, where materials for the purpose are dearer than in any navigable river in England; therefore experience demonstrates that the expense will be but a trifle to the value of the work performed by those sort of machines, which any person that knows the nature of those things may easily calculate." His treatise was illustrated by a drawing, of which the above is a copy on a reduced scale.

The inventor, aware of the novelty of his proposal and of the readiness of the public to ridicule novelties, deprecated rash censure of his project, and only claimed for it a fair and unprejudiced trial. In order to exhibit the powers of his steam-boat, he constructed an engine in 1737, and had it fixed on board a little vessel for trial in the river Avon at Evesham. The

trial was not satisfactory, and the engine was taken on shore again. "A failure! A failure!" cried the spectators, who stigmatised the projector as an ass.
The prophet had, indeed, no honour whatever in his own country. Long
after his steam-boat experiment had been forgotten, these lines about him
were remembered:

> Jonathan Hull,
> With his paper skull,
> Tried hard to make a machine
> That should go against wind and tide:
> But he, like an ass,
> Couldn't bring it to pass,
> So at last was ashamed to be seen.[12]

Not much more is known of Jonathan Hulls's history. In 1754 he published,
in conjunction with two others, a treatise on 'The Art of Measuring made
Easy, by the help of a new Sliding-rule;' and shortly after 'The Malt-maker's
Instructor;' but nothing more was heard of Jonathan Hulls's steam-boat.

We return to the Newcomen engine, which became increasingly employed
as a pumping power in all the mining districts. Borlase, writing in 1758, says
that "fire-engines" were then in regular use at North Downs near Redruth,
Pitt-louarn, Polgooth, Wheal-rith, Pool, Dolcoath, Herland, and many other
places.[13] Indeed there was scarcely a tin or copper mine of any importance
in Cornwall that had not one or more of Newcomen's engines at work.
They were also in general use in Staffordshire, Yorkshire, Lancashire, and
Northumberland. In the latter counties, where they were principally used for
pumping water out of the coal mines, fuel was ready at hand, cheap and abundant. But in Cornwall it was otherwise. The coal had to be brought thither
from a great distance, partly by sea and partly by land, and the cost of carriage
was very heavy. It, therefore, became an object of much importance to reduce
the consumption of fuel, to prevent the profits of the mines being absorbed
by the heavy cost of working the pumps. This, indeed, was the great objection
to Newcomen's engine, especially in Cornwall. The consumption of fuel at
some mines was so enormous, that it was doubtful whether the cost of steam
did not exceed that of an equal amount of horse power, and it became more
and more difficult to realise even a bare margin of profit. The two engines at
Wheal Rose and Wheal Busy, near Chacewater, of 66 and 72 inches diameter,
consumed each about thirteen tons of coal daily. To relieve the mining interest, in some measure, from this charge, government allowed a drawback of

Dartmouth, from the Harbour (by R.P. Leitch)

five shillings a chaldron on coal; but in some cases this was found insufficient, and it began to be complained that the consumption of coal was so great, that the mines were barely paying.

Invention, however, was constantly at work, and new improvements were from time to time introduced, with the object of economising fuel and increasing the efficiency of the engine. Among the ingenious men who devoted themselves to this work, were Payne, Brindley, and Smeaton. Of these, the last especially distinguished himself by his improvements of the Newcomen engine, which he may be said to have carried to the highest perfection of which it was capable. His famous Chacewater engine was the finest and most powerful work of the kind which had until then been constructed, and it remained unrivalled until superseded by the invention of Watt, to whose life and labours we now proceed to direct the attention of the reader.

NOTES

1   Newcomen's house occupies the centre of the engraving – the house with the peaked gable-end supported by timbers.

2   Pamphlet on 'Dartmouth: the advantages of its Harbour as a Station for Foreign Mail Packets, and a Short Notification of its Ancient and Present Condition.' By A.H. Holdsworth, London, 1841.

3   Switzer, 'Introduction to a System of Hydrostatics and Hydraulics,' p. 342

4   Harris, 'Lexicon Technicum.'

5   It has been stated that Newcomen took out a patent for his invention in
     1705; but this is a mistake, as no patent was ever taken out by Newcomen.
     It is supposed that Savery, having heard of his invention, gave him
     notice that he would regard his method of producing a speedy vacuum
     by condensation, as an infringement of his patent, and that Newcomen
     accordingly agreed to give him an interest in the new engine during the
     term of Savery's patent. It will, however, be observed that the principle
     on which Newcomen's engine worked was entirely different from that of
     Savery.

6   *Scogging* is a north country word, meaning skulking one's work, from
     which probably the boy gave the contrivance its name. Potter, however,
     grew up to be a highly skilled workman. He went abroad about the year
     1720, and erected an engine at a mine in Hungary. Described by Leupold
     in his 'Theatrum Machinarum,' with many encomiums upon Potter, who
     was considered the inventor.

7   The illustration shows the several parts of Newcomen's atmospheric engine.
     a is the boiler; *b*, the piston moving up and down; *c*, the cylinder; *d*, a
     pipe proceeding from the top of the boiler, and inserted into the bottom
     of the cylinder, having a cock, *e*, to interrupt the flow of steam at pleasure;
     f, cold-water cistern, from which the cold water is conveyed by the pipe
     g, called the injection-pipe, and thrown in a jet into the cylinder, *b*, on
     turning the injection-cock, *h*; the snifting-valve, *i*, enables the air to escape
     from the cylinder, while the siphon-pipe, *j*, enables the condensed steam
     to flow from the same cavity in the form of water; *k*, the main lever beam;
     l, the counterpoise or weight hung on the balance-beam, or on *m*, the
     pump-rod which works the pump, *n*.

8   Mr. Lemon eventually became the principal merchant and tin-smelter
     of Cornwall. Mr. Davies Gilbert says: – "The energies of his mind were
     not limited to these undertakings, great though they were. He cultivated
     a taste for literature, and, which is extremely unusual, acquired, amidst
     business, and at a middle age, the power of reading the classic authors in
     their original language ... He was distinguished in his district as "the great
     Mr. Lemon," but such were the impressions of his abilities, his exertions,
     and general merit, that a progress so rapid and unexampled does not
     appear to have excited envy, or any of those bad passions which usually
     alloy the enjoyment of prosperity." – 'History of Cornwall,' ii. 84

9   "It may be interesting to know that it required three hands to work
     Newcomen's first engines. I have heard it said that when the engine was

stopped, and again set at work, the words were passed "Snift Benjy!" "Blow the fire, Pomery!" "Work away, Joe!" The last let in the condensing water. Lifting the condensing clack was called "snifting," because on opening the valve, the air rushing through it made a noise like a man snifting. The fire was increased through artificial means by another hand, and all being ready, the machine was set in motion by a third." – Cyrus Redding, 'Yesterday and Today.' London, 1863. The "snifting clack" was a valve in the cylinder opening outwards, which permitted the escape of air or permanently elastic fluid, which could not be condensed by cold and run off through the eduction-pipe.

10   In 1737 he published a Treatise on the subject entitled, 'A description and Draught of a new-invented Machine for carrying Vessels or Ships out of or into any Harbour, Port, or River, against Wind or Tide, and in Calm,' by Jonathan Hulls.

11   In describing his mode of obtaining rotary motion by ratchet wheels, a weight, and ropes, Hulls states that he uses two axes, one behind the other, each of which is essential to the object; and he then adds, that when his tow boat is to be used in shallow rivers, the machine works by two cranks fixed to the hindermost axis; to which cranks are fixed two shafts (or poles) of proper length to reach the bottom of the river, and which move alternately forward from the motion of the wheels by which the vessel is carried on: so that the cranks, as described by Hulls, receive rotary motion from the axis on which they are placed, and do not, as has been erroneously stated, impart that motion to it. – Bennet Woodcroft, 'Sketch of the Origin and Progress of Steam Navigation.' London, 1848.

12   There are several versions of the same satire current to this day in the villages of Campden and Hanging Aston.

13   Borlase, 'Natural History of Cornwall,' p. 175.

James Watt

His Boyhood and Early Life: Mechanical Instrument Maker, Surveyor, and Inventor

Greenock and the Clyde, 1865 (by R.P. Leitch, after a sketch by J.S. Smiles)

Greenock harbour, 1768 (facsimile of an old print)

V

James Watt – Lineage and Birthplace – Boyhood and Apprenticeship

James Watt was born at Greenock, on the Clyde, on the 19th of January, 1736. His parents were of the middle class, industrious, intelligent, and religious people, with a character for probity which had descended to them from their "forbears," and was cherished as their proudest inheritance. James Watt was thus emphatically well-born. His father and grandfather both held local offices of trust, and honourable mention is made of them in the records of Greenock. His grandfather, Thomas Watt, was the first of the family who lived in that neighbourhood. He had migrated thither from the county of Aberdeen, where his father was a small farmer in the time of Charles I. It is supposed that he took part with the Covenanters in resisting the Marquis of Montrose in his sudden descent upon Aberdeen at the head of his wild Highlanders in the autumn of 1644; and that the Covenanting farmer was killed in one of the battles that ensued. The district was ravaged by the victorious Royalists; the crops were destroyed, cattle lifted, dwellings burnt; and many of the inhabitants fled southwards for refuge in more peaceful districts. Hence Thomas Watt's migration to Cartsdyke, where we find him settled as a teacher of navigation and mathematics, about the middle of the seventeenth century.

Cartsdyke, or Crawfordsdyke, was then a village situated a little to the east of Greenock, though now forming part of it. Crawfordsburn House, still standing, was the residence of the lord of the manor, and is a good specimen of the old-fashioned country mansion. It is beautifully situated on the high ground overlooking the Clyde. In former times a green slope stretched down from it towards the beach, along which lay the village, consisting of about a hundred cottages, mostly thatched. Cartsdyke was, however, in early times, a place of greater importance than Greenock. It had a pier, which

Greenock as yet had not; and from this pier the first Clyde ship which crossed the Atlantic sailed for Darien in 1697. What little enterprise existed in the neighbourhood was identified with Cartsdyke rather than with Greenock; and hence Thomas Watt's preference for it, in setting up there as a teacher. He, too, like his sire, seems to have been a sturdy Covenanter; for we find him, in 1683, refusing to take the test in favour of prelacy, and he was consequently proclaimed to be a "disorderly schoolmaster officiating contrary to law." He nevertheless continued the teaching of the mathematics, in which he seems to have prospered, as, besides marrying a wife, he shortly after bought the house and garden which he occupied, and subsequently added to his possessions a tenement in the neighbouring village of Greenock.

From the nature of his calling, it is obvious that he must have been a thoughtful and intelligent person;[1] and that he was a man of excellent character is clear from the confidence he inspired in those who had the best opportunities of knowing him. When William and Mary were confirmed in their occupancy of the British throne, shortly after the Revolution of 1688, one of the first acts of Mr. Crawford, of Crawfordsburn, the feudal superior, was to appoint Thomas Watt baillie of the barony – a position of local importance, involving the direction of public affairs within the limits of his jurisdiction.

A few years later, the Kirk Session of Greenock, having found him "blameless in life and conversation," appointed him an Elder of the parish, when it became part of his duty to overlook not only the religious observances, but the manners and morals, of the little community. Kirk Sessions did not then confine themselves to ecclesiastical affairs, but assumed the function of magistrates, and almost exercised the powers of an inquisition. One of their most important duties was to provide for the education of the rising generation, in pursuance of the injunction of John Knox, "that no father, of what estate or condition that ever be may be, use his children at his own fantasie, especially in their youthhead; but all must be compelled to bring up their children in learning and virtue," – words which lie at the root of much of Scotland's mental culture, as well as, probably, of its material prosperity. In 1696 the Act was passed by the Scotch Parliament which is usually regarded as the charter of the Scotch parish-school system; and in the following year the Kirk Session of Greenock proceeded to make provision for the establishment of their parish school, which continued until the Town Council superseded it by the Grammar School, at which James Watt, the future engineer, received the best part of his school education.

After holding the offices of Presbytery Elder and Kirk Treasurer for some time, Thomas Watt craved leave to retire into private life. He was seventy

Crawfordsburn House, Greenock

years old, and felt infirmities growing upon him. The plea was acknowledged, and the request granted; and on his retirement from office the Kirk Session recorded on their minutes that Thomas Watt had been found "diligent and faithful in the management of his trust." He died at the age of 92, and was buried in the old kirk-yard of Greenock, where his tombstone is still to be seen. He is there described as "Professor of Mathematics in Crawfordsdyk." Not far from his grave lie, "mouldering in silent dust," the remains of Burns's Highland Mary, who died while on a visit to a relative at Greenock.

Two sons survived the "Professor," John and James, who were well settled in life when the old man died. John, the elder, was trained by his father in mathematics and surveying; for some time officiating under him as clerk to the barony of Cartsdyke, and afterwards removing to Glasgow, where he began business on his own account. In the year that his father died (1734) he made the first survey of the river Clyde; but he died shortly after, and the map was published by his nephew. James, the engineer's father, was bound apprentice to a carpenter and shipwright at Cartsdyke, and on the expiry of his term he set up business for himself in the same line at Greenock.

About the beginning of the last century, Greenock, now one of the busiest ports in the kingdom, was but a little fishing-village, consisting of a single row of thatched cottages lying parallel with the sandy beach of the

Firth of Clyde, in what was then known as "Sir John's little bay." Sir John
Shaw was the superior, or lord of the manor, his mansion standing on a
height overlooking the town,[2] and commanding an extensive view of the
Clyde, from Rosneath to Dumbarton. Across the water lay the beautiful
north shore, broken by the long narrow sea-lochs running far away among
the Argyleshire hills. Their waters, now plashed by the paddles of innumerable Clyde steamers, were then only disturbed by the passing of an
occasional Highland coble; whilst their shores, now fringed with villages,
villas, and mansions, were as lonely as Glencoe.

  Greenock was in a great measure isolated from other towns by impassable
roads. The only route to Greenock, on the west, lay along the beach, and
when strong winds raised a high tide the communication was entirely cut
off. Greenock was separated from Cartsdyke, on the east, by the Ling Burn,
which was crossed by a plank, afterwards supplanted by an old ship's rudder;
and it was about the middle of the century before a bridge was built across the
stream. The other provisions of the place for public service and convenience
were of a like rude and primitive character: thus, Greenock could not boast of
a public clock until about the middle of the last century, when a town clock
was mounted in a wooden steeple. Till then, a dial, still standing, marked
the hours when the sun shone, and a bell hung upon a triangle summoned
the people to kirk and market. Besides the kirk, however, there was another
public building – the Black Hole, or prison, which, like the other houses in
the place, was covered with thatch. Before the prison were placed the "jougs,"
as a terror to evil-doers, as well as a few old pieces of cannon, taken from
one of the ships of the Spanish Armada wrecked near Pencores Castle. The
Black Hole, the jougs, and the cannon were thought necessary precautions
against the occasional visits to which the place was subject from the hungry
Highlandmen on the opposite shores of the firth.[3]

  The prosperity of Greenock dates from the year 1707, shortly after the
Union with England. The British Parliament then granted what the Scottish
Parliament had refused – the privilege of constructing a harbour. Before that
time there was no pier, – only a rude landing-stage which Sir John Shaw had
provided for his barge in the "Little Bay;" but the fishermen's boats and other
small craft frequenting the place were beached in the usual primitive way.
Vessels of burden requiring to load or unload their cargoes did so at the pier
at Cartsdyke above referred to. When the necessary powers were granted to
make a harbour at Greenock, the inhabitants proceeded to tax themselves to
provide the necessary means, paying a shilling and fourpence for every sack of
malt brewed into ale within the barony; ale, not whisky, being then the popu-

lar drink of Scotland. The devotion of the townspeople to their "yill caups" must have been considerable, as the harbour was finished and opened in 1710, and in thirty years the principal debt was paid off.

In course of time Greenock was made a custom-house port, and its trade rapidly increased. The first solitary vessel, freighted with Glasgow merchandise for the American colonies, sailed from the new harbour in 1719; and now the custom-house dues collected there amount to more than six times the whole revenue of Scotland in the time of the Stuarts.

Here James Watt, son of the Cartsdyke teacher of mathematics, and father of the engineer, began business about the year 1730. His occupation was of a very miscellaneous character, and embraced most branches of carpentry. He was a housewright, shipwright, carpenter, and undertaker, as well as a builder and contractor, having in the course of his life enlarged the western front of Sir John Shaw's mansion-house, and designed and built the Town-hall and Council-chambers. To these various occupations Mr. Watt added that of a general merchant. He supplied the ships frequenting the port with articles of merchandise as well as with ships' stores. He also engaged in foreign mercantile ventures, and held shares in several ships.

Three months after the death of his father, to a share of whose property he succeeded, Mr. Watt purchased a house on the Mid-Quay Head, at the lower end of William-street, with a piece of ground belonging to it, which extended to the beach. On this piece of ground stood Watt's carpenter's shop, in which a great deal of miscellaneous work was executed – household furniture and ships' fittings, chairs, tables, coffins, and capstans, as well as the ordinary sorts of joinery; while from his stores he was ready to supply blocks, pumps, gun-carriages, dead-eyes, and other articles used on board ship. He was ready to "touch" ships' compasses, and to adjust and repair nautical instruments generally; while in an emergency he could make a crane for harbour uses – the first in Greenock having been executed in his shops, and erected on the pier for the convenience of the Virginia tobacco-ships beginning to frequent the harbour. These multifarious occupations were necessitated by the smallness of the place, the business of a single calling being as yet too limited to yield a competency to an enterprising man, or sufficient scope for his powers.

Being a person of substance and respectability, Mr. Watt was elected by his fellow townsmen to fill various public offices, such as trustee for the burgh fund, town councillor, treasurer, and afterwards baillie or chief magistrate. He also added to his comfort as well as to his dignity by marrying a wife of character, Agnes Muirhead, a woman esteemed by her neighbours for her graces of person, as well as of mind and heart. She is said to have been not

James Watt Tavern, Greenock

less distinguished for her sound sense and good manners than for her cheerful temper and excellent housewifery.[4] Such was the mother of James Watt.
Three of her five children died in childhood; John, her fifth son perished at
sea when on a voyage to America in one of his father's ships; and James, the
fourth of the family, remained her only surviving child. He was born in the
house which stood at the corner between the present Dalrymple-street and
William-street, since taken down and replaced by the building now known as
the "James Watt Tavern."

From his earliest years James Watt was of an extremely fragile constitution, requiring the tenderest nurture. Struggling as it were for life all through
his childhood, he acquired an almost feminine delicacy and sensitiveness,
which made him shrink from the rough play of robust children; and hence,
during his early years his education was entirely conducted at home. His
mother taught him reading, and his father a little writing and arithmetic. His
mother, to amuse him, encouraged him to draw with a pencil on paper, or
with chalk upon the floor; and his father supplied him with a few tools from
the carpenter's shop, which he soon learnt to handle with expertness. In such
occupations he found the best resource against *ennui*. He took his toys to
pieces, and out of the parts ingeniously constructed new ones. The mechanical dexterity which he thus cultivated even as a child was probably in a great
measure the foundation upon which he built the speculations to which he
owes his glory; nor, without his early mechanical training, is there reason to

believe that he would afterwards become the improver and almost the creator of the steam-engine.

The invalid thus passed his early years almost entirely in the society of his mother, whose gentle nature, strong good sense, and unobtrusive piety, exercised a most beneficial influence in the formation of his character. Nor were his parents without their reward; for as the boy grew up to manhood he repaid their anxious care with obedience, respect, and affection. Mrs. Watt was in after life accustomed to say that the loss of her only daughter, which she had felt so severely, had been fully made up to her by the dutiful attentions of her son.

Spending his life indoors, without exercise, his nervous system became preternaturally sensitive. He was subject to violent sick headaches, which confined him to his room for weeks together; and it almost seems a marvel that, under such circumstances, he should have survived his boyhood It is in such cases as his that indications of precocity are generally observed; and parents would be less gratified at their display if they knew that they are usually the symptoms of disease. Several remarkable instances of this precocity are related of Watt. On one occasion, when he was bending over the hearth with a piece of chalk in his hand, a friend of his father said, "You ought to send that boy to a public school, and not allow him to trifle away his time at home." "Look how my child is occupied," said the father, "before you condemn him." Though only six years old, it is said he was found trying to solve a problem in geometry.

On another occasion he was reproved by Mrs. Muirhead, his aunt, for his indolence at the tea-table. "James Watt," said the worthy lady, "I never saw such an idle boy as you are: take a book or employ yourself usefully; for the last hour you have not spoken one word, but taken off the lid of that kettle and put it on again, holding now a cup and now a silver spoon over the steam, watching how it rises from the spout, catching and counting the drops it falls into." In the view of M. Arago, the little James before the tea-kettle becomes "the great engineer, preparing the discoveries which were soon to immortalize him." In our opinion the judgment of the aunt was the truest. There is no reason to suppose that the mind of the boy was occupied with philosophical theories on the condensation of steam, which he compassed with so much difficulty in his maturer years. This is more probably an afterthought borrowed from his subsequent discoveries. Nothing is commoner than for children to be amused with such phenomena, in the same way that they will form air-bubbles in a cup of tea, and watch them sailing over the surface till they burst. The probability is that little James was quite as idle as he seemed.

When he was at length sent to Mr. M'Adam's commercial school, the change caused him many trials and much suffering. He found himself completely out of place in the midst of the boisterous juvenile republic. Against the tyranny of the elders he was helpless; their wild play was most distasteful to him; he could not join in their sports, nor roam with them along the beach, nor shy stones into the water, nor take part in their hazardous exploits in the harbour. Accordingly they showered upon him contemptuous epithets; and the school being composed of both sexes, the girls joined in the laugh. He shone as little in the class as in the playground. He did not possess that parrot power of learning and confidence in self necessary to achieve distinction at school; and he was even considered dull and backward for his age.[5] His want of progress may, however, in some measure be accounted for by his almost continual ailments, which sometimes kept him for weeks together at home. It was not until he reached the age of about thirteen or fourteen, when he was put into the mathematical class, that his powers appeared to develop themselves, and from that time he made rapid progress.

When not quite fourteen, he was taken by his mother for change of air to Glasgow, then a quiet place without a single long chimney, somewhat resembling a rural market-town of the present day. He was left in charge of a relation, and his mother returned to Greenock. But he proved so wakeful during the visit, and so disposed to indulge in that habit of storytelling, which even Sir Walter Scott could afterwards admire in him, that Mr. Watt was very soon written to by his friend, and entreated to return to Glasgow and take home his son. "I cannot stand the excitement he keeps me in," said Mrs. Campbell; "I am worn out for want of sleep. Every evening, before retiring to rest, he contrives to engage me in conversation, then begins some striking tale, and whether humorous or pathetic, the interest is so overpowering, that the family all listen to him with breathless attention, and hour after hour strikes unheeded." He was taken back to Greenock accordingly; and, when well enough, was sent to the Grammar School of the town, then kept by Mr. Robert Arrol. Under him, Watt made fair progress in the rudiments of Latin and Greek; but he was still more successful in the study of mathematics, which he prosecuted under Mr. John Marr. It was only when he entered on this branch of learning that he discovered his strength, and he very soon took the lead in his class.

When at home the boy continued to spend much of his time in drawing or in cutting or carving with his penknife, or in watching the carpenters at work in his father's shop, sometimes trying his own hand at making little articles with the tools which lay about. In this he displayed a degree of dexterity which seemed so remarkable that the journeymen were accustomed to say of him that "little Jamie had gotten a fortune at his fingers' ends." Even when he had grown old he would recall to mind the pleasure as well as the profit which he had derived from working in his shirt-sleeves in his father's shop. He was, in fact, educating himself in the most effectual manner in his own way; learning to use his hands dexterously; familiarising himself with the art of handling tools; and acquiring a degree of expertness in working with them in wood and metal, which eventually proved of the greatest value to him. At the same time he was training himself in habits of application, industry, and invention. Most of his spare time was thus devoted to mechanical adaptations of his own contrivance. A small forge was erected for him, and a bench fitted up for his special use; and there he constructed many ingenious little objects, such as miniature cranes, pulleys, pumps, and capstans. Out of a large silver coin he fabricated a punch-ladle, which is still preserved. But the kind of work which most attracted him was the repairing of ships' compasses, quadrants, and nautical instruments, in executing which he exhibited so much neatness, dexterity, and accuracy, that it eventually led to his selection of the business he determined to follow, – that of a mathematical instrument maker.

The boy at the same time prosecuted his education at school; his improving health enabling him to derive more advantage from the instructions of his masters than in the earlier part of his career. Not the least influential part of his training, as regarded the formation of his character, consisted, as already observed, in the example and conversation of his parents at home. His frequent illnesses brought him more directly and continuously under their influence than is the case with most boys of his age; and reading became one of his chief sources of recreation and enjoyment. His father's library-shelf contained well-thumbed volumes of Boston, Bunyan, and 'The Cloud of Witnesses,' with Henry the Rymer's 'Life of Wallace,' and other old ballads, tattered by frequent use. These he devoured greedily, and re-read until he had most of them by heart. His father would also recount to him the sufferings of the Covenanters, – the moors and mosses which lay towards the south of Greenock having been among their retreats during the times of the persecution. Then there were the local and traditionary stories of the neighbourhood, – such as the exploits of the Greenock men under Sir John Shaw, at Worcester, in 1651,[6] – together with much of that unwritten history, heard only around firesides, which kindles the Scotchman's nationality, and influences his future life.

We may here mention, in passing, that one of the most vividly-remembered incidents of James Watt's boyhood was the Stuart rebellion of the "Forty-five,"

which occurred when he was about ten years old. Watt himself is so intimately identified with the material progress of the nineteenth century, that it
strikes one almost with surprise that he should have been a spectator, in however remote a degree, of incidents belonging to an altogether different age.
The Stuart Rebellion may be said to have been the end of one epoch and the
beginning of another; for certain it is that the progress of Scotland as an inte-
gral part of the British empire, and the growth of its skilled industry – which
the inventions of Watt did so much to develop – appeared as if to spring
from the very ashes of the rebellion. Like other lowland towns, Greenock
was greatly alarmed at the startling news from the Highlands of the threatened descent of the clans. Sir John Shaw had the trades mustered for drill on
the green in front of his mansion, and held them in readiness for defence of
the town, in case of attack. Greenock was otherwise secure, being protected
against the Highlands by the Clyde; besides, the western clans were either
neutral or adhered to the house of Hanover. The Pretender with his followers
passed southward by Stirling, and only approached Greenock on their return
from England, – a half-starved and ill-clad, though still unbroken army. They
halted at Glasgow, where they levied a heavy contribution on the inhabitants,
and sent out roving parties to try their fortunes in the neighbouring towns.
A small detachment one day approached Greenock, and came as near as the
Clune Brae; but the townspeople were afoot, and on guard; signal was given
to the ships of war moored near the old battery, and a few well-directed shots
speedily sent the Highlanders to the right-about. The alarm was over for the
present; but it was renewed in the following year, when the rumour reached
Edinburgh that Prince Charles, hunted from the Highlands, had landed at
Greenock, and lay concealed there. The consequence was that a strict search
was made throughout the town, and Mr. Watt's premises were searched like
the others; but, the Pretender had contrived to escape in another direction.
Such was one of the most memorable incidents in the boy-life of James Watt,
so strangely in contrast with the later events of his industrial career.

During holiday times, the boy sometimes indulged in rambles along
the Clyde, occasionally crossing to the north shore, and strolling up the
Gare Loch and Holy Loch, and even as far as Ben Lomond. He was of a
solitary disposition, and loved to wander by himself at night amidst the
wooded pleasure-grounds which surrounded the old mansion-house overlooking the town, watching through the trees the mysterious movements
of the stars. He became fascinated by the wonders of astronomy; and was
stimulated to inquire into the science by the examination of the nautical
instruments which he found amongst his father's shop-stores. For it was a

peculiarity which characterised him through life, that he could not look upon any instrument or machine without being seized with a desire to understand its meaning, to unravel its mystery, and master the rationale of its uses. Before he was fifteen he had twice gone through with great attention S'Gravande's 'Elements of Natural Philosophy,' a book belonging to his father. He performed many little experiments in chemistry, and even contrived to make an electrical machine, much to the marvel of those who felt its shocks. Like most invalids, he read eagerly such books on medicine and surgery as came in his way. He went so far as to practise dissection; and on one occasion he was found carrying off for this purpose the head of a child who had died of some uncommon disease. "He told his son," says Mr. Muirhead, "that, had he been able to bear the sight of the sufferings of patients, he would have been a surgeon."

In his solitary rambles, his love of wild-flowers and plants lured him on to the study of botany. Ever observant of the aspects of nature, the violent upheavings of the mountain-ranges on the north shores of Loch Lomond directed his attention to geology. He was a great devourer of books; reading all that came in his way. On a friend once advising him to be less indiscriminate in his reading, he replied, "I have never yet read a book without gaining information, instruction, or amusement." This was no answer to the admonition of his friend, who merely recommended him to bestow upon the best books the time he devoted to the worse. But the appetite for knowledge in inquisitive minds is, during youth, when curiosity is fresh and unslacked, too insatiable to be fastidious, and the volume which gets the preference is usually the first which comes in the way.

Watt was not, however, a mere bookworm. In his solitary walks through the country he would enter the cottages of the peasantry, gather their local traditions, and impart to them information of a similar kind from his own ample stores. Fishing, which suited his tranquil nature, was his single sport. When unable to ramble for the purpose, he could still indulge the pursuit from his father's yard, which was open to the sea, and the water of sufficient depth at high-tide to enable vessels of fifty or sixty tons to lie alongside.

But James Watt had now arrived at a suitable age to learn a trade; and his rambles must come to a close. His father had originally intended him to follow his own business; but having sustained some heavy losses about this time – one of his ships having foundered at sea, – and observing the strong bias of his son towards manipulative science and exact mechanics, he at length decided to send him to Glasgow, in the year 1754, when he was eighteen years old, to learn the trade of a mathematical instrument maker.

NOTES

1   Among the few household articles belonging to him which descended to his son, and afterwards to his grandson the engineer, were two portraits, one of Sir Isaac Newton, and the other John Napier, the inventor of Logarithms.

2   The mansion house of the Shaws is now principally occupied as manorial offices. The fine old garden and pleasure-grounds have been presented by Sir John Shaw to the people of Greenock as a public park for ever. It is now called "The Watt Park," and a more beautiful spot (bating the smoke of the busy town below) is scarcely to be found in Britain.

3   In 1715 the Greenock and Cartsdyke men kept strict watch and ward for eighty days against a threatened visit of Rob Roy and his caterans. The conduct of these unruly neighbours continued to cause apprehensions amongst the townspeople until a much later period, especially during fair time, then the great event of the year. The fair was the occasion of the annual gathering of the people from the neighbouring country to buy and to sell. Highlandmen came from opposite shores and from the lochs down the Clyde, men caring little for Lowland law, but duly impressed by a display of force. Their boats were drawn up on the beach with their prows to the High Street, the north side of which at that time lay open to the sea. The Highland folk lived and slept on board, each boat having a gangway between it and the shore. On the first day of the fair Sir John Shaw, the feudal superior, convened the local dignitaries, the deacons and the trades, and after drinking the King's health and throwing the glasses amongst the populace, they formed in procession and perambulated the town.

4   Some of her neighbours thought her stately and unbending, and that she affected a superior style of living. In the 'Memorials of Watt,' by the late George Williamson, Esq., Greenock, are to be found many curious and interesting details as to the Watt family; collected partly from tradition and partly from local records. Of Mrs. Watt's "superior style of living," compared with the custom of the period, the following anecdote is given: – "One of the author's informants on such points, a venerable lady in her eightieth year, was wont to speak of the worthy baillie's wife with much characteristic interest and animation. As illustrative of the internal economy of the family, the old lady related an occasion on which she had spent an evening, when a girl, at Mrs. Watt's house, and

remembered expressing with much naiveté to her mother on returning home, her childish surprise that 'Mrs. Watt had *two* lighted candles on the table.' Among these and other reminiscences of her youth, our venerable informant described James Watt's mother, in her expressive Doric, as 'a braw, braw woman – none now to be seen like her.'" p. 128–9.

5   The truth in regard to young Watt's first years in the public school is, that, owing doubtless to infirm health, to the suffering and depression which affected his whole powers, he was prevented for a considerable time displaying even a very ordinary and moderate aptitude for the common routine of school lessons; and during these years he was regarded by his schoolmasters as slow and inapt. Although to some minds facts of nature may be conceived to mar the romance of a great man's history, yet, seeing they rest on authenticity which cannot be impugned, there appears no reasonable ground on which it may be thought that they ought to be passed over as if they had not existed, or were altogether unfounded. – Williamson's 'Memorials of Watt,' p. 130.

6   The Shaw baronetcy was the reward of the feudal superior's services on the occasion. The banner carried by the tenantry in the civil war was long preserved in Greenock, and was hung up with the other town flags in one of the public rooms.

VI

James Watt, Mathematical Instrument Maker

When James Watt, a youth of eighteen, went to Glasgow in 1754 to learn his trade, the place was very different from the Glasgow of to-day. Not a steam-engine was then at work in the town; not a steam-boat disturbed the quiet of the Clyde. There was a rough quay along the Broomielaw, then, as the name implies, partly covered with broom. The quay was furnished with a solitary crane, for which there was very little use, as the river was full of sand-banks, and boats and gabberts of only six tons burden and under could then ascend the Clyde.[1] Often for weeks together not a single masted vessel was to be seen in the river. The principal buildings in the town were the Cathedral and the University. The west port, now in the centre of Glasgow, was then a real barrier between the town and the country. The ground on which Enoch-square stands consisted chiefly of gardens. A thick wood occupied the site of the present Custom-house and of that part of Glasgow situated behind West Clyde-street. Blythswood was grazing-ground. Not a house had yet been erected in Hutchinson-town, Laurieston, Tradeston, or Bridgeton. The land between Jamaica-street on the east, and Stobcross on the west, and south from Andereston-road to the river, now the most densely populated parts of Glasgow, consisted of fields and cabbage-gardens. The town had but two main streets, which intersected each other at the Cross or Market-place, and the only paved part of them was known as "The Plainstanes," which extended for a few hundred yards in front of the public offices and the Town-hall. The two main streets contained some stately well-built houses – Flemish-look-ing tenements with crow-stepped gables, – the lower stories standing on Doric columns, under which were the principal booths or shops – small, low-roofed, and dismal. But the bulk of the houses had only wooden fronts

Trongate, Glasgow

and thatched roofs, and were of a very humble character. The traffic along the unpaved streets was so small, that the carts were left standing in them at night. The town was as yet innocent of police;[2] it contained no Irish immigrants, and very few Highlanders. The latter then thought it beneath them to engage in any pursuit connected with commerce; and Rob Roy's contempt for the wabsters of Glasgow, as described by Sir Walter Scott in the novel, was no exaggeration. No Highland gentleman, however poor, would dream of condemning his son to the drudgery of trade; and even the poorest Highland cottar would shrink with loathing from the life of a weaver or a shopkeeper. He would be a hunter, a fisher, a cattle-lifter, or a soldier; but trade he would not touch – that he left to the Low landers.[3]

The principal men of business in Glasgow at the time of which we speak were the tobacco lords – importers of that article from the plantations in Virginia,[4] – who were often to be seen strutting along the Plainstanes, dressed in scarlet cloaks, cocked hats, and powdered wigs; the "boddies" who kept the adjoining shops eying them over their half-closed doors, and humbly watching for a nod of recognition from the mighty potentates. Yet even the greatest of the tobacco lords only lived in flats, entering from a common stair; and the domestic accommodation was so scanty and so primitive, that visitors were of necessity received in the bedrooms. This circumstance seems to have had some influence in the formation of the Clubs,[5] which then formed a curious feature of society in most Scotch towns. They consisted of knots of men of like tastes and pursuits, who met in the evenings at public-houses for purposes of gossip and social drinking. There they made new and cultivated old acquaintanceship and exchanged news with each other. The Club combined the use of the newspaper and the newsroom, which now accomplish the same objects without the drinking. But Glasgow had then no newspaper; and a London news-sheet of a week old was looked upon as a novelty. There was no coffee-room nor public library in the town; no theatre[6] nor place of resort open, except the "Change-house;" so that the Club was regarded as a social necessity. The drinking was sometimes moderate, and sometimes "hard." The better class confined themselves to claret and other French wines, which were then cheap, being free from duty. Those disposed to indulge in more frugal fare confined themselves to oat-cake and small-beer. It was not until heavy taxes were laid on foreign wines and malt that the hard whisky-drinking of Scotland set in. Whisky was introduced from the Highlands shortly after the "Forty-five;" and it soon became the popular drink. By 1780 the drinking of raw whisky in Glasgow at mid-day had become general.[7]

When young Watt arrived in Glasgow he carried with him but a small quantity of baggage; the articles in his trunk including amongst other things a quadrant, – probably a specimen of his own handiwork, – a leather apron, about a score of carpenters' and other tools, and "a pair of bibels." On making inquiry for a proper master, under whom to learn the business of mathematical instrument making, it was found that there was no such person in Glasgow. There was, however, a mechanic in the town, who dignified himself with the name of "optician," under whom Watt was placed for a time. He was a sort of Jack-of-all-trades, who sold and mended spectacles, repaired fiddles, tuned spinets, made and repaired the simpler instruments used in mechanical drawing, and eked out a slender living by making and selling fishing-rods and fishing-tackle. Watt was as handy at dressing trout and salmon flies as at most other things, and his master, no doubt, found him useful enough; but there was nothing to be learnt in return for his services. Though his master was an ingenious workman, in a small way, and could turn his ready hand to anything, it soon became clear to Watt's relations, the Muirheads, with whom he lived during his stay, that the instructions of such an artist were little likely to advance him in mathematical instrument making. Among the gentlemen to whom Watt was introduced by his relatives was Dr. Dick, Professor of Natural Philosophy in Glasgow College, who strongly recommended him to proceed to London, and there place himself under the instruction of some competent master. Watt consulted his father on the subject, who readily gave his sanction to the proposal; and, with a letter of introduction from Dr. Dick in his pocket, he set out for the great city accordingly.

No stage-coach then ran between Glasgow and London; so it was determined that young Watt should proceed on horseback, then the most convenient and speedy mode of travelling. His chest was sent by sea. Old Mr. Watt's memorandum-book at Heathfield contains the following entry, under date the 6th June, 1755:

> To send James Watt's chist to the care of Mr. William Oman, Ventener in Leith, to be shypt for London to ye care of Captain William Watson, at the Hermitage, London.
>
> P^d. 3s. 6d. for wagon carage to Edenbrouglh of chist.
>
> P^d. to son James 2l. 2s.
>
> P^d. Plaster and Pomet, 1s. 4d.
>
> P^d. 4 doz. pencels, 1s. 6d.

The "plaster and pomet" may possibly have been provided in view of the long journey on horseback and its contingencies. It was arranged that the youth should travel in the company of a relative, Mr. Marr, a sea-captain, who was on his way to join his ship, then lying in the Thames. They set out on the 7th of June, travelling by way of Coldstream and Newcastle, where they joined the great north road, then comparatively practicable to the south of Durham. They reached London safely on the 19th, having been about a fortnight on the road.

Mr. Marr immediately proceeded to make inquiries for a mathematical instrument maker with whom to place his young friend. But it was found that a serious obstacle presented itself in the rules of the trade, which prescribed that those employed must either be apprentices serving under a seven years' apprenticeship, or, if journeymen, that they should have served for that term. Watt, however, had no intention of binding himself to serve for so long a period, and he had no pretensions to rank as a journeyman. His object was to learn the business in the shortest possible time, and then return to Glasgow and set up for himself. The two went about from shop to shop, but only met with rebuffs. "I have not yet got a master," Watt wrote to his father about a fortnight after his arrival; "we have tried several, but they all made some objection or other. I find that, if any of them agree with me at all, it will not be for less than a year; and even for that time they will be expecting some money."

Mr. Marr continued to exert himself on behalf of the youth. Anxious to be employed in any way rather than not at all, Watt offered his services gratuitously to a watchmaker named Neale, with whom Mr. Marr did business, and he was allowed to occupy himself in his shop for a time, cutting letters and figures in metal. At length a situation of a more permanent character was obtained for him; and he entered the shop of Mr. John Morgan, a respectable mathematical instrument maker in Cornhill, on the terms of receiving a year's instruction in return for a fee of twenty guineas and the proceeds of his labour during that time. He soon proved himself a ready learner and skilful workman. That division of labour, the result of an extensive trade, which causes the best London carriages to be superior to any of provincial construction, was even then applied to mathematical instruments. "Very few here," wrote Watt, "know any more than how to make a rule, others a pair of dividers, and such like." His first employment was in making brass scales, rules, parallels, and the brass-work of quadrants; and by the end of a month he was able to finish a Hadley's quadrant in better style than any apprentice in the shop. From rule and quadrant making he proceeded to azimuth compasses, brass sectors, theodolites, and the more delicate kinds of instruments. At the end of the year he wrote home to his father that he had made "a brass sector with a French joint, which is reckoned as nice a piece of framing-work as is in the trade;" and he expressed the hope that be would soon be able to work for himself, and earn his bread by his own industry.

Up to this time he had necessarily been maintained by his father, on whom he drew from time to time. Mr. Watt's memorandum-books show that on the 27th of June he remitted him 10*l*.; on the 24th of August following he enters: "Sent George Anderson by post 8*l*. to buy a bill of 7*l*. or 8*l*. to send Wheytbread and Gifferd, and ballance of my son's bill, 2*l*. 2*s*. 3*d*., for which ame to remite him more;" and on the 11th September following, the balance was forwarded through the same channel. On the 24th October, 4*l*. 10*s*. was in like manner sent to George Anderson "on son James's second bill;" and on the 31st December, 10*l*. was remitted, "to be put to the credit of son James's last bill." To relieve his father as much as possible for the cost of his maintenance in London, Watt lived in a very frugal style, avoiding all unnecessary expenses. His living cost him only eight shillings a week and he could not reduce it below that, he wrote to his father, "without pinching his belly." He also sought for some remunerative work on his own account; and when he could obtain it he sat up at night to execute it.

During Watt's stay in London he was in a great measure prevented from stirring abroad by the hot press for sailors which was then going on. As many as forty pressgangs were at work, seizing all able-bodied men they could lay hands on. In one night they took not fewer than a thousand men. Nor were the kidnappers idle. These were the agents of the East India Company, who had crimping-houses in different parts of the city for receiving the men whom they had seized upon for service in the Indian army. Even when the demand for soldiers abated, the kidnappers continued their trade, and sold their unhappy victims to the planters in Pennsylvania and other North American colonies. Sometimes severe fights took place between the pressgangs and the kidnappers for possession of those who had been seized, the law and police being apparently powerless to protect them. "They now press anybody they can get," Watt wrote in the spring of 1756, "landsmen as well as seamen, except it be in the liberties of the city, where they are obliged to carry them before the Lord Mayor first; and unless one be either a prentice or a creditable tradesman, there is scarce any getting off again. And if I was carried before my Lord Mayor, I durst not avow that I wrought in the city, it being against their laws for any unfreeman to work even as a journeyman within the liberties."[8] What a curious glimpse does this give us into the practice of man-hunting in London in the eighteenth century!

Watt's enforced confinement, together with his sedentary habits and unremitting labour, soon told upon his weak frame. When he hurried to his lodgings at night, his body was wearied, and his nerves exhausted, so that his hands shook like those of an old man; yet he persevered with the extra work which he imposed upon himself, in order to earn a little honest money to help to pay for his living. His seat in Mr. Morgan's shop being placed close to the door, which was often opened and shut in the course of the day, he caught a severe cold in the course of the winter; and he was afflicted by a racking cough and severe rheumatic pains, from the effects of which he long continued to suffer. Distressed by a gnawing pain in his back, and greatly depressed in spirits, he at length, with his father's sanction, determined to return to Greenock, to seek for renewal of health in his native air. His father made him a further remittance to enable him to purchase some of the tools required for his trade, together with materials for, making others, and a copy of Bion's work on the construction and use of Mathematical Instruments. Having secured these, he set out on his return journey for Scotland, and reached Greenock in safety in the autumn of 1756. There his health soon became sufficiently restored to enable him to return to work; and with the concurrence and help of his father, he shortly after proceeded to Glasgow, in his twentieth year, to begin business on his own account.

In endeavouring to establish himself in his trade, Watt encountered the same obstacle which in London had almost prevented his learning it. Although there were no mathematical instrument makers in Glasgow, and it must have been a public advantage to have so skilled a mechanic settled in the place, Watt was opposed by the corporation of hammermen on the ground that he was neither the son of a burgess nor had served an apprenticeship within the borough.[9] Failing in his endeavours to open a place of business, he next tried to prevail on the corporation to allow him to make use of a small workshop wherein to make experiments; but this also was peremptorily refused. The hammermen were doubtless acting in a very narrow spirit, in thus excluding the young mechanic from the privileges of citizenship; but such was the custom of the times, – those who were within the favoured circles usually putting their shoulders together to exclude those who were without. Watt had, however, already been employed by Dr. Dick, Professor of Natural Philosophy, to repair some mathematical instruments which had been bequeathed to the University by a gentleman in the West Indies; and the professors, having an absolute authority within the area occupied by the college buildings, determined to give him an asylum there, and thus free him from the incubus of the guilds.

In the heart of old Glasgow city, not far from the cathedral of St. Mungo, which Knox with difficulty preserved from the fury of the Scotch iconoclasts, stands the venerable University, a curiously black and sombre building, more than 400 years old. Inside the entrance, on the right-hand side, is a stone staircase, guarded by fabulous beasts in stone. The buildings consist of several quadrangles; but there is not much regularity in their design, each part seeming to stand towards the other parts, in a state of independent crookedness and irregularity. There are turrets in the corners of the quadrangles, – turrets with peaked tops, like witches' caps. In the inner quadrangle, entered from the left-hand side of the outer court, a workshop was found for our mechanician, in which he was securely established by the midsummer of 1757. The apartment appropriated to Watt by the professors is still to be seen in nearly the same rude state in which he left it. It is situated on the first floor of the range of building forming the northwest side of the inner quadrangle, immediately under the gallery of the Natural Philosophy class, with which it communicates. It is lighted by three windows, two of which open into the quadrangle, and the third, at the back, into the Professors' court. There is a small closet in the corner of

Inner Quadrangle, Glasgow College

the room, where some students have cut their names in the plaster, – date "1713." The access to the room used to be from the court by a spiral stone staircase; but that entrance is now closed. The apartment is only about twenty feet square; but it served Watt, as it has since served others, for high thinking and noble working.[10]

In addition to his workshop under the Natural Philosophy class, a shop for the sale of his instruments was also appropriated to Watt by the Professors. It formed the ground-floor of the house situated next to the Principal's Gate, being part of the University Buildings, and was entered directly from the pavement of the High Street. It has been described to us, on the authority of Professor Fleming, as an old house, with a sort of arcade in front, supported on pillars. In making some alterations in the building the pillars were too much weakened, and the house, excepting the basement, had to be taken down. The shop occupied by Watt is the little tenement shown on the right hand of the following engraving; but the lower story of the building has since been altered and repaired, and is now totally different from what it was in Watt's time.

Though his wants were few, and he lived on humble fare, Watt found it very difficult to earn a subsistence by his trade. His father sent him remittances from time to time; but the old man had suffered serious losses in his own business, and had become much less able to help his son with money. After a year's trial, Watt wrote to his father, that "unless it be the Hadley's instruments there is little

Isometric view of Glasgow College, 1693, from Sleyer's
'Theatrum Scottæ'[11]

to be got by it, as at most other jobs I am obliged to do the most of them myself;
and, as it is impossible for one person to be expert at everything, they often cost
me more time than they should do." Of the quadrants, he could make three in
a week, with the help of a lad; but the profit upon the three was not more than
40*s*. The customers for these were very few in number, as seagoing ships with
their captains could not yet reach Glasgow.[12]

Failing sufficient customers for his instruments, Watt sent those which he
had made to Port Glasgow and Greenock, where his father helped him to
dispose of them. He also bethought him of taking a journey to Liverpool
and London, for the purpose of obtaining orders for instruments; though,
for some reason or other – most probably because he was averse to "pushing," and detested the chaffering of trade – his contemplated journey was not
undertaken. He therefore continued to execute only such orders as came to
him; so that his business remained very small. He began to fear that he must
give up the trade that would not keep him, and he wrote to his father: "If
this business does not succeed, I must fall into some other." To eke out his
income, he took to map and chart selling, and, amongst other things, offered
for sale the Map of the River Clyde,[13] originally surveyed by his uncle John.

It is well for the world at large that Watt's maps and quadrants remained
on his hands unsold. The most untoward circumstances in life have often

the happiest results. It is not Fortune that is blind, but man. Had his instrument-making business prospered, Watt might have become known as a first-class maker of quadrants, but not as the inventor of the condensing steam-engine. It was because his own special business failed that he was driven to betake himself to other pursuits, and eventually to prosecute the invention on which his fame mainly rests. At first he employed part of his leisure in making chemical and other experiments; but as these yielded him no returns in the shape of money, he was under the necessity of making some sort of article that was in demand, and for which he could find customers. Although he had no ear for music, and scarcely knew one note from another, he followed the example of the old spectacle-maker, his first master, in making fiddles, flutes, and guitars, which met with a readier sale than his quadrants. These articles were what artists call "pot-boilers," and kept him in funds until a maintenance could be earned by higher-class work. We are informed, through a lady at Glasgow, that her father bought a flute from Watt, who said to him, in selling it: "Woe be to ye, Tam, if you're no guid luck; for this is the first I've sold!"

His friend Dr. Black, probably to furnish him with some profitable employment, asked Watt to make a barrel-organ for him, which he at once proceeded to construct. Watt was not the man to refuse work of any kind requiring the exercise of constructive skill. He first carefully studied the principles of harmony, – making science, in a measure, the substitute for want of ear,[14] and took for his guide the profound but obscure work on 'Harmonics,' published by Dr. H. Smith of Cambridge. He next made a model of the instrument; after which he constructed the organ, which, when finished, was considered a great success. About the same time the office-bearers of a Mason's Lodge in Glasgow sent to ask him if he would undertake to build for them a finger-organ. As he had successfully repaired an instrument of the same kind, besides making the barrel-organ, he readily accepted the order. Watt was always, as he said, dissatisfied with other people's work, as well as his own; and this habit of his mind made him study to improve upon whatever came before him. Thus, in the process of building this organ, he devised a number of novel expedients, such as a sustained monochord, indicators and regulators of the strength of the blast, means of tuning the instrument according to any system of temperament, with sundry contrivances for improving the efficiency of the stops. The qualities of the organ when finished are said to have elicited the surprise and admiration of musicians.[15]

The leisure time which Watt did not occupy with miscellaneous work of this sort, he spent in reading. He did not want for books, as the College library was near at hand; and the professors as well as students were willing to lend him from their stores. He was not afraid of solid, heavy, dry books, provided he could learn something from them. All were alike welcome; and one of his greatest pleasures was in devouring a novel, when it fell in his way. He is even said to have occupied himself in writing tales and verses when he had nothing else to do. As none of his attempts have been preserved, we cannot offer an opinion upon them; but it is doubtful whether Watt's poetry and fiction would display the same originality and power of invention as his steam-engine. The only youthful exercises of his which have been preserved are anything but poetical. One of them, at Heathfield, is a 'Treatise on Practical Megethometry;' and another is a 'Compendium of Definitions,' in Latin, by Gerard de Yries, both written in a neat round hand.

Like most of the Glasgow citizens of that time, Watt occasionally visited his club, where he cultivated the society of men of greater culture and experience than himself.[16] As he afterwards observed to a friend, "Our conversations then, besides the usual subjects with young men, turned principally on literary topics, religion, morality, belles-lettres, &c.; and to those conversations my mind owed its first bias towards such subjects, in which they were all much my superiors, I never having attended a college, and being then but a mechanic."

There was another circumstance connected with his situation at this time which must have been peculiarly agreeable to a young man of his character, aspirations, and thirst for knowledge. His shop, being conveniently situated within the College, was a favourite resort of the professors and the students. They were attracted by the ingenious instruments and models which the shop contained, and the pleasure always felt in witnessing the proceedings of a skilful mechanic at his work, but more particularly by the easy, unaffected, and original conversation of Watt himself. Though a comparative youth, the professors were usually glad to consult him on points of mechanical knowledge and practice; and the acuteness of his observation, the accuracy of his knowledge, and the readiness with which he communicated what he knew, soon rendered him a general favourite. Among his most frequent visitors were Dr. Joseph Black, the distinguished professor of chemistry, who there contracted a friendship with Watt which lasted, uninterrupted, for a period of forty years, until the Doctor's death; Professor Simson, one of the most eminent men of his day, whom Lord Brougham has described as the restorer of the science of geometry; Dr. Dick, the Professor of Natural Philosophy; and Professor Anderson.[17] Dr. Moor and Dr. Adam Smith were also frequent callers. But of all Watt's associates, none is more closely connected with his name and history than John Robison, then a student at Glasgow College, and afterwards Professor of Natural Philosophy at Edinburgh.

Robison was nearer Watt's age than the rest, and stood in the intimate relation to him of bosom friend, as well as fellow inquirer in science. He was handsome and prepossessing in appearance, frank and lively, full of fancy and humour, and a general favourite in the College. He was a capital talker, an accomplished linguist, and a good musician; yet, with all his versatility, he was a profound thinker and a diligent student, especially in mathematical and mechanical science, as he afterwards proved in his elaborate 'System of Mechanical Philosophy,' edited by Sir David Brewster, and his many able contributions to the 'Encyclopedia Britannica,' of which he was the designer and editor.

Robison's introduction to Watt has been described by himself. After feasting his eyes on the beautifully finished instruments in his shop, Robison entered into conversation with him. Expecting to find only a workman, he was surprised to discover a philosopher. "I had the vanity," says Robison, "to think myself a pretty good proficient in my favourite study (mathematical and mechanical philosophy), and was rather mortified at finding Mr. Watt so much my superior. But his own high relish for these things made him pleased with the chat of any person who had the same tastes with himself; and his innate complaisance made him indulge my curiosity, and even encourage my endeavours to form a more intimate acquaintance with him. I lounged much about him, and, I doubt not, was frequently teasing him. Thus our acquaintance began."

In Watt's workshop also, Robison first met Dr. Black, and there initiated a friendship which ended only with death. "My first acquaintance with him," Robison afterwards wrote Watt, "began in your rooms when you were rubbing up Macfarlane's instruments. He used to come in, and, standing with his back to us, amuse himself with Bird's quadrant, whistling softly to himself, in a manner that thrilled me to the heart."

In 1757 Robison applied for the office of assistant to Dr. Dick, Professor of Natural Philosophy, in the place of the son of that gentleman, who had just died; but though he had already taken the degree of Master of Arts, he was thought too young to hold so important an office, being only about nineteen years old. His friends wished him to study for the church; but, preferring some occupation in which his mechanical tastes might be indulged, he turned his eyes to London. Furnished with letters from Professor Dick and Dr. Simson, he obtained an introduction to Admiral Knowles, who engaged him to take charge of his son's instruction while at sea. In that capacity he sailed from Spithead in 1759, with the fleet which assisted the land forces in the taking of Quebec; he and his pupil being rated as midshipmen in the Admiral's ship. Robison was on duty in the boat which carried Wolfe to the point where the army scaled the heights of Montcalm the night before the battle; and as the sun was setting in the west, the General, doubtless from an association of ideas suggested by the dangers of the coming struggle, recited, in an under tone, Gray's 'Elegy on a Country Churchyard;' and when he had finished, said, "Now, gentlemen, I would rather have been the author of that poem than take Quebec."

When Robison returned from his voyagings in 1763, a travelled man, – having had the advantage, during his absence, of acting as confidential assistant of Admiral Knowles in his marine surveys and observations, – he reckoned himself more than on a par with Watt; but he soon found that, during the period of his absence from Glasgow, his friend had been even busier than himself. When they entered into conversation, he found Watt continually striking into new paths where he was obliged to be his follower. The extent of the mathematical instrument maker's investigations was no less remarkable than the depth to which he had pursued them. Not only had he mastered the principles of engineering, civil and military, but diverged into studies in antiquity, natural history, languages, criticism, and art. Every pursuit became science in his hands, and he made use of his subsidiary knowledge for the purpose of helping him towards his favourite objects.

Before long, Watt came to be regarded as one of the ablest men about college. "When to the superiority of knowledge in his own line," said Robison, "which every man confessed, there was joined the naïve simplicity and candour of his character, it is no wonder that the attachment of his acquaintances was so strong. I have seen something of the world," he continued, "and I am obliged to say that I never saw such another instance of general and cordial attachment to a person whom all acknowledged to be their superior. But this superiority was concealed under the most amiable candour, and liberal allowance of merit to every man. Mr. Watt was the first to ascribe to the ingenuity of a friend things which were very often nothing but his own surmises followed out and embodied by another. I am well entitled to say this, and have often experienced it in my own case."

There are few traits in biography more charming than this generous recognition of merit mutually attributed by the one friend to the other. Arago, in quoting the words of Robison, has well observed that it is difficult to determine whether the honour of having thus recorded them be not as great as that of having inspired them.

The Broomielaw in 1760

Professor Robison
(by T. D. Scott, after
Raeburn)

NOTES

1   According to Smeaton's report in 1755, there were in spring tides only 3 feet 8 inches water at Pointhouse Ford. Measures were taken to deepen the river, and operations with that object were begun in 1768. Salmon abounded in the Clyde, and was so common that servants and apprentices were accustomed to stipulate that they should not have salmon for dinner more than a certain number of days in the week.

2   The "middens" in the street were sometimes complained of as a nuisance; and in 1776, the magistrate threatened a penalty of 5s. if middens of which complaint had been made were not removed within 48 hours.

3   The Highland gentry and people regarded the Lowlanders as their natural enemies, fair subjects for plunder at all times as opportunities offered. The Lowlanders, on their part, regarded the Highlanders very much as the primitive settlers of North America regarded the Cherokee and Chocktaw Inaians. Sometimes a band of uncouth half-clad Highland-men would suddenly rush down upon the Lowlands, swoop up all the cattle within their reach, and drive them off into the mountains. Hence the Lowlanders and the Highlanders were always in a state of feud. Long after the '45 a Highlandman would "thank God that he had not a drop of Lowland blood in his veins."

4   The only trade which Glasgow carried on with foreign countries previous to the Union, was in coal, grindstones, and fish, – Glasgow-cured herrings being in much repute abroad. After the Union partnerships were formed; vessels were built down the Clyde, and chartered for carrying on the trade with Virginia, Maryland, and Carolina. The first *honest* vessel crossed the Atlantic from the Clyde in 1719; in 1735 the Virginia merchants in Glasgow had fifteen vessels engaged in the trade, and the town shortly after became the great mart for tobacco. Of the 90,000 hogsheads imported into the United Kingdom in 1772, Glasgow alone imported 49,000, or more than one-half. The American Revolution had the effect of completely ruining the tobacco trade of Glasgow, after which the merchants were compelled to turn to other fields of enterprise and industry. The capital which they had accumulated from tobacco enabled them to enter upon their new undertakings with spirit, and the steam-engine which had by that time been invented by their townsman James watt, proved their best helper in advancing the prosperity of modern Glasgow. The rapidity of its progress may be inferred from the

following facts. In 1735, though the Glasgow merchants owned half the entire tonnage of Scotland, it amounted to only 5600 tons. In that year the whole shipping of Scotland was only one-fortieth part of that of England: it is now about one fifth. From 1752 to 1770 the total tonnage dues of the harbour of Glasgow amounted to only 147*l.*, or equal to an average of about 8*l.* per annum. In 1780, the Clyde having been deepened in the interval, they reached 1515*l.*; and in 1854, they amounted to 85,580*l.* The increase has been quite as great in later years. In point of value of exports, Glasgow ranks fourth among the ports of the United Kingdon; and Greenock now takes precedence of Bristol.

5   For many curious particulars of Old Glasgow and its society, see Dr. Strang's 'Glasgow and its Clubs.'

6   A temporary wooden theatre was run up in 1752, but the religious prejudices of the population were violently excited by the circumstance, and the place was attacked by a mob and seriously damaged. The few persons who went there had to be protected from insults. In 1762, when some persons proposed to build a theatre, not a single individual who had ground within the burgh would grant them a site. Two years later the theatre was erected outside the precincts, and on the night on which it was opened it was willfully set on fire by some persons instigated by the preaching of a neighbouring Methodist, when it narrowly escaped destruction.

7   When the Lowlanders want to drink a cheering cup, they go to the public-house, called the Change-house, and call for a chopin of twopenny, which is their yeasty beverage, made of malt, not quite so strong as the table-beer of England ... The Highlanders, on the contrary, despise the liquor, and regale themselves with whisky, or malt spirit, as strong as Geneva, which they swallow in great quantities, without any signs of inebriation: they are used to it from the cradle, and find it an excellent preservative against the winter cold, which must be extreme on these mountains. – Smollett, 'Expedition of Humphry Clinker.'

8   Letter to his father quoted in Muirhead's 'Life of Watt,' p. 39

9   The following "letter to Guildry" embodied the local regulations which existed for the purpose of preventing "loss and skaith" to the burgesses and craftsmen of Glasgow by the intrusion of "strangers": – "The Dean of Guild and his Council shall have the full power to discharge, punish, and unlaw all persons, unfreemen, using the liberty of a freeman within the burgh, as they shall think fit, ay and while the said unfreemen be put off the town, and restrained, or else be made free with the town and their crafts; and sic like, to pursue, upon the judges competent, all persons

dwelling within the burgh, and usurping the liberty thereof, obtain decrets against them, and cause the same to be put to speedy execution."

10   When we visited the room some years since, we found lain there the galvanic apparatus employed by Professor Thomson for perfecting the invention of his delicate process of signaling through the wires of the Atlantic Telegraph.

11   The illustration does not show the Inner Quadrangle, situated to the left of the Main Court, that part of the building having been added since the view was published.

12   The author of 'Glasgow, Past and Present' thus writes: – "Last week (Nov. 1851) I was crossing the ferry at the west end of Tradeston, and in the course of our passage over we turned round the bow of a large ship. The ferryman, looking up to her leviathan bulwarks, exclaimed, 'She came up here yesterday, drawing eighteen feet water!' Now, upon this very spot seventy years ago, when a very little boy, I waded across the river, my feet never being off the ground, and the water not reaching above my arm-pits. The depth at that time could not have been much more than three feet."

13   The 'Glasgow Courant' of Oct. 22, 1759, contains the following advertisement: –

"Just Published,

And to be Sold by James Watt, at his Shop in the College of Glasgow,
      price 2s. 6d.,

A large Sheet Map of the River Clyde, from Glasgow to Portincross, from
      an Actual Survey.

To which is added,

A Draught of Part of the North Channel, with the Frith of the Clyde
      according to the best authorities."

14   General T. Perronet Thompson is another remarkable instance of a person without ear for music, who has mastered the principles of harmony and applied them in the invention of his "Enharmonic Organ."

15   Watt seems to have made other organs besides those above mentioned. Not long since a barrel-organ of his construction was offered for sale at Glasgow. It was originally in the form of a table, about three feet square, having no appearance of a musical instrument externally. At this table, when Watt and his friends were seated, he would set the concealed mechanism in action, and surprise them with the production of the music. It has since been mounted with an organ front and sides, with gilt pipes. When in proper tune it is of condiserable power and pleasing harmony; and continues orthodox in its psalm tunes, which range from "Martyrs" to

the "Old Hundred." A correspondent writes as follows: – "A large organ made and used by Watt when he had his shop in Glasgow, was disposed of by him, when he first left this city. It came into the possession of the late Mr. Archibald M'Lellan, coach-builder, Miller Street, Glasgow, and he had it fitted up in his elegant residence in that fine old street. I have heard it played by Mr. M'Lellan. After his death it was sold, and purchased by Mr. James G. Adam of the Denny print-works. Mr. Adam died, and the organ was advertised for sale, in 1864, and purchased for 10*l.*, by Adam Sim, Esq., of Coulter Mains, in whose possession it now is. Mr. Sim has authentic documents to prove that this organ was really James Watt's."

16   The club he frequented was called the Anderston Club, of which Mr. (afterwards Professor) Millar, Dr. Robert Simson, the mathematician, Dr. Adam Smith, Dr. Black, and Dr. Cullen, were members. The standing dish of the club was henbroth, consisting of a decoction of "how-towdies" (fowls), thickened with black beans, and seasoned with pepper. Dr. Strang says Profesor Simson was in the habit of counting the steps from his house to the club, so that he could tell the distance to a fraction of an inch. But it is not stated whether he counted the steps on his return, and found the number of steps the same.

17   John Anderson was a native of Greenock, and an intimate friend of James Watt. He was appointed professor of Hebrew in his twenty-seventh year, and succeeded Dr. Dick as professor of Natural Philosophy in 1757. Watt spent many of his evenings at his residence within the college, and had free use of his excellent private library. Professor Anderson is entitled to the honour of being the first to open classes for the instruction of working men – "anti-toga classes," as he called them – in the principles of Natural Philosophy; and at his death he bequeathed his property for the purpose of founding an institution with the same object. The Andersonian University was opened in 1796, long before the age of Mechanics' Institutes.

VII

Watt's Experiments on Steam – Invents the Separate Condenser

It was in the year 1759 that Robison first called the attention of his friend Watt to the subject of the steam engine. Robison was then only in his twentieth, and Watt in his twenty-third year. Robison's idea was that the power of steam might be advantageously applied to the driving of wheel-carriages, and he suggested that it would be the most convenient for the purpose to place the cylinder with its open end downwards to avoid the necessity of using a working beam. Watt admits that he was very ignorant of the steam-engine at the time; nevertheless, he began making a model with two cylinders of tinplate, intending that the pistons and their connecting-rods should act alternately on two pinions attached to the axles of the carriage-wheels. But the model, being slightly and inaccurately made, did not answer his expectations. Other difficulties presented themselves, and the scheme was laid aside on Robison leaving Glasgow to go to sea. Indeed, mechanical science was not yet ripe for the locomotive. Robison's idea had, however, dropped silently into the mind of his friend, where it grew from day to day, slowly and at length fruitfully.

At his intervals of leisure and in the quiet of his evenings, Watt continued to prosecute his various studies. He was shortly attracted by the science of chemistry, then in its infancy. Dr. Black was at that time occupied with the investigations which led to his discovery of the theory of latent heat, and it is probable that his familiar conversations with Watt on the subject induced the latter to enter upon a series of experiments with the view of giving the theory some practical direction. His attention again and again reverted to the steam-engine, though he had not yet seen even a model of one. Steam was as yet almost unknown in Scotland as a working power. The first engine was erected at Elphinstone Colliery, in Stirlingshire, about the year 1750;

and the second more than ten years later, at Govan Colliery, near Glasgow, where it was known by the startling name of "The Firework." This had not, however, been set up at the time Watt began to inquire into the subject. But he found that the College possessed the model of a Newcomen engine for the use of the Natural Philosophy class, which had been sent to London for repair. On hearing of its existence, he suggested to his friend Dr. Anderson, Professor of Natural Philosophy, the propriety of getting back the model; and a sum of money was placed by the Senatus at the Professor's disposal "to recover the steam-engine from Mr. Sisson, instrument maker, in London."

In the mean time Watt sought to learn all that had been written on the subject of the steam-engine. He ascertained from Desaguliers, from Switzer, and other writers, what had been accomplished by Savery, Newcomen, Beighton, and others: and he went on with his own independent experiments. His first apparatus was of the simplest possible kind. He used common apothecaries' phials for his steam reservoirs, and canes hollowed out for his steam pipes.[1] In 1761 he proceeded to experiment on the force of steam by means of a small Papin's digester and a syringe. The syringe was only the third of an inch in diameter, fitted with a solid piston; and it was connected with the digester by a pipe furnished with a stopcock, by which the steam was admitted or shut off at will. It was also itself provided with a stopcock, enabling a communication to be opened between the syringe and the outer air to permit the steam in the syringe to escape. The apparatus, though rude, enabled the experimenter to ascertain some important facts. When the steam in the digester was raised and the cock turned, enabling it to rush against the lower side of the piston, he found that the expansive force of the steam raised a weight of fifteen pounds with which the piston was loaded. Then, on turning the cock and shutting off the connexion with the digester at the same time that a passage was opened to the air, the steam was allowed to escape, when the weight upon the piston, being no longer counteracted, immediately forced it to descend

Watt saw that it would be easy to contrive that the cocks should be turned by the machinery itself instead of by the hand, and the whole be made to work by itself with perfect regularity. But there was an objection to this method. Water is converted into vapour as soon as its elasticity is sufficient to overcome the weight of the air which keeps it down. Under the ordinary pressure of the atmosphere water acquires this necessary elasticity at 212°; but as the steam in the digester was prevented from escaping, it acquired increased heat, and by consequence increased elasticity. Hence it was that the steam which issued from the digester was not only able to support the piston and the air which pressed upon its upper surface, but the additional

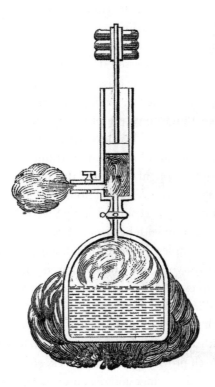

load with which the piston was weighted. With the imperfect mechanical construction, however, of those days, there was a risk lest the boiler should be burst by the steam, which was apt to force its way through the ill-made joints of the machine. This, conjoined with the great expenditure of steam on the high-pressure system, led Watt to abandon the plan; and the exigencies of his business for a time prevented him pursuing his experiments. Watt's own account of his early experiments will be found appended as notes to Brewster's edition of the articles 'Steam and Steam-engines,' written by Dr. Robison for the 'Encyclopædia Britannica,' and afterwards published in a separate form.

At length the Newcomen model arrived from London; and, in 1763, the little engine, which was destined to become so famous, was put into the hands of Watt. The boiler was somewhat smaller than an ordinary tea-kettle. The cylinder of the engine was only of two inches diameter and six inches stroke. Watt at first regarded it as merely "a fine plaything." It was, however, enough to set him upon a track of thinking which led to the most important results. When he had repaired the model and set it to work, he found that the boiler, though apparently large enough, could not supply steam in suf-

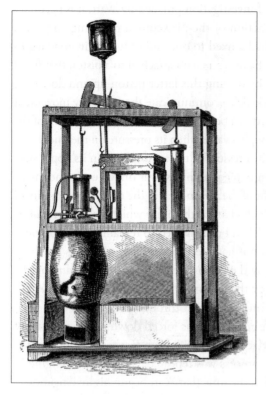

The Newcomen model

ficient quantity, and only a few strokes of the piston could be obtained, when the engine stopped. The fire was urged by blowing, and more steam was produced, but still it would not work properly. Exactly at the point at which another man would have abandoned the task in despair, the mind of Watt became thoroughly roused. "Everything," says Professor Robison, "was to him the beginning of a new and serious study; and I knew that he would not quit it till he had either discovered its insignificance, or had made something of it." Thus it happened with the phenomena presented by the model of the steam-engine. Watt referred to his books, and endeavoured to ascertain from them by what means he might remedy the defects which he found in the model; but they could tell him nothing. He then proceeded with an independent course of experiments, resolved to work out the problem for himself. In the course of his inquiries he came upon a fact which, more than any other, led his mind into the train of thought which at last conducted him to the invention of which the results were destined to prove so stupendous. This fact was the existence of Latent Heat.

In order to follow the track of investigation pursued by Watt, it is necessary for a moment to revert to the action of the Newcomen pumping-engine. A beam, moving upon a centre, had affixed to one end of it a chain attached to the piston of the pump, and at the other a chain attached to a piston that fitted into the steam cylinder. It was by driving this latter piston up and down the cylinder that the pump was worked. To communicate the necessary movement to the piston, the steam generated in a boiler was admitted to the bottom of the cylinder, forcing out the air through a valve when its pressure on the under side of the piston counterbalanced the pressure of the atmosphere on its upper side. The piston, thus placed between two equal forces, was drawn up to the top of the cylinder by the greater weight of the pump-gear at the opposite extremity of the beam. The steam, so far, only discharged the office which was performed by the air it displaced; but, if the air had been allowed to remain, the piston once at the top of the cylinder could not have returned, being pressed as much by the atmosphere underneath as by the atmosphere above it. The steam, on the contrary, which was admitted by the exclusion of the air, *could be condensed*, and a vacuum created, by injecting cold water through the bottom of the cylinder. The piston being now unsupported, was forced down by the pressure of the atmosphere on its upper surface. When the piston reached the bottom, the steam was again let in, and the process was repeated. Such was the engine in ordinary use for pumping water at the time that Watt begun his investigations.

Among his other experiments, he constructed a boiler which showed by inspection the quantity of water evaporated in any given time, and the quantity of steam used in every stroke of the engine. He was astonished to discover that a *small* quantity of water in the form of steam, heated a *large* quantity of cold water injected into the 'cylinder for the purpose of cooling it; and upon further examination he ascertained that steam heated *six times* its weight of cold water to 212°, which was the temperature of the steam itself. "Being struck with this remarkable fact," says Watt, "and not understanding the reason of it, I mentioned it to my friend Dr. Black, who then explained to me his doctrine of latent heat, which he had taught for some time before this period (the summer of 1764); but having myself been occupied by the pursuits of business, if I had heard of it I had not attended to it, when I thus stumbled upon one of the material facts by which that beautiful theory is supported."[2]

When Watt found that water, in its conversion into vapour, became such a reservoir of heat, he was more than ever bent on economising it; for the great waste of heat involving so heavy a consumption of fuel, was felt to be the principal obstacle to the extended employment of steam as a motive power. He accordingly endeavoured, with the same quantity of fuel, at once to increase the production of steam, and to diminish its waste. He increased the heating surface of the boiler, by making flues through it; he even made his boiler of wood, as being a worse conductor of heat than the brickwork which surrounds common furnaces; and he cased the cylinders and all the conducting-pipes in materials which conducted heat very slowly. But none of these contrivances were effectual; for it turned out that the chief expenditure of steam, and consequently of fuel, in the Newcomen engine, was occasioned by the reheating of the cylinder after the steam had been condensed, and the cylinder was consequently cooled by the injection into it of the cold water. Nearly four-fifths of the whole steam employed was condensed on its first admission, before the surplus could act upon the piston. Watt therefore came to the conclusion, that to make a perfect steam-engine, it was necessary that *the cylinder should be always as hot as the steam that entered it*; but it was equally necessary that the steam should be condensed when the piston descended, – nay, that it should be cooled down below 100, or a considerable amount of vapour would be given off, which would resist the descent of the piston, and diminish the power of the engine. Thus the cylinder was never to be at a less temperature than 212°, and yet at each descent of the piston it was to be less than 100; conditions which, on the very face of them, seemed to be wholly incompatible.

We revert for a moment to the progress of Watt's instrument-making business. The shop in the College was not found to answer, being too far from the principal thoroughfares. If he wanted business he must go nearer to the public, for it was evident that they would not come to him. But to remove to a larger shop, in a more central quarter, involved an expenditure of capital for which he was himself unequal. His father had helped him with money as long as he could, but could do so no longer. Though he was as much respected by his neighbours as ever, he had grown poor by his losses; and, instead of giving help, himself needed it. Watt therefore looked about him for a partner with means, and succeeded in finding one in a Mr. John Craig, in conjunction with whom he opened a retail shop in the Salt-market, nearly opposite St. Andrew's Street, about the year 1760; removing from thence to Buchanan's Land, on the north side of the Trongate, a few years later.[3] Watt's partner was not a mechanic, but he supplied the requisite capital, and attended to the books. The partnership was on the whole successful, as we infer from the increased number of hands employed. At first Watt could execute all his orders himself, and afterwards by the help of a man and a boy; but by the end of 1764, the number of hands employed by the firm had increased to sixteen.

His improving business brought with it an improving income, and Watt – always a frugal and thrifty man – began to save a little money. He was

Watt's House, Delftfield Lane

encouraged to economise by another circumstance – his intended marriage with his cousin, Margaret Miller. In anticipation of this event, he had
removed from his rooms in the College to a house in Delftfield Lane – a
narrow passage then parallel with York Street, but now converted into the
spacious thoroughfare of Watt Street. Having furnished his house in a plain
yet comfortable style, he brought home his young wife, and installed her there
in July, 1764. The step was one of much importance to his personal wellbeing.
Mrs. Watt was of a lively, cheerful temperament; and as Watt himself was of
a meditative disposition, prone to melancholy, and a frequent sufferer from
nervous headache, her presence at his fireside could not fail to have a beneficial influence upon his health and comfort.

Watt continued to pursue his studies as before. Though still occupied with
his inquiries and experiments as to steam, he did not neglect his proper business, but was constantly on the look-out for improvements in instrument
making. A machine which he invented for drawing in perspective proved a

success; and he made a considerable number of them to order, for customers in London as well as abroad. He was also an indefatigable reader, and continued to extend his knowledge of chemistry and mechanics by perusal of the best books on these sciences.

Above all other subjects, however, the improvement of the steam-engine continued to keep the fastest hold upon his mind. He still brooded over his experiments with the Newcomen model, but did not seem to make much way in introducing any practical improvement in its mode of working. His friend Robison says he struggled long to condense with sufficient rapidity without injection, trying one expedient after another, finding out what would do by what would *not* do, and exhibiting many beautiful specimens of ingenuity and fertility of resource. He continued, to use his own words, "to grope in the dark, misled by many an *ignis fatuus*." It was a favourite saying of his, that "Nature has a weak side, if we can only find it out;" and he went on groping and feeling for it, but as yet in vain. At length light burst upon him, and all at once the problem over which he had been brooding was solved.

One Sunday afternoon, in the spring of 1765, he went to take an afternoon walk on the Green, then a quiet, grassy meadow, used as a bleaching and grazing-ground. On week-days the Glasgow lasses came thither with their largest kail-pots, to boil their clothes in; and sturdy queans might be seen, with coats kilted, tramping blankets in their tubs. On Sundays the place was comparatively deserted, and hence Watt, who lived close at hand, went there to take a quiet afternoon stroll. His thoughts were as usual running on the subject of his unsatisfactory experiments with the Newcomen engine, when the first idea of the separate condenser suddenly flashed upon his mind. But the notable discovery is best told in his own words, as related to Mr. Robert Hart, many years after: –

"I had gone to take a walk on a fine Sabbath afternoon. I had entered the Green by the gate at the foot of Charlotte Street, and had passed the old washing-house. I was thinking upon the engine at the time, and had gone as far as the herd's house, when the idea came into my mind that as steam was an elastic body it would rush into a vacuum, and if a communication were made between the cylinder and an exhausted vessel, it would rush into it, and might be there condensed without cooling the cylinder. I then saw that I must get rid of the condensed steam and injection-water if I used a jet, as in Newcomen's engine. Two ways of doing this occurred to me. First, the water might be run off by a descending pipe, if an off-let could be got at the depth of 35 or 36 feet, and any air might be extracted by a small pump. The second was to make the pump large enough to extract both water and air. He continued: I had not walked further than the Golf-house[4] when the whole thing was arranged in my mind."[5]

Great and prolific ideas are almost always simple. What seems impossible at the outset appears so obvious when it is effected that we are prone to marvel that it did not force itself at once upon the mind. Late in life Watt, with his accustomed modesty, declared his belief that if he had excelled, it had been by chance and the neglect of others." To Professor Jardine he said "that when it was analysed the invention would not appear so great as it seemed to be. In the state," said he, "in which I found the steam-engine, it was no great effort of mind to observe that the quantity of fuel necessary to make it work would for ever prevent its extensive utility. The next step in my progress was equally easy – to inquire what was the cause of the great consumption of fuel: this, too, was readily suggested, viz., the waste of fuel which was necessary to bring the whole cylinder, piston, and adjacent parts from the coldness of water to the heat of steam, no fewer than from fifteen to twenty times in a minute." The question then occurred, how was this to be avoided or remedied? It was at this stage that the idea of carrying on the condensation in a separate vessel flashed upon his mind, and solved the difficulty.[6]

Mankind has been more just to Watt than he was to himself. There was no accident in the discovery. It had been the result of close and continuous study; and the idea of the separate condenser was merely the last step of a long journey – a step which could not have been taken unless the road which led to it had been traversed. Dr. Black says, "This capital improvement flashed upon his mind at once, and filled him with rapture;" a state which, spite of the unimpassioned nature of Watt, we can readily believe.

On the morning following his Sunday afternoon's walk on Glasgow Green, Watt was up betimes making arrangements for a speedy trial of his new plan. He borrowed from a college friend a large brass syringe, an inch and a third in diameter, and ten inches long, of the kind used by anatomists for injecting arteries with wax previous to dissection. The body of the syringe served for a cylinder, the piston-rod passing through a collar of leather in its cover. A pipe connected with the boiler was inserted at both ends for the admission of steam, and at the upper end was another pipe to convey the steam to the condenser. The axis of the stem of the piston was drilled with a hole, fitted with a valve at its lower end, to permit the water produced by the condensed steam on first filling the cylinder to escape. The first condenser made use of was an improvised cistern of tinned plate, provided with a pump to get rid of the water formed by the condensation of the steam, both the condensing-pipes and the air-pump being placed in a reservoir of cold water.

"The steam-pipe," says Watt, "was adjusted to a small boiler. When steam was produced, it was admitted into the cylinder, and soon issued through the perforation of the rod, and at the valve of the condenser; when it was judged that the air was expelled, the steam-cock was shut, and the air-pump piston-rod was drawn up, which leaving the small pipes of the condenser in a state of vacuum, the steam entered them and was condensed. The piston of the cylinder immediately rose and lifted a weight of about 18 lbs., which was hung to the lower end of the piston-rod. The exhaustion-cock was shut, the steam was readmitted into the cylinder, and the operation was repeated. The quantity of steam consumed and the weights it could raise were observed, and, excepting the non-application of the steam-case and external covering, the invention was complete, in so far as regarded the savings of steam and fuel."

But, although the invention was complete in Watt's mind, it took him many long and laborious years to work out the details of the engine. His friend Robison, with whom his intimacy was maintained during these interesting experiments, has given a graphic account of the difficulties

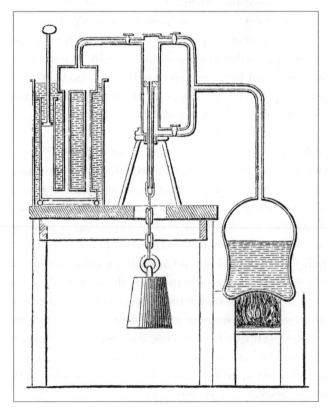

Watt's first improved
Apparatus

which he successively encountered and overcame. He relates that on his return from the country, after the College vacation in 1785, he went to have a chat with Watt and communicate to him some observations be had made on Desaguliers' and Belidor's account of the steam-engine. He went straight into the parlour, without ceremony, and found Watt sitting before the fire looking at a little tin cistern which he had on his knee. Robison immediately started the conversation about steam, his mind, like Watt's, being occupied with the means of avoiding the excessive waste of heat in the Newcomen engine. Watt, all the while, kept looking into the fire, and after a time laid down the cistern at the foot of his chair, saying nothing. It seems that Watt felt rather nettled at Robison having communicated to a mechanic of the town a contrivance which he had hit upon for turning the cocks of his engine. When Robison therefore pressed his inquiry, Watt at length looked at him and said briskly, "You need not fash yourself any more about that, man; I have now made an engine that shall not waste a particle of steam. It shall all be boiling hot, – ay, and hot water injected, if I please." He then pushed the little tin cistern with his foot under the table.

Robison could learn no more of the new contrivance from Watt at that time; but on the same evening he accidentally met a mutual acquaintance, who, supposing he knew as usual the progress of Watt's experiments, observed to him, "Well, have you seen Jamie Watt?" "Yes." "He'll be in fine spirits now with his engine?" "Yes," said Robison, "very fine spirits." "Gad!" said the other, "the separate condenser's the thing: keep it but cold enough, and you may have a perfect vacuum, whatever be the heat of the cylinder." This was Watt's secret, and the nature of the contrivance was clear to Robison at once.

It will be observed that Watt had not made a secret of it to his other friends. Indeed Robison himself admitted that one of Watt's greatest delights was to communicate the results of his experiments to others, and set them upon the same road to knowledge with himself; and that no one could display less of the small jealousy of the tradesman than he did. To his intimate friend, Dr. Black, he communicated the progress made by him at every stage; and the Doctor kindly encouraged him in his struggles, cheered him in his encounter with difficulty, and, what was of still more practical value at the time, he helped him with money to enable him to prosecute his invention. Communicative though Watt was disposed to be, he learnt reticence when he found himself exposed to the depredations of the smaller fry of inventors. Robison says that had he lived in Birmingham or London at the time, the probability is that some one or other of the numerous harpies who live by sucking other people's brains, would have secured patents for his more impor-

J.COOPER.S^t   Dr. Joseph Black

tant inventions, and thereby deprived him of the benefits of his skill, science, and labour. As yet, however, there were but few mechanics in Glasgow capable of understanding or appreciating the steam-engine; and the intimate friends to whom he freely spoke of his discovery were too honourable-minded to take advantage of his confidence. Shortly after, Watt fully communicated to Robison the different stages of his invention, and the results at which he had arrived, much to the delight of his friend.

It will be remembered that in the Newcomen engine the steam was only employed for the purpose of producing a vacuum, and that its working power was in the down stroke, which was effected by the pressure of the air upon the piston; hence it is now usual to call it the atmospheric engine. Watt perceived that the air which followed the piston down the cylinder would cool the latter, and that steam would be wasted in re-heating it. In order, therefore, to avoid this loss of heat, he resolved to put an air-tight cover upon the cylinder, with a hole and stuffing-box for the piston-rod to slide through, and to admit steam above the piston, to act upon it instead of the atmosphere. When the steam had done its duty in driving down the piston, a communication was opened between the upper and lower part of the cylinder, and the same steam, distributing itself equally in both compartments, sufficed to restore equilibrium. The piston was now drawn up by the weight of the pump-gear; the steam beneath it was then condensed in the separate vessel so as to produce a vacuum, and a fresh jet of steam from the boiler was let in above the piston, which forced it again to the bottom of the cylinder. From an atmospheric it had thus become a true steam-engine, and with a much greater economy of steam than when the air did half the duty. But it was not only important to keep the air from flowing down the inside of the cylinder: the air which circulated within cooled the metal and condensed a portion of the steam within; and this Watt proposed to remedy by a second cylinder, surrounding the first with an interval between the two which was to be kept full of steam.

One by one these various contrivances were struck out, modified, settled, and reduced to definite plans; the separate condenser, the air and water pumps, the use of fat and oil (instead of water as in the Newcomen engine) to keep the piston working in the cylinder air-tight, and the enclosing of the cylinder itself within another to prevent the loss of heat. They were all but emanations from the first idea of inventing an engine working by a piston, in which the cylinder should be kept continually hot and perfectly dry. "When once," says Watt, "the idea of separate condensation was started, all these improvements followed as corollaries in quick succession; so that in the course of one or two days the invention was thus far complete in my mind."

The next step was to construct a model engine for the purpose of embodying the invention in a working form. With this object Watt hired an old cellar, situated in the first wide entry to the north of the beef-market in King Street, and there proceeded with his model. He found it much easier, however, to prepare his plan than to execute it. Like most ingenious and inventive men, Watt was extremely fastidious; and this occasioned considerable delay in the execution of the work. His very inventiveness to some extent proved a hinderance; for new expedients were perpetually occurring to him, which he thought would be improvements, and which he, by turns, endeavoured to introduce. Some of these expedients he admits proved fruitless, and all of them occasioned delay. Another of his chief difficulties was in finding competent workmen to execute his plans. He himself had been accustomed only to small metal work, with comparatively delicate tools, and had very little experience "in the practice of mechanics *in great*," as he termed it. He was therefore under the necessity of depending, in a great measure, upon the handiwork of others. But mechanics capable of working out Watt's designs in metal were then with difficulty to be found. The beautiful self-acting tools and workmanship which have since been called into being, principally by his own invention, did not then exist. The only available hands in Glasgow were the blacksmiths and tinners, little capable of constructing articles out of their ordinary walks; and even in these they were often found clumsy, blundering, and incompetent. The result was, that in consequence of the malconstruction of the larger parts, Watt's first model was only partially successful. The experiments made with it, however, served to verify the expectations he had formed, and to place the advantages of the invention beyond the reach of doubt. On the exhausting-cock being turned, the piston, when loaded with 18 lbs., ascended as quick as the blow of a hammer; and the moment the steam-cock was opened, it descended with like rapidity, though the steam was weak, and the machine snifted at many openings.

Satisfied that he had laid hold of the right principle of a working steam-engine, Watt felt impelled to follow it to an issue. He could give his mind to no other business in peace until this was done. He wrote to a friend that he was quite barren on every other subject. "My whole thoughts," said he, "are bent on this machine. I can think of nothing else."[7] He proceeded to make another and bigger, and, he hoped, a more satisfactory engine, in the following August; and with that object he removed from the old cellar in King-street to a larger apartment in the then disused pottery or delftwork near the Broomielaw. There he shut himself up with his assistant, John Gardiner, for the purpose of erecting his engine. The cylinder was five or six inches in diameter, with a two-feet stroke. The inner cylinder was enclosed in a wooden steam-case, and placed inverted, the piston working through a hole in the bottom of the steam-case. After two months' continuous application and labour it was finished and set to work; but it leaked in all directions, and the piston was far from air-tight. The condenser also was in a bad way, and needed many alterations. Nevertheless, the engine readily worked with 10½ lbs. pressure on the inch, and the piston lifted a weight of 14 lbs. The improvement of the cylinder and piston continued Watt's chief difficulty, and taxed his ingenuity to the utmost. At so low an ebb was the art of making cylinders that the one he used was not bored but hammered, the collective mechanical skill of Glasgow being then unequal to the boring of a cylinder of the simplest kind; nor, indeed, did the necessary appliances for the purpose then exist anywhere else. In the Newcomen engine a little water was poured upon the upper surface of the piston, and sufficiently filled up the interstices between the piston and the cylinder. But when Watt employed steam to drive down the piston, he was deprived of this resource, for the water and the steam could not coexist. Even if he had retained the agency of the air above, the drip of water from the crevices into the lower part of the cylinder would have been incompatible with keeping the surface hot and dry, and, by turning into vapour as it fell upon the heated metal, it would have impaired the vacuum during the descent of the piston.

While he was occupied with this difficulty, and striving to overcome it by the adoption of new expedients, such as leather collars and improved workmanship, he wrote to a friend, "My old white-iron man is dead;" the old white-iron man, or tinner, being his leading mechanic. Unhappily, also, just as he seemed to have got the engine into working order, the beam broke, and having great difficulty in replacing the damaged part, the accident threatened, together with the loss of his best workman, to bring the experiment to an end. But though discouraged by these misadventures, he was far from defeated, but went on as before, battling down difficulty inch by inch, and holding good the ground he had won, becoming every day more strongly convinced that he was in the right track, and that the important uses of the invention, could he but find time and means to perfect it, were beyond the reach of doubt.

But how to find the means! Watt himself was a comparatively poor man; having no money but what he earned by his business of mechanical instrument making, which he had for some time been neglecting through his devotion to the construction of his engine. What he wanted was capital, or the help of a capitalist willing to advance him the necessary funds to perfect his invention. To give a fair trial to the new apparatus would involve an expenditure of several thousand pounds; and who on the spot could be expected to invest so large a sum in trying a machine so entirely new, depending for its success on physical principles very imperfectly understood?

There was no such help to be found in Glasgow. The tobacco lords, though rich, took no interest in steam power, and the manufacturing class, though growing in importance, had full employment for their little capital in their own concerns.

NOTES

1 At a meeting held in Glasgow in 1839 to erect a monument to Watt, Dr. Ure observed: – "As to the latent heat of steam," said Mr. Watt to me "it was a piece of knowledge essential to my inquiries, and I worked it out myself in the best way that I could. I used apothecaries' phials for my

apparatus, and by means of them I got approximations sufficient for my purpose at the time." The passage affords a striking illustration of the large results that may be arrived at by means of the humblest instruments. In like manner Cavendish, when asked by a foreigner to be shown over his laboratories, pointed to an old tea-tray on the table, containing a few watch-glasses, test papers, a balance, and a blow-pipe, and observed "There is all the laboratory I possess."

2 Watt's notes to Robison's Articles on 'Steam and Steam-engines.'

3 The following advertisement in the 'Glasgow Journal' of the 1st Dec., 1763, fixes the date of this last removal: "James Watt has removed his shop from the Saltmercat to Mr. Buchanan's land in the Trongate, where he sells all sorts of Mathematical and Musical Instruments, with a variety of toys, and other goods. "

4 About the site of the Humane Society's House.

5 Mr. Robert Hart's 'Reminiscences of James Watt,' in 'Transactions of the Glasgow Archæological Society, 1859.'

6 "The last step of all,' says Professor Jardine, "was more difficult – the forming of the separate condensing vessel. The great knowledge he had acquired of the mechanical powers enabled him to construct it, but I have often heard him say this was a work of great difficulty, and that he met with many disappointments before be succeeded. I have often made use of this beautiful analysis received from Mr. Watt, in another department in which I have been long engaged, to illustrate and encourage the progress of genius in youth, to show, that once in possession of a habit of attention, under proper direction, it may be carried from one easy step to another, till the mind becomes qualified and invigorated for uniting and concentrating effort – the highest exertion of genius."

7 "I have now (April, 1765) almost a certainty of the *facturum* of the fire-engine, having determined the following particulars: The quantity of steam produced; the ultimatum of the lever engine; the quantity of steam destroyed by the cold of its cylinder; the quantity destroyed in mine; and if there be not some devil in the hedge, mine ought to raise water to 44 feet with the same quantity of steam that theirs does to 32 (supposing my cylinder as thick as theirs), which I think I can demonstrate. I can now make a cylinder 2 feet diameter and 3 feet high, only a 40th of an inch thick, and strong enough to resist the atmosphere; *sed tace*. In short, I can think of nothing else but this machine." – Watt to Dr. Lind, quoted in Muirhead's 'Life of Watt,' 94–5.

VIII

Watt's Connexion with Dr. Roebuck – Watt acts as Surveyor and Engineer

Dr. Black continued to take a lively interest in Watt's experiments, and lent him occasional sums of money from time to time to enable him to prosecute them to an issue. But the Doctor's means were too limited to permit him to do more than supply Watt's more pressing necessities. Meanwhile, the debts which the latter had already incurred, small though they were in amount, hung like a millstone round his neck. Black then bethought him whether it would not be possible to associate Watt with some person possessed of sufficient means, and of an active commercial spirit, who should join as a partner in the risk, and share in the profits of the enterprise. Such a person, be thought, was Dr. Roebuck, the founder of the Carron Iron Works, an enterprising man, of undaunted spirit, not scared by difficulties, nor a niggard of expense when he saw before him any reasonable prospect of advantage.[1]

Roebuck was at that time engaged in sinking for coal on a large scale near Boroughstoness, where he experienced considerable difficulty in keeping the shafts clear of water. The Newcomen engine, which he had erected, was found comparatively useless, and he was ready to embrace any other scheme which held out a reasonable prospect of success. Accordingly, when his friend Dr. Black informed him of an ingenious young mechanic at Glasgow who had invented a steam-engine, capable of working with increased power, speed, and economy, Roebuck immediately felt interested, and entered into correspondence with Watt on the subject. He was at first somewhat sceptical as to the practicability of the new engine, so different in its action from that of Newcomen; and he freely stated his doubts to Dr. Black. He was under the impression that condensation might in some way be effected in the cylinder without injection; and he urged Watt to try whether this might not be done.

Contrary to his own judgment, Watt tried a series of experiments with this object, and at last abandoned them, Roebuck himself admitting his error.

Up to this time Watt and Roebuck had not met, though they carried on a long correspondence on the subject of the, engine. In September, 1765, we find Roebuck inviting Watt to come over with Dr. Black to Kinneil (where Roebuck lived), and discuss with him the subject of the engine. Watt wrote to say that "if his foot allowed him" he would visit Carron on a certain day, from which we infer that he intended to walk. But the way was long and the road miry, and Watt could not then leave his instrument shop, so the visit was postponed. In the mean time Roebuck urged Watt to press forward his invention with all speed, "whether he pursued it as a philosopher or as a man of business."

In the month of November following, Watt forwarded to Roebuck the detailed drawings of a covered cylinder and piston to be cast at the Carron Works. Though the cylinder was the best that could be made there, it was very ill-bored, and was eventually laid aside as useless. The piston-rod was made at Glasgow, under Watt's own supervision; and when it was completed he was afraid to tend it on a common cart, lest the workpeople should see it, which would "occasion speculation." "I believe," he wrote in July, 1766, "it would be best to send it in a box." These precautions would seem to have been dictated, in some measure, by fear of piracy; and it is obvious that the necessity of acting by stealth increased the difficulty of getting the various parts of the proposed engine constructed. Watt's greatest obstacle continued to be the clumsiness and inexpertness of his mechanics. "My principal hinderance in erecting engines," he wrote to Roebuck, "is always the smith-work."

In the mean time it was necessary for Watt to attend to the maintenance of his family. He found that the steam-engine experiments brought nothing in, while they were a constant source of expense. Besides, they diverted him from his retail business, which needed constant attention. It ought also to be mentioned that his partner having lately died, the business had been somewhat neglected and had consequently fallen off. At length he determined to give it up altogether, and begin the business of a surveyor. He accordingly removed from the shop in Buchanan's Land to an office on the east side of King-street, a little south of Prince's-street. It would appear that he succeeded in obtaining a fair share of business in his new vocation. He already possessed a sufficient knowledge of surveying from the study of the instruments which it had been his business to make; and application and industry did the rest. His first jobs were in surveying lands, defining boundaries, and surveyor's work of the ordinary sort; from which he gradually proceeded to surveys of a more important character.

It affords some indication of the local estimation in which Watt was held, that the magistrates of Glasgow should have selected him as a groper person to survey a canal for the purpose of opening up a new coal-field in the neighbourhood, and connecting it with the city, with a view to a cheaper and more abundant supply of fuel. He also surveyed a ditch-canal for the purpose of connecting the rivers Forth and Clyde, by what was called the Loch Lomond passage; though the scheme of Brindley and Smeaton was eventually preferred as the more direct line. Watt came up to London in 1767, in connexion with the application to Parliament for powers to construct his canal; and he seems to have been very much disgusted with the proceedings before "the confounded committee of Parliament," as he called it; adding, "I think I shall not long to have anything to do with the House of Commons again. I never saw so many wrong-headed people on all sides gathered together." The fact, however, that they had decided against him had probably some share in leading him to form this opinion as to the wrong-headedness of the Parliamentary Committee.

Though interrupted by indispensable business of this sort, Watt proceeded with the improvement of his steam-engine whenever leisure permitted. Roebuck's confidence in its eventual success was such that in 1767 he undertook to pay debts to the amount of 1000*l.* which Watt had incurred in prosecuting his project up to that time, and also to provide the means of prosecuting further experiments, as well as to secure a patent for the engine. In return for this outlay Roebuck was to have two-thirds of the property in the invention. Early in 1768 Watt made trial of a new and larger model, with a cylinder of seven or eight inches diameter. But the result was not very satisfactory. "By an unforeseen misfortune," he wrote Roebuck, "the mercury found its way into the cylinder, and played the devil with the solder. This throws us back at least three days, and is very vexatious, especially as it happened in spite of the precautions I had taken to prevent it." Roebuck, becoming impatient, urged Watt to meet him to talk the matter over; and suggested that as Watt could not come as far as Carron, they should meet at Kilsyth, about fifteen miles from Glasgow. Watt replied, saying he was too unwell to be able to ride so far, and that his health was such that the journey would disable him from doing anything for three or four days after. But he went on with his experiments, patching up his engine, and endeavouring to get it into working condition. After about a month's labour, he at last succeeded to his heart's content; and he at once communicated the news to his partner, intimating his intention of at last paying his long-promised visit to Roebuck at Kinneil. "I sincerely wish you joy of this successful result," he said, "and hope it will make some return for the obligations I owe you."

Kinneil House

Kinneil House, to which Watt hastened to pay his visit of congratulation to Dr. Roebuck, is an old-fashioned building, somewhat resembling an old French château. It was a former country-seat of the Dukes of Hamilton, and is finely situated on the shores of the Firth of Forth. The mansion is rich in classical associations, having been inhabited, since Roebuck's time, by Dugald Stewart, who wrote in it his 'Philosophy of the Human Mind.'[2] There he was visited by Wilkie, the painter, when in search of subjects for his pictures; and Dugald Stewart found for him, in an old farmhouse in the neighbourhood, the cradle-chimney introduced in the "Penny Wedding." But none of these names can stand by the side of that of Watt; and the first thought at Kinneil, of every one who is familiar with his history, would be of the memorable day when he rode over in exultation to wish Dr. Roebuck joy of the success of the steam-engine. His note of triumph was, however, premature. He had yet to suffer many sickening delays and bitter disappointments; for, though he had contrived to get his model executed with fair precision, the skill was still wanting to manufacture the parts of their full size with the requisite unity; and this present elation was consequently doomed to be succeeded by repeated discomfiture.

The model went so well, however, that it was determined at once to take out a patent for the engine. The first step was to secure its provisional protection, and with that object Watt went to Berwick-upon-Tweed, and made a declaration before a Master in Chancery of the nature of the invention. In August, 1768, we find him in London on the business of the patent. He became utterly wearied with the delays interposed by sluggish officialism, and disgusted with the heavy fees which he was required to pay in order to protect his invention. He wrote home to his wife at Glasgow in a very desponding mood. Knowing her husband's diffidence and modesty, but having the fullest confidence in his genius, she replied, "I beg that you will not make yourself uneasy, though things should not succeed to your wish. If it [the condensing engine] will not do, *something else will; never despair.*" Watt must have felt cheered by these brave words of his noble helpmate, and encouraged to go onward cheerfully in hope.

He could not, however, shake off his recurring fits of despondency, and on his return to Glasgow, we find him occasionally in very low spirits. Though his head was full of his engine, his heart ached with anxiety for his family, who could not be maintained on hope, already so often deferred. The more sanguine Roebuck was elated with the good working of the model, and impatient to bring the invention into practice. He wrote Watt in October, 1768, "You are now letting the most active part of your life insensibly glide away. A day, a moment, ought not to be lost. And you should not suffer your thoughts to be diverted by any other object, or even improvement of this, but only the speediest and most effectual manner of executing an engine of a proper size, according to your present ideas."

Watt, however, felt that his invention was capable of many improvements, and he was never done introducing new expedients. He proceeded, in the intervals of leisure which he could spare from his surveying business, to complete the details of the drawings and specification, – making various trials of pipe-condensers, plate-condensers, and drum-condensers, – contriving steam-jackets to prevent the waste of heat and new methods for securing greater tightness of the piston, – inventing condenser-pumps, oil-pumps, gauge-pumps, exhausting-cylinders, loading-valves, double cylinders, beams, and cranks. All these contrivances had to be thought out and tested, elaborately and painfully, amidst many failures and disappointments; and Dr. Roebuck began to fear that the fresh expedients which were always starting up in Watt's brain, would endlessly protract the consummation of the invention. Watt, on his part, felt that he could only bring the engine nearer to perfection by never resting satisfied with imperfect devices, and hence he left no means untried to overcome the many practical defects in it of which he was so conscious. Long after, when a noble lord was expressing to him the admiration with which he regarded his great achievement, Watt replied: "The public only look at my success, and not at the intermediate failures and uncouth constructions which have served me as so many steps to climb to the top of the ladder."

As to the lethargy from which Roebuck sought to raise Watt, it was merely the temporary reaction of a mind strained and wearied with long-continued application to a single subject, and from which it seemed to be occasionally on the point of breaking down altogether. To his intimate friends, Watt bemoaned his many failures, his low spirits, his bad health, and his sleepless nights. He wrote to his friend Dr. Small[3] in January, 1769, "I have many things I could talk to you about – much contrived, and little executed. How much would good health and spirits be worth to me!" A month later he wrote, "I am still plagued with head-aches, and sometimes heart-aches."

It is nevertheless a remarkable proof of Watt's indefatigable perseverance in his favourite pursuit, that at this very time, when apparently sunk in the depths of gloom, he learnt German for the purpose of getting at the contents of a curious book, the *Theatrum Machinarum* of Leupold, which just then fell into his hands, and contained an account of the machines, furnaces, methods of working, profits, &c., of the mines in the Upper Hartz. His instructor in the language was a Swiss dyer,[4] settled in Glasgow. With the like object of gaining access to untranslated books in French and Italian – then the great depositories of mechanical and engineering knowledge – Watt had already mastered both those languages.

In preparing his specification, Watt viewed the subject in all its bearings. The production of power by steam is a very large one, but Watt grasped it thoroughly. The insight with which he searched, analysed, arranged, and even provided for future modifications, was the true insight of genius. He seems with an almost prophetic eye to have seen all that steam was capable of accomplishing. This is well illustrated by his early plan of working steam expansively by cutting it off at about half-stroke, thereby greatly economising its use;[5] as well as by his proposal to employ high-pressure steam where cold water could not be used for purposes of condensation.[6] The careful and elaborate manner in which he studied the specification, and the consideration which he gave to each of its various details, are clear from his correspondence with Dr. Small, which is peculiarly interesting, as showing Watt's mind actively engaged in the very process of invention. At length the necessary specification and drawings were completed and lodged early in 1769, – a year also remarkable as that in which Arkwright took out the patent for his spinning-machine.

In order to master thoroughly the details of the ordinary Newcomen engine, and to ascertain the extent of its capabilities as well as of its imperfections, Watt undertook the erection of several engines of this construction; and during his residence at Kinneil took charge of the Schoolyard engine near Boroughstoness, in order that he might thereby acquire a full practical knowledge of its working. Mr. Hart, in his interesting 'Reminiscences of James Watt,' gives the following account: "My late brother had learned from an old man who had been a workman at Dr. Roebuck's coal-works when Mr. Watt was there, that be had erected a small engine on a pit they called Taylor's Pit. The workman could not remember what kind of engine it was, but it was the fastest-going one he ever saw. From its size, and from its being placed in a small timber-house, the colliers called it 'the Box Bed.' We thought it likely to have been the first of the patent engines made by Mr. Watt, and took the opportunity of mentioning this to him at our interview. He said he had erected that engine, but he did not wish at the time to venture on a patent one until he had a little more experience."[7]

At length he proceeded to erect the trial engine after his new patent, and made arrangements to stay at Kinneil until the work was finished. It had been originally intended to erect it in the little town of Boroughstoness; but as prying eyes might have there watched his proceedings, and as he wished to avoid display, being determined, as he said, "not to puff," he fixed upon an outhouse behind Kinneil, close by the burn-side in the glen, where there was abundance of water and secure privacy. The materials were brought to the place, partly from Watt's small works at Glasgow, and partly from Carron, where the cylinder – of eighteen inches diameter and five feet stroke – had been cast; and a few workmen were placed at his disposal

The process of erection was very tedious, owing to the clumsiness of the mechanics employed on the job. Watt was occasionally compelled to be absent on other business, and on his return he usually found the men at a standstill, not knowing what to do next. As the engine neared completion, his "anxiety for his approaching doom" kept him from sleep; for his fears, as he said, were at least equal to his hopes. He was easily cast down by little obstructions, and especially discouraged by unforeseen expense. Roebuck, on the contrary, was hopeful and energetic, and often took occasion to rally the other on his despondency under difficulties, and his almost painful want of confidence in himself. Roebuck was, doubtless, of much service to Watt in encouraging him to proceed with his invention, and also in suggesting some important modifications in the construction of the engine. It is probable, indeed, that but for his help, Watt could not have gone on. Robison says, "I remember Mrs. Roebuck remarking one evening, 'Jamie is a queer lad, and, without the Doctor, his invention would have been lost; but Dr. Roebuck won't let it perish.'"

The outhouse behind
Kinneil

The new engine, on which Watt had expended so much labour, anxiety, and ingenuity, was completed in September, 1759, about six months from the date of its commencement. But its success was far from decided. Watt himself declared it to be "a clumsy job." His new arrangement of the pipe-condenser did not work well; and the cylinder having been badly cast, was found almost useless. One of his greatest difficulties consisted in keeping the piston tight. He wrapped it round with cork, oiled rags, tow, old hat, paper, horse-dung, and other things, but still there were open spaces left, sufficient to let the air in and the steam out. Watt was grievously depressed by his want of success; and he had serious thoughts of giving up the thing altogether. Before abandoning it, however, the engine was again thoroughly overhauled, many improvements were introduced in it, and a new trial was made of its powers. But this proved not more successful than the earlier ones had been. "You cannot conceive," he wrote to Small, "how mortified I am with this disappointment. It is a damned thing for a man to have his all hanging by a single string. If I had wherewithal to pay the loss, I don't think I should so much fear a failure; but I cannot bear the thought of other people becoming losers by my schemes; and I have the happy disposition of always painting the worst."

Watt was therefore bound to prosecute his project by honour not less than by interest; and summoning up his courage he went on with it anew. He continued to have the same confidence as ever in the principles of his engine: where it broke down was in workmanship. Could mechanics but be found capable of accurately executing its several parts, he believed that its success was certain. But there were no such mechanics then at Carron.

By this time Roebuck was becoming embarrassed with debt, and involved in various difficulties. The pits were drowned with water, which no existing machinery could pump out, and ruin threatened to over take him before Watt's engine could come to his help. He had sunk in the coal-mine, not only his own fortune, but much of the property of his relatives; and he was so straitened for money that he was unable to defray the cost of taking out the engine patent according to the terms of his engagement, and Watt had accordingly to borrow the necessary money from his never-failing friend, Dr. Black. He was thus adding to his own debts, without any clearer prospect before him of ultimate relief. No wonder that be should, after his apparently fruitless labour, express to Small his belief that, "of all things in life, there is nothing more foolish than inventing." The unhappy state of his mind may be further inferred from his lamentation expressed to the same friend on the 31st of January, 1770. "To day," said he, "I enter the thirty-fifth year of my life, and I think I have hardly yet done thirty-five pence worth of good in the world; but I cannot help it."

Notwithstanding the failure of his engine thus far, and the repeated resolution expressed to Small that he would invent no more, leading, as inventing did, to only vexation, failure, loss, and increase of head-ache, Watt could not control his irrepressible instinct to invent; and whether the result might be profitable or not, his mind went on as before, working, scheming, and speculating. Thus, at different times in the course of his correspondence with Small, who was a man of a like ingenious turn of mind, we find him communicating various new things, "gimcracks," as he termed them, which he had contrived. He was equally ready to contrive a cure for smoky chimneys, a canal sluice for economising water, a method of determining "the force necessary to dredge up a cubic foot of mud under any given depth of water," and a means of "clearing the observed distance of the moon from any given star of the effects of refraction and parallax;" illustrating his views by rapid but graphic designs embodied in the text of his letters to Small and other correspondents. One of his minor inventions was a new method of readily measuring distances by means of a telescope.[8] At the same time he was occupied in making experiments on kaolin, with the intention of introducing the manufacture of porcelain in the pottery work on the Broomielaw, in which he was a partner. He was also concerned with Dr. Black and Dr. Roebuck in pursuing experiments with the view of decomposing sea-salt by lime, and thereby obtaining alkali for purposes of commerce. A patent for the process was taken out by Dr. Roebuck, but eventually proved a failure, like most of his other projects. We also find Watt inventing a muffling furnace for melting metals, and sending the drawings to Mr. Boulton at Birmingham for trial. At other times he was occupied with Chaillet, the Swiss dyer, experimenting on various chemical substances; corresponding with Dr. Black as to the new fluoric or spar acid; and at another time making experiments to ascertain the heats at which water boils at every inch of mercury from vacuo to air. Later we find him inventing a prismatic micrometer for measuring distances, which he described in considerable detail in his letters to Small.[9] He was at the same time busy inventing and constructing a new surveying quadrant by reflection, and making improvements in barometers and hygrometers. "I should like to know," he wrote to Small, "the principles of *your* barometer: De Luc's hygrometer is nonsense. *Pro bavi*." Another of his contrivances was his dividing-screw, for dividing an inch accurately into 1000 equal parts. He states that he found this screw exceedingly useful, as it saved him much needless compass-work, and, moreover, enabled him to divide lines into the ordinates of any curve whatsoever.

Such were the multifarious pursuits in which this indefatigable student and inquirer was engaged; all tending to cultivate his mind and advance his education, but comparatively unproductive, so far as regarded pecuniary return. So unfortunate, indeed, had Watt's speculations proved, that his friend Dr. Hutton, of Edinburgh, addressed to him a New-year's day letter, with the object of dissuading him from proceeding further with his unprofitable brain-distressing work. "A happy new year to you!" said Hutton; "may it be fertile to you in lucky events, but no new inventions!" He went on to say that invention was only for those who live by the public, and those who from pride choose to leave a legacy to the public. It was not a thing likely to be well paid for under a system where the rule was to be the best paid for the work that was easiest done. It was of no use, however, telling Watt that he must not invent. One might as well have told Burns that he was not to sing because it would not pay, or Wilkie that he was not to paint, or Hutton himself that he was not to think and speculate as to the hidden operations of nature. To invent was the natural and habitual operation of Watt's intellect, and he could not restrain it.

Watt had already been too long occupied with this profitless work: his money was all gone; he was in debt; and it behoved him to turn to some other employment by which he might provide for the indispensable wants of his family. Having now given up the instrument-making business, he confined himself almost entirely to surveying. Among his earliest surveys was one of a coal canal from Monkland to Glasgow, in 1769; and the Act authorising its construction was obtained in the following year. Watt was invited to superintend the execution of the works, and he had accordingly to elect whether he would go on with the engine experiments, the event of which was doubtful, or embrace a honourable and perhaps profitable employment, attended with much less risk and uncertainty. His necessities decided him. "I had," he said, "a wife and children, and saw myself growing grey without having any settled way of providing for them." He accordingly accepted the appointment offered him by the directors of the canal, and undertook to superintend the construction of the works at a salary of 200*l.* a year. At the same time he determined not to drop the engine, but to proceed with it at such leisure moments as he could command.

The Monkland Canal was a small concern, and Watt had to undertake a variety of duties. He acted at the same time as surveyor, superintendent, engineer, and treasurer, assisted only by a clerk. But the appointment proved useful to him. The salary he earned placed his family above want, and the out-doors life he was required to lead improved his health and spirits. After a few months he wrote Dr. Small that he found himself more strong, more resolute, less lazy, and less confused, than when he began the occupation. His pecuniary affairs were also more promising. "Supposing the engine to stand good for itself," he said, "I am able to pay all my debts and some little thing more, so that I hope in time to be on a par with the world." But there was a dark side to the picture. His occupation exposed him to fatigue, vexation, hunger, wet, and cold. Then, the quiet and secluded habits of his early life did not fit him for the out-door work of the engineer. He was timid and reserved, and had nothing of the navvy in his nature. He had neither the roughness of tongue nor stiffness of back to enable him to deal with rude labour gangs. He was nervously fearful lest his want of practical experience should betray him into scrapes, and lead to impositions on the part of his workmen. He hated higgling, and declared that he would rather "face a loaded cannon than settle an account or make a bargain." He had been "cheated," he said, "by under-takers, and was unlucky enough to know it."

Watt continued to act as engineer for the Monkland Canal Company for about a year and a half,[10] during which he was employed in other engineer-ing works. Among these was a survey of the river Clyde, with a view to the improvement of the navigation. Watt sent in his report; but no steps were taken to carry out his suggestions until several years later, when the beginning was made of a series of improvements, which have resulted in the conversion of the Clyde from a pleasant trouting and salmon stream into one of the busi-est navigable highways in the world.[11]

Among Watt's other labours about the same period may be mentioned his survey of a canal between Perth and Cupar Angus, through Strathmore; of the Crinan Canal, afterwards carried out by Rennie; and other projects in the western highlands. The Strathmore Canal survey was conducted at the instance of the Commissioners of Forfeited Estates. It was forty miles long, through a very rough country. Watt set out to make it in September, 1770, and was accompanied by snow-storms through almost the entire survey. He suffered severely from the cold: the winds swept down from the Grampians with fury and chilled him to the bone. The making of this survey occupied him forty-three days, and the remuneration he received for it was only eighty pounds, which included expenses. The small pay of engineers at that time may be further illustrated by the fee paid him in the same year for supplying the magistrates of Hamilton with a design for the proposed new bridge over the Clyde at that town. It was originally intended to employ Mr. Smeaton; but as his charge was ten pounds, which was thought too high, Watt was employed in his stead. The Burgh minutes record that, after the Act had been

Hamilton Bridge

obtained in 1770, Baillie Naismith was appointed to proceed to Glasgow to see Mr. Watt on the subject of a design, and his charge being only 7*l.* 7*s.*, he was requested to supply it accordingly. "I have lately," wrote Watt to Small, "made a plan and estimate of a bridge over our river Clyde, eight miles above this: it is to be of five arches and 220 feet waterway, founded upon piles on a muddy bottom."[12] The bridge, after Watt's plan, was begun in 1771, but it was not finished until 1780.[13]

About the same time Watt prepared plans of docks and piers at Port Glasgow, and of a new harbour at Ayr. The Port Glasgow works were carried out, but those at Ayr were postponed. When Rennie came to examine the design for the improvement of the Ayr navigation, of which the new harbour formed part, he took objections to it, principally because of the parallelism of the piers, and another plan was eventually adopted. His principal engineering job, and the last of the kind on which Watt was engaged in Scotland, was a survey of the Caledonian Canal, long afterwards carried out by Telford. The survey was made in the autumn of 1773, through a country without roads. "An incessant rain," said he, "kept me for three days as wet as water could make me; I could hardly preserve my journal book."

In the midst of this dreary work, Watt was summoned to Glasgow by the intelligence which reached him of the illness of his wife; and when he reached home

Port Glasgow (by R.P. Leitch)

he found that she had died in childbed.[14] Of all the heavy blows he had suffered, this he felt to be the worst. His wife had struggled with him through poverty; she had often cheered his fainting spirit when borne down by doubt, perplexity, and disappointment; and now she was gone, without being able to share in his good fortune as she had done in his adversity. For some time after, when about to enter his humble dwelling, he would pause on the threshold, unable to summon courage to enter the room where he was never more to meet "the comfort of his life." "Yet this misfortune," he wrote to Small, "might have fallen upon me when I had less ability to bear it, and my poor children might have been left suppliants to the mercy of the wide world."

Watt tried to forget his sorrow, as was his custom, in increased application to work, though the recovery of the elasticity of his mind was in a measure beyond the power of his will. There were, at that time, very few bright spots in his life. A combination of unfortunate circumstances threatened to overwhelm him. No further progress had yet been made with his steam-engine, which he almost cursed as the cause of his misfortunes. Dr. Roebuck's embarrassments had reached their climax. He had fought against the water which drowned his coal until he could fight no more, and he was at last delivered into the hands of his creditors a ruined man. "My heart bleeds for him;" said Watt, "but I can do nothing to help him. I have stuck by him, indeed, till I have hurt myself."

But the darkest hour is nearest the dawn. Watt had passed through a long night, and a gleam of sunshine at last beamed upon him. Matthew Boulton, of Birmingham, was at length persuaded to take up the invention on which Watt had expended so many of the best years of his life, and the turning-point in Watt's fortunes had arrived.

NOTES

1   For Memoir of Roebuck, see 'Industrial Biography,' p. 133

2   When we visited the place many years ago, Miss Stewart's spinet still stood in the drawing-room, but there was not a tone left in it. Like many other old houses, Kinneil has the reputation of being haunted. The ghost is that of "Lady Lilburne," wife of the Parliamentary General, who is said to have thrown herself out of one of the windows during her husband's absence.

3   Dr. Small was born in 1734 at Carmylie, Angus, Scotland, of which parish his father was the minister. He had been for some time the professor of Natural Philosophy in the University of Williamsburg, Virginia, from whence he returned to England and settled at Birmingham.

4   "I have," he writes, "just now got a curious book, being on account of all the machines, furnaces, methods of working, profits, &c., of the mines of the Upper Hartz. It is unluckily in German, which I understand little of, but am improving in by the help of a truly Chymical Swiss Dryer, who is come here to dye standing red on linen and cotton, in which he is successful. He is according to the custom of philosophers ennuyé to a great degree, but seems to be more modest than usual, and, what is still more unusual, is attached only to his dyeing, though he has a tolerable knowledge of chymestry. He promises to make me a coat that will not wet though boiled in water. This would be a great use to a hundred people I see just now running by, wet to the skin … I verily believe the drops are an inch in diameter! To return to the book – it contains an account of all the unsuccessful experiments that have been tried in the Hartz, and I assure you it gives me some consolation to see the great Liebnitz, the rival of Newton, bungling repeatedly, applying wind mills to raise ore while water ran idle past him. There is among other machines the fellow of Blackie's, only worked by water, and a full and true account of why it did not succeed, which he should read. Their machines in general display great ingenuity though ignorance of principles." – Watt to Small, May 28, 1769. Boulton MSS.

5   "I mentioned to you a method of still doubling the effect of the steam,
     and that tolerably easy, by using the power of steam rushing into a
     vacuum, at present lost. This would do a little more than double the effect,
     but it would too much enlarge the vessels to use it all. It is peculiarly
     applicable to wheel engines, and may supply the want of a condenser
     where force of steam is only used; for, open one of the steam valves and
     admit steam, shut the valve, and the steam will continue to expand and
     press round the wheel with a diminishing power, ending one-fourth of its
     first exertion. The sum of this series you will find greater than one-half,
     though only one-fourth steam was used. The power will indeed be un-
     equal, but this can be remedied by a fly, or in several other ways." – Watt
     to Small, 28th May, 1769.
     Boulton MSS.

6   He anticipated the use of high-pressure steam, as afterwards employed in
     the locomotive by Trevithick, in the following passage: – "I intend," he
     said, "in many cases to employ the expansive force of steam to press on
     the piston, or whatever is used instead of one, in the same manner as the
     weight of the atmosphere is now employed in common fire-engines. In
     some cases I intend to use both the condenser and this force of steam, so
     that the powers of these engines will as much exceed those pressed only by
     the air, as the expansive power of the steam is greater than the weight of
     the atmosphere. In other cases, when plenty of cold water cannot be had, I
     intend to work the engines by the force of steam only, and to discharge it
     into the air by proper outlets after it has done its office." – Watt to Small,
     March, 1769. Boulton MSS.

7   Mr. Hart's "Reminiscences of James Watt," in 'Transactions of the
     'Glasgow Archæological Society,' Part 1. 1859.

8   The telescope was mounted with two parallel horizontal hairs in the
     focus of the eyeglass, crossed by one perpendicular hair. The measuring
     pole was dividied into feet and inches, so that, wrote Watt, "if the hairs
     comprehend one foot at one chain distance, they will comprehend ten feet
     at ten chains," and so on. This invention Watt made in 1770, and used the
     telescope in his various surveys. Eight years later, in 1778, the Society of
     Arts awarded to a Mr. Green a premium for precisely the same invention.

9   Letter to Small, 24th Nov. 1772. Watt, however, took no steps to bring this
     invention before the public, and in 1777, a similar instrument having been
     invented by Dr. Maskelyne, was presented by him to the Royal Society.
     Thus Watt also lost the credit of this invention.

10   The Company afterwards came to grief. The original subscription list was

not filled up, and the stagnation in trade which took place at the outbreak of the American war, brought the works to a standstill. In 1782 the concern was sold to the Messrs. Stirling, who eventually became the sole proprietors and finished the undertaking.

11 There was then a ford at Dumbuck, a few miles below Glasgow, which prevented boats of more than ten tons burden ascending to the Broomielaw. This was shortly after removed by the Clyde Trust, who have expended 3,564,397*l.* in improvement of the navigation between 1770 and 1863, the revenue collected during the same time in dues having been 2,288,000*l.* Vessels drawing 21 feet can now ascend to the Broomielaw; and when the present improvements are completed the depth at high water is expected to be upwards of 24 feet.

12 Watt to Small, 21ˢᵗ Dec. 1770. Boulton MSS.

13 The bridge was partially destroyed by a flood in 1806, when one of the central piers was thrown down. Two of the arches fell, and were re-built, but the others stand as originally constructed.

14 The child was stillborn. Of four other children who were the fruit of this marriage, two died young. A son and daughter survived; the son, James, succeeded his father, and died unmarried, at Aston Hall, near Birmingham, in 1848. The daughter married Mr. Miller, of Glasgow, whose grandson, the present J. W. Gibson Watt, Esq., succeeded to the Watt property.

Boulton and Watt

Engineers, Birmingham

Above: Birmingham (By Percival Skelton)

Below: Mathew Boulton, F.RS. Engraved by W. Holt, after portrait by
Sir W. Beechy, R.A.

IX

Birmingham – Matthew Boulton

From an early period, Birmingham has been one of the principal centres of mechanical industry in England. The neighbourhood abounds in coal and iron, and has long been famous for the skill of its artisans. Swords were forged there in the time of the Ancient Britons. The first guns made in England bore the Birmingham mark. In 1538 Leland found "many smiths in the town that use to make knives and all manner of cutting tools, and many loriners that make bittes, and a' great many nailers." About a century later Camden described the place as "full of inhabitants, and resounding with hammers and anvils, for the most part of them smiths." As the skill of the Birmingham artisans increased, they gradually gave up the commoner kinds of smithery, and devoted themselves to ornamental metal-work, in brass, steel, and iron. They became celebrated for their manufacture of buckles, buttons, and various fancy articles; and they turned out such abundance of toys that toward the close of last century Burke characterised Birmingham as "the great toy-shop of Europe."

The ancient industry of Birmingham was of a staid and steady character, in keeping with the age. Each manufacturer kept within the warmth of his own forge. He did not go in search of orders, but waited for the orders to come to him. Ironmongers brought their money in their saddle-bags, took away the goods in exchange, or saw them packed ready for the next waggon before they left. Notwithstanding this quiet way of doing business, many comfortable fortunes were made in the place; the manufacturers, like their buttons, moving off so soon as they had received the stamp and the gilt. Hutton, the Birmingham bookseller, says he knew men who left the town in chariots who had first approached it on foot. Hutton himself entered the town a poor boy, and lived to write its history, and make a fortune by his industry.

Until towards the end of last century the town was not very easy of approach from any direction. The roads leading to it had become worn by the traffic of many generations. The hoofs of the pack-horses, helped by the rains, had deepened the tracks in the sandy soil, until in many places they were twelve or fourteen feet deep, so that it was said of travellers that they approached the town by sap. One of these old hollow roads, still called Holloway-head, though now filled up, was so deep that a waggon-load of hay might pass along it without being seen. There was no direct communication between Birmingham and London until about the middle of the century. Before then, the Great Road from London to Chester passed it four miles off, and the Birmingham manufacturer, when sending wares to London, had to forward his package to Castle Bromwich, there to await the approach of the packhorse train or the stage-waggon journeying south. The Birmingham men, however, began to wake up, and in 1747 a coach was advertised to run to London in two days "if the roads permit." Twenty years later a stage-waggon was put on, and the communication by coach became gradually improved.

When Hutton entered Birmingham in 1740, he was struck by the activity of the place and the vivacity of the inhabitants, which expressed itself in their looks as he passed them in the streets. "I had," he says, "been among dreamers, but now I saw men awake. Their very step showed alacrity. Every man seemed to know and to prosecute his own affairs." The Birmingham men were indeed as alert as they looked – steady workers and clever mechanics – men who struck hard on the anvil. The artisans of the place had the advantage of a long training in mechanical skill. It had been bred in their bone, and descended to them from their fathers as an inheritance.[1] In no town in England were there then to be found so many mechanics capable of executing entirely new work; nor, indeed, has the ability yet departed from them, the Birmingham artisans maintaining their individual superiority in intelligent execution of skilled work to the present day. We are informed that inventors of new machines, foreign as well as English, are still in the practice of resorting to them for the purpose of getting their inventions embodied in the best forms, with greater chances of success than in any other town in England.

About the middle of last century the two Boultons, father and son, were recognised as among the most enterprising and prosperous of Birmingham manufacturers. The father of the elder Matthew Boulton was John Boulton of Northamptonshire, in which county Boultons or Boltons have been settled for a long period, and where there are records of many clergymen of the name. About the end of the seventeenth century, this John Boulton settled at Lichfield, where he married Elizabeth, heir of Matthew Dyott of

Stitchbrooke, by whom he obtained considerable property. His means must, however, have become reduced; in consequence of which his son Matthew was sent to Birmingham to enter upon a career of business, and make his own way in the world. He became established in the place as a silver stamper and piecer, to which he added other branches of manufacture, which his son Matthew afterwards largely extended.

Matthew Boulton the younger was born at Birmingham on the 3rd September, 1728. Little is known of his early life, beyond that he was a bright, clever boy, and a general favourite with his companions. He received his principal education at a private academy at Deritend, kept by the Rev. Mr. Ansted, under whom he acquired the rudiments of a good ordinary English education. Though he left school early for the purpose of following his father's business, he nevertheless continued the work of self-instruction, and afterwards acquired considerable knowledge of Latin and French, as well as of drawing and mathematics. But his chief pleasure was in pursuing the study of chemistry and mechanics, in which, as we shall shortly find, he became thoroughly accomplished. Long after he joined his father in business, he delighted to revert to his classical favourites. From an entry in his private memorandum book of expenses at the age of about thirty, though then very economical in other respects, we find him expending considerable sums in experiments on electricity, and on one occasion laying out a guinea on a copy of Virgil, from which it appears that trade had not spoilt his taste for either science or letters.

Young Boulton appears to have engaged in business with much spirit. By the time he was seventeen he had introduced several important improvements in the manufacture of buttons, watch-chains, and other trinkets; and he had invented the inlaid steel buckles which shortly after became the fashion. These buckles were exported in large quantities to France, from whence they were brought back to England and sold as the most recent productions of French ingenuity. The elder Boulton, having every confidence in his son's discretion and judgment, adopted him as a partner so soon a he came of age, and from that time forward he took almost the entire management of the concern. Although in his letters he signed "for father and self," he always spoke in the first person of matters connected with the business. Thus, in 1757, we find him writing to Timothy Holles, London, as to the prices of "coat-link and vest buttons," intimating that to lower them would be to beat down price and quality until it became no business at all; "yet," said he, "as I have put myself to greater expense than anybody else in erecting the best conveniences and the completest tools for the purpose,

I am not willing that any interlopers should run away with it." We find him at the same time carrying on a correspondence with Benjamin Huntsman, of Sheffield, the celebrated inventor of cast-steel.[2] On the 19th January, 1757, he sends Huntsman "a parcel of goods of the newest patterns," and at the same time orders a quantity of Huntsman's steel. "When thou hast some of a proper size and quality for me, and an opportunity of sending it, thou may'st, but I should be glad to have it a little tougher than the last." He concludes – "I hope thy Philosophic Spirit still laboureth within thee, and may it soon bring forth Fruit useful to mankind, but more particularly to thyself, is the sincere wish of Thy Obliged Friend." With a view to economy, Boulton in course of time erected a steel-house of his own for the purpose of making steel; and he frequently used it to convert the cuttings and scraps of the small iron wares which he manufactured, into ordinary steel, afterwards melting and converting it into cast-steel in the usual way.

From the earliest glimpses we can get of Boulton as a man of business, it would appear to have been his aim to be at the top of whatsoever branch of manufacture he undertook. He endeavoured to produce the best possible articles in regard of design, material, and workmanship. Taste was then at a low ebb, and "Brummagem" had become a byword for everything that was gaudy, vulgar, and meretricious. Boulton endeavoured to get rid of this reproach, and aimed at raising the standard of taste in manufacture to the highest point. With this object, he employed the best artists to design his articles, and the cleverest artisans to manufacture them. Apart from the question of elevating the popular taste, there can be no doubt that this was good policy on his part, for it served to direct public attention to the superior and honest quality of the articles produced by his firm, and eventually brought him a large accession of business.

In 1759, Boulton's father died, bequeathing to him the considerable property which he had accumulated by his business. The year following, when thirty-two years of age, Matthew married Anne, the daughter of Luke Robinson, Esq., of Lichfield. The lady was a distant relation of his own; the Dyotts of Stitchbrooke, whose heir his grandfather had married, being nearly related to the Babingtons of Curborough, from who Miss Robinson was lineally descended – Luke Robinson having married the daughter and co-heir of John Babington of Curborough and Patkington. Considerable opposition was offered to the marriage by the lady's friends, on account of Matthew Boulton's occupation; but he pressed his suit, and with good looks and a handsome presence to back him, he eventually succeeded in winning the heart and hand of Anne Robinson. He was now, indeed, in a position to

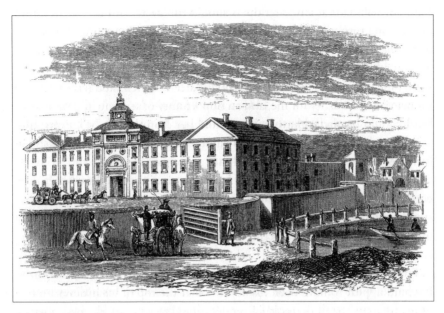

Soho Manufactory

have retired from business altogether. But a life of inactivity had no charms for him. He liked to mix with men in the affairs of active life, and to take his full share in the world's business. Indeed, he hated ease and idleness, and found his greatest pleasure in constant occupation.

Instead, therefore, of retiring from trade, he determined to engage in it more extensively. He entertained the ambition of founding a manufactory that should be the first of its kind, and serve as a model for the manufacturers of his neighbourhood. His premises on Snow-hill,[3] Birmingham, having become too small for his purpose, he looked about him for a suitable spot on which to erect more commodious workshops; and he was shortly attracted by the facilities presented by the property afterwards so extensively known as the famous Soho.

Soho is about two miles north of Birmingham, on the Wolverhampton road. It is not in the parish of Birmingham, nor in the county of Warwick, but just over the border in the county of Stafford. Down to the middle of last century the ground on which it stands was a barren heath, used only as a rabbit-warren. The sole dwelling on it was the warrener's hut, which stood near the summit of the hill, on the spot afterwards occupied by Soho House; and the warrener's well is still to be found in one of the cellars of the mansion. In 1756, Mr. Edward Ruston took a lease of the ground for ninety-nine years from Mr. Wyerley, the lord of the manor, with liberty to make a cut about half a mile in length for the purpose of turning the waters of Hockley Brook into a pool under the brow of the hill. The head of water thus formed was used to drive a feeble mill below, which Mr. Ruston had established for laminating metals. He also built a small dwelling-house about 150 yards from the mill, and expended upon the place a sum of about 1000*l.* in all. When Mr. Boulton was satisfied that the place would suit his purpose, he entered into arrangements with Mr. Ruston for the purchase of his lease,[4] on the completion of which he proceeded to rebuild the mill on a large scale, and in course of time removed thither the whole of his tools, machinery, and workmen. The new manufactory, when finished, consisted of a series of roomy workshops conveniently connected with each other, and capable of accommodating upwards of a thousand workmen. The building and stocking of the premises cost upwards of 20,000*l.*

Before removing to Soho, Mr. Boulton took into partnership Mr. John Fothergill, with the object of more vigorously extending his business operations. Mr. Fothergill possessed a very limited capital, but he was a man of good character and active habits of business, with a considerable knowledge of foreign markets. On the occasion of his entering the concern, stock was taken of the warehouse on Snow Hill; and some idea of the extent of Boulton's business at the time may be formed from the fact that his manager, Mr. Zaccheus Walker, assisted by Farquharson, Nuttall, Frogatt, and half-a-dozen labourers, were occupied during eight days in weighing metals, counting goods, and preparing an inventory of the effects and stock in trade. The partnership commenced at midsummer, 1762, and shortly after the principal manufactory was removed to Soho.

Steps were immediately taken to open up new connexions and agencies at home and abroad; and a large business was shortly established with many of the principal towns and cities of Europe, in filagree and inlaid work, livery and other buttons, buckles, clasps, watch-chains, and various kinds of ornamental metal wares. The firm shortly added the manufacture of silver plate and plated goods to their other branches,[5] and turned out large quantities of candlesticks, urns, brackets, and various articles in ormolu. The books of the firm indicate the costly nature of their productions, 500 ounces of silver being given out at a time, besides considerable quantities of gold and platina for purposes of fabrication. Boulton himself attended to the organization and management of the works and to the extension of the trade at home, while Fothergill devoted himself to establishing and superintending the foreign agencies.

From the first, Boulton aimed at establishing a character for the excellence of his productions. They must not only be honest in workmanship, but tasteful in design. He determined, so far as in him lay, to get rid of the "Brummagem" reproach. Thus we find him writing to his partner from London: – "The prejudice that Birmingham hath so justly established against itself makes every fault conspicuous in all articles that have the least pretensions to taste. How can I expect the public to countenance rubbish from Soho, while they can procure sound and perfect work from any other quarter ?"

He frequently went to town for the express purpose of reading and making drawings of rare works in metal in the British Museum, sending the results down to Soho. When rare objects of art were offered for sale, he endeavoured to secure them. "I bid five guineas," he wrote his partner on one occasion, "for the Duke of Marlborough's great blue vase, but it sold for ten … I bought two figures, which are sent herewith." He borrowed antique candlesticks, vases, and articles in metal from the Queen and from various members of the nobility. "I wish Mr. Eginton," he wrote, "would take good casts from the Hercules and the Hydra, and then let it be well gilt and returned with the seven vases; for 'tis the Queen's. I perceive we shall want many such figures, and therefore we should omit no opportunity of taking good casts." The Duke of Northumberland lent Boulton many of his most highly prized articles for imitation by his workmen. Among his other liberal helpers in the same way, we find the Duke of Richmond, Lord Shelburne, and the Earl of Dartmouth. The Duke gave him an introduction to Horace Walpole, for the purpose of enabling him to visit and examine the art treasures of Strawberry Hill. "The vases," said he, in writing to Boulton, "are, in my opinion, better worth your seeing than anything in England, and I wish you would have exact drawings of them taken, as I may very possibly like to have them copied by you." Lord Shelburne's opinion of Boulton may be gathered from his letter to Mr. Adams, the architect, in which he said: – "Mr. Boulton is the most enterprising man in different ways in Birmingham, and is very desirous of cultivating Mr. Adams's taste in his productions, and has bought his Dioclesian by Lord Shelburne's advice."

Boulton, however, did not confine himself to England; he searched the Continent over for the best specimens of handicraft as models for imitation; and when he found them he strove to equal, if not to excel them in style and quality. He sent his agent, Mr. Wendler, on a special mission of this sort, to Venice, Rome, and other Italian cities, to purchase for him the best specimens of metal-work, and obtain for him designs of various ornaments – vases, cameos, intaglios, and statuary. On one occasion we find Wendler sending him

456 prints, Boulton acknowledging that they will prove exceedingly useful for the purposes of his manufacture. At the same time, Fothergill was travelling through France and Germany with a like object, while he was also establishing new connexions with a view to extended trade.[6]

While Boulton was ambitious of reaching the highest excellence in his own line of business, he did not confine himself to that, but was feeling his way in various directions outside of it. Thus to his friend Wedgwood he wrote on one occasion, that he admired his vases so much that he "almost wished to be a potter." At one time, indeed, he had serious thoughts of beginning the fictile manufacture; but he rested satisfied with mounting in metal the vases which Wedgwood made. "The mounting of vases," he wrote, "is a large field for fancy, in which I shall indulge, as I perceive it possible to convert even a very ugly vessel into a beautiful vase."[7]

Another branch of business that he sought to establish was the manufacture of clocks. It was one of his leading ideas, that articles in common use might be made much better and cheaper if manufactured on a large scale with the help of the best machinery; and he thought this might be successfully done in the making of clocks and timepieces. The necessary machinery was erected accordingly, and the new branch of business was started. Some of the timepieces were of an entirely novel arrangement. One of them, invented by Dr. Small, contained but a single wheel, and was considered a piece of very ingenious construction. Boulton also sought to rival the French makers of ornamental timepieces, by whom the English markets were then almost entirely supplied; and some of the articles of this sort turned out by him were of great beauty. One of his most ardent encouragers and admirers, the Hon. Mrs. Montagu, wrote to him, – "I take greater pleasure in our victories over the French in the contention of arts than of arms. The achievements of Soho, instead of making widows and orphans, make marriages and christenings. Your noble industry, while elevating the public taste, provides new occupations for the poor, and enables them to bring up their families in comfort. Go on, then, sir, to triumph over the French in taste, and to embellish your country with useful inventions and elegant productions."

Boulton's efforts to improve the industrial arts did not, however, always meet with such glowing eulogy as this. Two of his most highly finished astronomical clocks could not find purchasers at his London sale; on which he wrote to his wife at Soho, "I find philosophy at a very low ebb in London, and I have therefore brought back my two fine clocks, which I will send to a market where common sense is not out of fashion.

If I had made the clocks play jigs upon bells, and a dancing bear keeping time, or if I had made a horse-race upon their faces, I believe they would have had better bidders. I shall therefore bring them back to Soho, and some time this summer will send them to the Empress of Russia, who, I believe, would be glad of them."[8] During the same visit to London, he was more successful with the king and queen, who warmly patronised his productions. "The king," he wrote to his wife, "hath bought a pair of cassolets, a Titus, a Venus clock, and some other things, and inquired this morning how yesterday's sale went. I shall see him again, I believe. I was with them, the queen and all the children, between two and three hours. There were, likewise, many of the nobility present. Never was man so much complimented as I have been; but I find that compliments don't make fat nor fill the pocket. The queen showed me her last child, which is a beauty, but none of 'em are equal to the General of Soho or the fair Maid of the Mill.[9] God bless them both, and kiss them for me."

In another letter he described a subsequent visit to the palace. "I am to wait upon their majesties again so soon as our Tripod Tea-kitchen arrives, and again upon some other business. The queen, I think, is much improved in her person, and she now speaks English like an English lady. She draws very finely, is a great musician, and works with her needle better than Mrs. Betty. However, without joke, she is extremely sensible, very affable, and a great patroness of English manufactures. Of this she gave me a particular instance; for, after the king and she had talked to me for nearly three hours, they withdrew, and then the queen sent for me into her boudoir, showed me her chimneypiece, and asked me how many vases it would take to furnish it; 'for,' said she, 'all that china shall be taken away.' She also desired that I would fetch her the two finest steel chains I could make. All this she did of her own accord, without the presence of the king, which I could not help putting a kind construction upon."[10]

Thus stimulated by royal and noble patronage, Boulton exerted himself to the utmost to produce articles of the highest excellence. Like his friend Wedgwood, he employed Flaxman and other London artists to design his choicer goods; but he had many foreign designers and skilled workmen, French and Italian, in his regular employment. He attracted these men by liberal wages, and kept them attached to him by kind and generous treatment. On one occasion we find the Duke of Richmond applying to him to recommend a first-class artist to execute some special work in metal for him. Boulton replies that he can strongly recommend one of his own men, an honest, steady workman, an excellent metal turner. "He hath made for me some exceeding good acromatic telescopes [another branch of Boulton's business] ... I give him two

guineas a week and a house to live in. He is a French and formerly worked with
the famous M. Germnain; he afterwards worked for the Academy of Sciences
at Berlin, and he hath worked upwards of two years for me."[11]

Before many years had passed, Soho was spoken of with pride, as one of
the best schools of skilled industry in England. Its fame extended abroad as
well as at home, and when distinguished foreigners came into England, they
usually visited Soho as one of the national sights. When the manufactory was
complete[12] and in full work, Boulton removed from his house on Snow-hill to
the mansion of Soho, which he had by this time considerably enlarged and
improved. There he continued to live until the close of his life, maintaining a
splendid hospitality. Men of all nations, and of all classes and opinions, were
received there by turns, – princes, philosophers, artists, authors, merchants,
and poets. In August, 1767, while executing the two chains for the queen,
we find him writing to his London agent as his excuse for a day's delay in
forwarding it: "I had lords and ladies to wait on yesterday; I have French
and Spaniards to-day; and to-morrow I shall have Germans, Russians, and
Norwegians." For many years the visitors at Soho House were so numerous
and arrived in such constant succession, that it more resembled an hotel than
a private mansion.

The rapid extension of the Soho business necessarily led to the increase
of the capital invested in it. Boulton had to find large sums of money for
increased stock, plant, and credits. He raised 3000l. on his wife's estate; he
borrowed 5000l. from his friend Baumgarten; and he sold considerable portions of the property left him by his father, by which means he was enabled
considerably to extend his operations. There were envious busybodies about
who circulated rumours to his discredit, and set the report on foot, that to
carry on a business on so large a scale would require a capital of 80,000l.
"Their evil speaking," said he to a correspondent, "will avail but little, as our
house is founded on so firm a rock that envy and malice will not be able to
shake it; and I am determined to spare neither pains, nor money to establish
such a house as will acquire both honour and wealth." The rapid strides he
was making may be inferred from the statement made to the same correspondent, which showed that the gross returns of the firm, which were 7000l. in
1763, had advanced to 30,000l. in 1767, with orders still upon the increase.

Though he had a keen eye for business, Boulton regarded character more
than profit. He would have no connexion with any transaction of a dis-
creditable kind. Orders were sent to him from France for base money, but
he spurned them with indignation. "I will do anything," he wrote to M.
Motteaux, his Paris agent, "short of being common informer against particu-

Soho House

lar persons, to stop the malpractices of the Birmingham coiners." He declared
he was as ready to do business on reasonable terms as any other person, but he
would not undersell; "for," said he, "to run down prices would be to run down
quality, which could only have the effect of undermining confidence, and
eventually ruining trade." His principles were equally honourable as regarded
the workmen of rival employers. "I have had many offers and opportunities,"
he said to one, "of taking your people, whom I could, with convenience to
myself, have employed; but it is a practice I abhor. Nevertheless, whatever
game we play at, I shall always avail myself of the rules with which 'tis played,
or I know I shall make but a very indifferent figure in it."[13]

He was frequently asked to take gentlemen apprentices into his works, but
declined to receive them, though hundreds of pounds' premium were in many
cases offered with them. He preferred employing the humbler class of boys,
whom he could train up as skilled workmen. He was also induced to prefer
the latter for another reason, of a still more creditable kind. "I have," said
he, in answer to a gentleman applicant, "built and furnished a house for the
reception of one kind of apprentices – fatherless children, parish apprentices,
and hospital boys; and gentlemen's sons would probably find themselves out
of place in such companionship."

While occupied with his own affairs, and in conducting what he described
as "the largest hardware manufactory in the world," Boulton found time to

take an active part in promoting the measures then on foot for opening up the internal navigation of the country. He was a large subscriber to the Grand Trunk and Birmingham Canal schemes, the latter of which was of the greater importance to him personally, as it passed close by Soho, and thus placed his works in direct communication both with London and the northern coal and manufacturing districts.[14]

Coming down to a few years later, in 1770, we find his business still growing, and his works and plant absorbing still more capital, principally obtained by borrowing. In a letter to Mr. Adams, the celebrated architect, requesting him to prepare the design of a new sale-room in London, he described the manufactory at Soho as in full progress, from 700 to 800 persons being employed as metallic artists and workers in tortoiseshell, stones, glass, and enamel. "I have almost every machine," said he, "that is applicable to those arts; I have two water-mills employed in rolling, polishing, grinding, and turning various sorts of lathes. I have trained up many, and am training up more plain country lads into good workmen; and wherever I find indications of skill and ability, I encourage them. I have likewise established correspondence with almost every mercantile town in Europe, and am thus regularly supplied with orders for the grosser articles in common demand, by which I am enabled to employ such a number of hands as to provide me with an ample choice of artists for the finer branches of work; and I am thereby encouraged to erect and employ a more extensive apparatus than it would be prudent to provide for the production of the finer articles only."

It is indeed probable – though Boulton was slow to admit it – that he had been extending his business more rapidly than his capital would conveniently allow; for we find him becoming more and more pressed for means to meet the interest on the borrowed money invested in buildings, tools, and machinery. He had obtained 10,000*l.* from a Mr. Tonson of London; and on the death of that gentleman, in 1772, he had considerable difficulty in raising the means to pay off the debt. His embarrassment was increased by a serious commercial panic, aggravated by the failure of Fordyce brothers, by which a considerable sum deposited with them remained locked up for some time, and he was eventually a loser to the extent of 2000*l.* Other failures and losses followed; and trade came almost to a stand-still. Yet he bravely held on. "We have a thousand mouths at Soho to feed," he says; "and it has taken so much labour and pains to get so valuable and well-organised a staff of workmen together, that the operations of the manufactory must be carried on at whatever risk." He continued to receive distinguished visitors at his works. "Last week," he wrote Mr. Ebbenhouse, "we had Prince Poniatowski, nephew of the

King of Poland, and the French, Danish, Sardinian, and Dutch Ambassadors; this week we have had Count Orloff, one of the five celebrated brothers who are such favourites with the Empress of Russia; and only yesterday I had the Viceroy of Ireland, who dined with me. Scarcely a day passes without a visit from some distinguished personage."

Besides carrying on the extensive business connected with his manufactory at Soho, this indefatigable man found time to prosecute the study of several important branches of practical science. It was scarcely to be supposed that he had much leisure at his disposal; but in life it often happens that the busiest men contrive to find the most leisure; and he who is "up to the ears" in work, can, nevertheless, snatch occasional intervals to devote to inquiries in which his heart is engaged. Hence we find Boulton ranging at intervals over a wide field of inquiry; at one time studying geology, and collecting fossils, minerals, and specimens for his museum; at another, reading and experimenting on fixed air; and at another studying Newton's works with the object of increasing the force of projectiles.[15] But the subject which perhaps more than all interested him was the improvement of the Steam Engine, which shortly after led to his introduction to James Watt.

NOTES

1   There seems reason to believe that the capacity for skilled industry is to a certain extent transmissible; and that the special aptitude for mechanics which characterises the population of certain districts, is in a great measure the result of centuries of experience, transmitted from one generation to another. Mr. Morell takes the same view: "We have every reason to believe," he says, "that the power of specialised instincts is transmitted, and when the circumstances favour it, goes on increasing from age to age in intensity, and in a particular adaptation to the purposes demanded. All confirmed habits which become a part of the animal nature, seem to be imparted by hereditary descent; and thus what *seems* to be an original instinct may, after all, be but the accumulated growth and experience of many generations."

2   For Memoir of Huntsman, see 'Industrial Biography,' 102–110

3   While on Snow-hill, Boulton's business was principally confined to the making of buttons, shoe-buckles, articles in steel, and various kinds of trinkets. His designation was that of "toymaker," as is shown by the following document copied from the original: – "Received of Matthew

Boulton, toymaker, Snow-hill, three shillings and sixpence, for which sum
I solemnly engage, if he should be chosen by lot to serve in the militia for
this parish, at the first meeting for that purpose, to procure a substitute
that shall be approved of. Birmingham, January 11, 1762, Henry Brookes,
Sergt." The Birmingham toymaker was, however, often a man doing a large
business, producing articles of utility as well as ornament. Mr. Osler, the
Birmingham manufacturer of glass beads and other toys, when examined
before a Committee of the House of Commons many years since,
astonished the members by informing them that trifling though dolls' eyes
might appear to be as an article of manufacture, he had once obtained
an order for 500*l.* worth of the article "Eighteen years ago," said he, "on
my first going to London, a respectable-looking man in the city asked me
if I could supply him with dolls' eyes; and I was foolish enough to feel
half offended; I thought it derogatory to my dignity as a manufacturer
to make dolls' eyes. He took me into a room quite as wide, and perhaps
twice the length of this, and we had just room to walk between the stacks,
from the floor to the ceiling, of parts of dolls. He said, These are only the
legs and the arms; the trunks are below.' But I saw enough to convince
me, that he wanted a great many eyes ... He ordered various quantities,
and of various sizes and qualities. On returning to the Tavistock Hotel, I
found that the order a to upwards of 500*l* ... Calculating on every child
in this country not using a doll till two years old, and throwing it aside at
seven, and having a new one annually, I satisfied myself that the eyes alone
would produce a circulation of a great many thousand pounds. I mention
this merely to show the importance of trifles." – Babbage, 'Economy of
Machinery and Manufactures,' 243–5.

4   Mr. Boulton afterwards purchased the fee simple of the property, together
with much of the adjoining land. The nature of his tenure caused him to
take a lively interest in the question of common lands enclosure, and at a
much later period (17th April, 1790) we find him writing to the Right Hon.
Lord Hawkesbury as follows: "The argument of robbing the poor [by
enclosures of wastes] is fallacious. They have no legal title to the common
land; and the more of it that is cultivated, the more work and the more
bread there will be for them. I speak from experience; for I founded my
manufactory upon one of the most barren commons in England, where
there existed but a few miserable huts filled with idle beggarly people,
who by the help of the common land and a little thieving made shift to
live without working. The scene is now entirely changed. I have employed
a thousand men, women, and children, in my aforesaid manufactory for

nearly thirty years past. The Lord of the Manor hath exterminated these very poor cottages, and hundreds of clean comfortable cheerful houses are found erected in their place. Thus the inhabitants of the parish have been trebled without at all increasing the poor levies. I am more confirmed in this view when I turn my eyes to a neighbouring parish (Sutton Colefield), where there are 10,000 acres of common land uncultivated, and spirited men; and the poor will then have plenty of work, and the next generation of them will be fully reconciled to earning their bread instead of begging for it." – Boulton MSS.

5   Mr. Keir, in a MS. Memoir of Mr. Boulton now before us, says he was the first to introduce the silver plate business at Birmingham, and to make complete services in solid silver. But the business was not profitable, in consequence of the great value of the material, the loss of interest upon which was not compensated by the additional price put upon it for workmanship. One good consequence of the silver plate business, however, was the establishment of an assay office in Birmingham, the necessary Act for which was obtained at Boulton's expense, and proved of much advantage to the town.

6   "If, in the course of your future traveling," he wrote Mr. Wendler (July, 1767), "You can pick up for me any metallic ores or fossil substances, or any other curious natural productions, I should be much obliged to you, as I am fond of all those things that have a tendency to improve my knowledge in mechanical arts, in which my manufactory will every year become more and more general, and therefore wish to know the taste, the fashions, the toys, both useful and ornamental, the implements, vessels, &c., that prevail in all the different parts of Europe, as I should be glad to work for all of Europe in all things that they may have occasion for – gold, silver, copper, plated, gilt, pinchbeck, steel, platina, tortoiseshell, or anything else that may become an article of general demand. I have lately begun to make snuff-boxes, instrument-cases, tooth-picks, &c., in metal, gilt, and in tortoiseshell inlaid, likewise gilt and pinchbeck watch-chains. We are now being completely fixed at Soho, and when Mr. Fothergill returns (which will not be for six months), I shall then have more time to attend to improvements than I have at present." – Boulton, MSS.

7   Boulton to Wedgwood, January, 1769 – Wedgwood was one of his most intimate friends, the two alike aiming at excellence in their respective branches of production. Their kindred efforts seem to have excited the ire of some satirist, whose effusion against them in the 'Public Ledger' is thus

referred to in the postscript of a letter from Wedgwood to Boulton, dated 19th February, 1771: – "If you take in the 'Public Ledger' you'll see that Mr. Antipuffado has done me the honour to rank me with the most *stupendous geniuses* of the age, and has really *cut me up very cleanly*. He talks, too, that he should not wonder if some genius at Birmingham should be tempted o make *Roman medals* and *tenpenny nails*, or *Corinthian knives* and *daggers*, and style himself Roman medal and Etruscan tenpenny nail-maker to the Empress of Abyssinia. But see the paper: I believe it is the first week in February, and is one of the better sort of this class." – Boulton MSS.

8   The clocks, with several other articles, were sent out to Russia, and submitted to the Empress through the kindness of the Earl Cathcart. His lordship, in communicating the result to Mr. Boulton, said – "I have the pleasure to inform you that her Imperial Majesty not only bought them all, last week, but did me the honour to tell me that she was extremely pleased with them, and thought them superior in every respect to the French, as well as cheaper, which entitled them in all lights to a preference."

9   Pet names of his two children, Matthew Robinson and Anne Boulton.

10 These letters are without date, but we infer that they were written in the summer of 1767.

11 Boulton to the Duke of Richmond, April 8, 1770. The Duke was engaged at the time in preparing a set of machines for making the various experiments in Natural Philosophy described in S'Gravande's book. The Duke was himself a good turner and worker in metal.

12 The manufactory was complete so far as regarded the hardware manufacture. But additions were constantly being made to it; and, as other branches of industry were added, it became more than doubled in extent and accommodation.

13 Boulton to John Taylor, 23rd January, 1769. Boulton MSS.

14 When the canal came to be constructed at the point at which it passed Soho, it occasioned him great anxiety through the leakage of the canal banks and loss of water for the purposes of his manufactory. The supply, especially in dry summers, was already too limited; but the canal threatened to destroy it altogether. Writing to Mr. Thomas Gilbert, M.P., on the subject in February, 1769, he said, "The very holes which Mr. Smeaton hath dug to try the ground, drink up the water nearly as fast as you can pour it in ... Let Smeaton or Brindley, or all the engineers upon earth give what evidence they will before Parliament, I am convinced by last summer's experience that if the proprietors of the canal continue to

take the two streams on which my mill depends, it is ruined. I might as well have built it upon the summit of the hill." After the act had passed he wrote his friend Garbett, "I have seen the testimony of the two engineers, Smeaton and Yeoman, but I value the opinions of neither of them, nor of Brindley nor Simcox (in this case), nor of the whole tribe of jobbing ditchers, who are retained as evidence on any side which first applies for them." His alarms, however, proved unfounded, as the leakage of the canal was eventually remedied; and in November, 1772, we find him writing to the Earl of Warwick, "Our navigation goes on prosperously; the junction with the Wolverhampton Canal is complete and we already sail from Birmingham to Bristol and to Hull." – Boulton MSS.

15   Among Boulton's scientific memoranda, we find some curious speculations, bearing the date of 1765, relative to improvements which he was trying to work out in gunnery. He proposed the truer boring of the guns, the use of a telescopic sight, and a cylindrical shot with its end of a parabolic form as presenting in his opinion the least resistance to the air.

Boulton and the Steam Engine – Correspondence with Watt

Want of water-power was one of the great defects of Soho as a manufacturing establishment, and for a long time Boulton struggled with the difficulty. The severe summer droughts obliged him to connect a horse-mill with the water-wheel. From six to ten horses were employed as an auxiliary power, at an expense of from five to eight guineas a week: But this expedient, though costly, was found very inconvenient. Boulton next thought of erecting a pumping-engine after Savery or Newcomen's construction, for the purpose of raising the water from the mill-stream and returning it back into the reservoir – thereby maintaining a head of water sufficient to supply the water-wheel and keep the mill in regular work. "The enormous expense of the horse-power," he wrote to a friend, "put me upon thinking of turning the mill by fire, and I made many fruitless experiments on the subject."

In 1766 we find him engaged in a correspondence with the distinguished Benjamin Franklin as to steam power. Eight years before, Franklin had visited Boulton at Birmingham and made his acquaintance. They were mutually pleased with each other, and continued to correspond during Franklin's stay in England, exchanging their views on magnetism, electricity, and other subjects.[1] When Boulton began to study the fire-engine with a view to its improvement, Franklin was one of the first whom he consulted. Writing him on the 22nd February, 1766, he said, –

My engagements since Christmas have not permitted me to make any further progress with my fire-engine; but, as the thirsty season is approaching apace, necessity will oblige me to set about it in good earnest. Query, – Which of the steam-valves do you like best? Is it better to introduce the jet of cold water at the bottom of the receiver, or at the top? Each has its advantages and disadvantages. My thoughts about the secondary or mechanical contrivances of the engine are too numerous to trouble you with in this letter, and yet I have not been lucky enough to hit upon any that are objectionless. I therefore beg, if any thought occurs to your fertile genius which you think may be useful, or preserve me from error in the execution of this engine, you'll be so kind as to communicate it to me, and you'll very greatly oblige me.

From a subsequent letter it appears that Boulton, like Watt – who was about the same time occupied with his invention at Glasgow – had a model constructed for experimental purposes, and that this model was now with Franklin in London; for we find Boulton requesting the latter to "order a porter to nail up the model in the box again and take it to the Birmingham carrier at the Bell Inn, Smithfield." After a silence of about a month Franklin replied, –

You will, I trust, excuse my so long omitting to answer your kind letter, when you consider the excessive hurry and anxiety I have been engaged in with our American affairs ... I know not which of the valves to give the preference to, nor whether it is best to introduce your jet of cold water above or below. Experiments will best decide in such cases. I would only repeat to you the hint I gave, of fixing your grate in such a manner as to burn all your smoke. I think a great deal of fuel will then he saved, for two reasons. One, that smoke is fuel, and is wasted when it escapes uninflamed. The other, that it forms a sooty crust on the bottom of the boiler, which crust not being a good conductor of heat, and preventing flame and hot air coming into immediate contact with the vessel, lessens their effect in giving heat to the water. All that is necessary is, to make the smoke of fresh coals pass descending through those that are already thoroughly ignited. I sent the model last week, with your papers in it, which I hope got safe to hand.[2]

The model duly arrived at Soho, and we find Boulton shortly after occupied in making experiments with it, the results of which are duly entered in his note-books. Dr. Erasmus Darwin, with whom be was on very intimate terms, wrote him from Lichfield, inquiring what Franklin thought of the model and what suggestions he had made for its improvement. "Your model of a steam-engine, I am told," said he, "has gained so much approbation in London, that I cannot but congratulate you on the mechanical fame you have acquired by it, which, assure yourself, is as great a pleasure to me as it could possibly be to yourself."[3] Another letter of Darwin to Boulton is preserved, without date, but apparently written earlier than the preceding, in which the Doctor lays before the mechanical philosopher the scheme of "a fiery chariot" which he had conceived, – in other words, of a locomotive steam-carriage. He proposed to apply an engine with a pair of cylinders working alternately, to drive the proposed vehicle;[4] and he sent Boulton some rough diagrams illustrative of his views, which he begged might be kept a profound secret, as it was his intention, if Boulton approved of his plan and would join him as a partner, to endeavour to build a model engine, and, if it answered, to take out a joint patent for it. But Dr. Darwin's scheme was too crude to be capable of being embodied in a working model; and nothing more was heard of his fiery chariot.

Another of Boulton's numerous correspondents about the same time was Dr. Roebuck, of Kinneil, then occupied with his enterprise at Carron, and about to engage in working the Boroughstoness coal mines, of the results of which he was extremely sanguine. He also wished Boulton to join him as a partner, offering a tenth share in the concern, and to take back the share if the result did not answer expectations. But Boulton's hands were already full of business nearer home, and he declined the venture. Roebuck then informed him of the invention made by his ingenious friend Watt, and of the progress of the model engine. This was a subject calculated to excite the interest of Boulton, himself occupied in studying the same subject, and he expressed a desire to see Watt, if he could make it convenient to visit him at Soho.

It so happened that Watt had occasion to be in London in the summer of 1767 on the business connected with the Forth and Clyde Canal Bill, and he determined to take Soho on his way home. When Watt paid his promised visit, Boulton was absent; but he was shown over the works by his friend Dr. Small, who had settled in Birmingham as a physician, and already secured a high place in Boulton's esteem. Watt was much struck with the admirable arrangements of the Soho manufactory, and recognised at a glance the admirable power of organisation which they displayed. Still plodding wearily with his model, and contending with the "villanous bad workmanship" of his Glasgow artisans, he could not but envy the precision of the Soho tools and the dexterity of the Soho workmen. Some conversation on the subject must have occurred between him and Small, to whom he explained the nature of his invention; for we find the latter shortly after writing Watt, urging him to come to Birmingham and join partnership with Boulton and himself in the manufacture of steam-engines.[5] Although nothing came of this proposal at the time, it had probably some effect, when communicated to Dr. Roebuck, in inducing him to close with Watt as a partner, and thus anticipate his Birmingham correspondents, of whose sagacity he had the highest opinion.

In the following year Watt visited London on the business connected with the engine patent. Small wrote to him there, saying, "Get your patent and come to Birmingham, with as much time to spend as you can." Watt accordingly again took Birmingham on his way home. There he saw his future partner for the first time, and they at once conceived a hearty liking for each other. They had much conversation about the engine, and it greatly cheered Watt to find that the sagacious and practical Birmingham manufacturer should augur so favourably of its success as he did. Shortly after, when Dr. Robison visited Soho, Boulton told him that although he had begun the construction of his proposed pumping-engine, he had determined to proceed no further with it until he saw what came of Watt and Roebuck's scheme. "In erecting my proposed engine," said he, "I would necessarily avail myself of what I learned from Mr. Watt's conversation; but this would not now be right without his consent." Boulton's conduct in this proceeding was thoroughly characteristic of him, and merely affords another illustration of the general fairness and honesty with which he acted in all his business transactions.

Watt returned to Glasgow to resume his engine experiments and to proceed with his canal surveys. He kept up a correspondence with Boulton, and advised him from time to time of the progress made with his model. Towards the end of the year we find him sending Boulton a package from Glasgow containing "one dozen German flutes at 5s., and a copper digester 1l. 10s." He added, "I have almost finished a most complete model of my reciprocating-engine: when it is tried, I shall advise the success." To Dr. Small he wrote more confidentially, sending him in January, 1769, a copy of the intended specification of his steam-engine. He also spoke of his general business: "Our pottery," said he, "is doing tolerably, though not as I wish. I am sick of the people I have to do with, though not of the business, which I expect will turn out a very good one. I have a fine scheme for doing it all by fire or water mills, but not in this country nor with the present people."[6] Later, he wrote: "I have had another three days of fever, from which I am not quite recovered. This cursed climate and constitution will undo me." Watt must have told Small when at Birmingham of the probability of his being able to apply his steam-engine to locomotion; for the latter writes him, "I told Dr. Robison and his pupil that I hoped soon to travel in a fiery chariot of your invention." Later, Small wrote: "A linendraper at London, one Moore, has taken out a patent for moving wheel-carriages by steam. This comes of thy delays. I dare say he has heard of your inventions ... Do come to England with all possible speed.

At this moment, how I could scold you for negligence! However, if you will come hither soon, I will promise to be very civil, and buy a steam-chaise of you and not of Moore. And yet it vexes me abominably to see a man of your superior genius neglect to avail himself properly of his great talents. These short fevers will do you good."[7] Watt replied: "If linendraper Moore does not use *my* engines to drive his chaises, he can't drive them by steam. If he does, I will stop them. I suppose by the rapidity of his progress and puffing he is too volatile to be dangerous … You talk to me about coming to England, just as if I was an Indian that had nothing to remove but my person. Why do we encumber ourselves with anything else? I can't see you before July at soonest, unless you come here. If you do I can recommend you to a fine sweet girl, who will be anything you want her to be if you can make yourself agreeable to her." Badinage apart, however, there was one point on which Watt earnestly solicited the kind services of his friend. He had become more than ever desirous of securing the powerful co-operation of Matthew Boulton in introducing his invention to public notice: –

"Seriously," says he, "you will oblige me if you will negotiate the following affair: – I find that if the engine succeeds my whole time will be taken up in planning and erecting Reciprocating engines, and the Circulator must stand still unless I do what I have done too often, neglect certainty for hope. Now, Mr. Boulton wants one or more engines for his own use. If he will make a model of one of 20 inches diameter at least, I will give him my advice and as much assistance as I can. He shall have liberty to erect one of any size for his own use. If he should choose to have more the terms will be easy, and I shall consider myself much obliged to him. If it should answer, and he should not think himself repaid for his trouble by the use of it, he shall make and use it until he is repaid. If this be agreeable to him let me know, and I will propose it to the Doctor [Roebuck], and doubt not of his consent. I wish Mr. Boulton and you had entered into some negotiation with the Doctor about coming in as partners. I am afraid it is now too late; for the nearer it approaches to certainty, he grows the more tenacious of it.[8] For my part, I shall continue to think as I did, that it would be for our mutual advantage. His expectations are solely from the Reciprocator. Possibly he may be tempted to part with the half of the Circulator to you. This I say of myself. Mr. Boulton asked if the Circulator was contrived since our agreement. It was; but it is a part of the scheme, and virtually included in it."[9]

From this it will be seen how anxious Watt was to engage Boulton in taking an interest in his invention. But though the fly was artfully cast over the nose of the fish, still he would not rise. The times were out of joint, business was stagnant, and Boulton was of necessity cautious about venturing upon new enterprises. Small doubtless communicated the views thus confidentially conveyed to him by Watt; and in his next letter he again pressed him to come to Birmingham and have a personal interview with Boulton as to the engine, adding, "bring this pretty girl with you when you come." But, instead of Watt, Roebuck himself went to see Boulton on the subject. During the time of this visit, Watt again communicated to Small his anxiety that Boulton should join in the partnership. "As for myself," said he, "I shall say nothing; but if you three can agree among yourselves, you may appoint me what share you please, and you will find me willing to do my best to advance the good of the whole; or, if this [the engine] should not succeed, to do any other thing I can to make you all amends, only reserving to myself the liberty of grumbling when I am in an ill humour."[10]

Small's reply was discouraging. Both Boulton and he had just engaged in another scheme, which would require all the ready money at their command. Possibly the ill-success of the experiment Watt had by this time made with his new model at Kinneil may have had some influence in deterring them from engaging in what still looked a very unpromising speculation. Watt was greatly cast down at this intelligence, though he could not blame his friend for the caution he displayed in the matter.[11]He nevertheless again returned to the subject in his letters to Small; and at last Boulton was persuaded to enter into a conditional arrangement with Roebuck, which was immediately communicated to Watt, who received the intelligence with great exultation. "I shake hands," he wrote to Small, "with you and Mr. Boulton in our connexion, which I hope will prove agreeable to us all." His joy, however, proved premature, as it turned out that the agreement was only to the effect, that if Boulton thought proper to exercise the option of becoming a partner in the engine to the extent of one-third, he was to do so within a period of twelve months, paying Roebuck a sum of 1000l.; but this option Boulton never exercised, and the engine enterprise seemed to be as far from success as ever.

In the mean time Watt became increasingly anxious about his own position. He had been spending more money on fruitless experiments, and getting into more debt. The six months he had been living at Kinneil had brought him in nothing. He had been neglecting his business, and could not afford to waste more time in prosecuting an apparently hopeless speculation. He accordingly returned to his regular work, and proceeded with the survey of the river Clyde, at the instance of the Glasgow Corporation. "I would not have meddled with this," he wrote to Dr. Small, "had I been certain of being able to bring the engine to bear. But I cannot, on an uncertainty, refuse every piece of business that offers. I have refused some common fire-engines, because they must have taken my attention so up as to hinder my going on with my own. However, if I cannot make it answer soon, I shall certainly undertake the next that offers, for I cannot afford to trifle away my whole life, which – God knows – may not be long. Not that I think myself a proper hand for keeping men to their duty; but I must use my endeavours to make myself square with the world, though I much fear I never shall."[12]

Small lamented this apparent abandonment of the engine to its fate. But though he had failed in inducing Boulton heartily to join Watt in the enterprise, he did not yet despair. He continued to urge Watt to complete his engine, as the fourteen years for which the patent lasted would soon be gone. At all events he might send drawings of his engine to Soho; and Mr. Boulton and he would undertake to do their best to have one constructed for the purpose of exhibiting its powers.[13] To this Watt agreed, and about the beginning of 1770, the necessary drawings were sent to Soho, and an engine was immediately put in course of execution. Patterns were made and sent to Coalbrookdale to be cast; but when the castings were received, they were found exceedingly imperfect, and were thrown aside as useless. They were then sent to an ironfounder at Bilston to be executed; but the result was only another failure.

About the beginning of 1770, another unsuccessful experiment was made by Watt and Roebuck with the engine at Kinneil. The cylinder had been repaired and made true by beating, but as the metal of which it was made was soft, it was feared that the working of the piston might throw it out of form. To prevent this, two firm parallel planes were fixed, through which the piston worked, in order to prevent its vibration. "If this should fail," Roebuck wrote to Boulton, in giving an account of the intended trial, "then the cylinder must be made of cast-iron. But I have great confidence that the present engine will work completely, and by this day se'nnight you may expect to hear the result of our experiments."[14] The good news, however, never went to Birmingham; on the contrary, the trial proved a failure. There was some more tinkering at the engine, but it would not work satisfactorily; and Watt went back to Glasgow with a heavy heart.

Small again endeavoured to induce Watt to visit Birmingham, to super-intend the erection of the engine, the materials for which were now lying at Soho. He also held out to Watt the hope of obtaining some employment for him in the midland counties as a consulting engineer. But Watt could not afford to lose more time in erecting trial-engines; and he was too much occupied at Glasgow to leave it for the proposed uncertainty at Birmingham. He accordingly declined the visit, but invited Small to continue the correspondence; "for," said he, "we have abundance of matters to discuss, though the damned engine sleep in quiet." Small wrote back, professing himself satisfied that Watt was so fully employed in his own profession at Glasgow. "Let nothing," he said, "divert you from the business of engineering. You are sensible that both Boulton and I engaged in the patent scheme much more from inclination to be in some degree useful to you than from any other principle; so that if you are prosperous and happy, we do not care whether you find the scheme worth prosecuting or not."[15] Replying to Small's complaint of himself, that he felt *ennuyé* and stupid, taking pleasure in nothing but sleep, Watt said: "You complain of physic; I find it sufficiently stupifying to be obliged to think on any subject but one's hobby; and I really am become monstrously stupid, and can seldom think at all. I wish to God I could afford to live without it; though I don't admire your sleeping scheme. I must fatigue myself, otherwise I can neither eat nor sleep. In short, I greatly doubt whether the silent mansion of the grave be not the happiest abode. I am cured of most of my youthful desires, and if ambition or avarice do not lay hold of me, I shall be almost as much *ennuyé* as you say you are."[16]

Small again recurred to the subject of Watt's removal to Birmingham, informing him that he had provided accommodation for him, "having kept a whole house in my power, in hopes you may come to live here."

Watt's prospects were, however, brightening. He was then busily occupied in superintending the construction of the Monkland Canal. He wrote Small that he had a hundred men working under him, who had "made a confounded gash in a hill," at which they had been working for twelve months; that by frugal living he had contrived to save money enough to pay his debts, and that he had plenty of remunerative work before him. He had also become concerned in a pottery, which, he said, "does very well, though we make monstrous bad ware."[17] He had not, indeed, got rid of his headaches, though he was not so much afflicted by low spirits as he had been. But he confessed that after all he hated the business of engineering, and wished himself well rid of it, for the reasons stated in a preceding chapter.

This comparatively prosperous state of Watt's affairs did not, however, last long. The commercial panic of 1772 put a sudden stop to most of the canal schemes then on foot. The proprietors of the Monkland Canal could not find the necessary means for carrying on the works, and Watt consequently lost his employment as their engineer. He was thus again thrown upon the world, and where was he to look for help? Naturally enough, he reverted to his engine. But it was in the hands of Dr. Roebuck, who was overwhelmed with debt, and upon the verge of insolvency. It was clear that no help was to be looked for in that quarter. Again he bethought him of Small's invitations to Birmingham, and of the interest that Boulton had taken in the engine scheme. Could he be induced at last to become a partner? He again broached the subject to Small, telling him how business had failed him; that he was now ready to go to Birmingham and engage in English surveys, or do anything that would bring him in an honest income. But, above all, would Boulton and Small, now that Roebuck had failed, join him as partners in the engine business?

By this time Boulton himself had become involved in difficulties arising out of the commercial pressure of the time, and was more averse than ever to enter upon such an enterprise. But having lent Roebuck a considerable sum of money, it occurred to Watt that the amount might be taken as part of the price of Boulton's share in the patent, if he would consent to enter into the proposed partnership. He represented to Small the great distress of Roebuck's situation, which he had done all that he could to relieve. "What little I can do for him," he said, "is purchased by denying myself the conveniences of life my station requires, or by remaining in debt, which it galls me to the bone to owe." Reverting to the idea of a partnership with Boulton, he added, "I shall be content to hold a very small share in it, or none at all, provided I am to be freed from my pecuniary obligations to Roebuck, and have any kind of recompense for even a part of the anxiety and ruin it has involved me in." And again: "Although I am out of pocket a much greater sum upon these experiments than my proportion of the profits of the engine, I do not look upon that money as the price of my share, but as money spent on my education. I thank God I have now reason to believe that I can never, while I have health, be at any loss to pay what I owe, and to live at least in a decent manner; more, I do not violently desire."[18]

In a subsequent letter Watt promised Small that he would pay an early visit to Birmingham, and added, "there is nowhere I so much wish to be." In replying, Small pointed out a difficulty in the way of the proposed partnership: "It is impossible," he wrote, "for Mr. Boulton and me, or any other honest man, to purchase, especially from two particular friends, what has no market price, and at a time when they might be inclined to part with the commodity at an under value."[19] He added that the high-pressure wheel-engine constructing at Soho, after Watt's plans, was nearly ready, and that Wilkinson, of Bradley, had promised that the boiler should be sent next week. "Should the experiment succeed, or seem likely to succeed," he said, "you ought to come hither immediately upon receiving the notice, which I will instantly send. In that case we propose to unite three things under your direction, which would altogether, we hope, prove tolerably satisfactory to you, at least until your merit shall be better known."[20]

But before the experiment with the wheel-engine could be tried at Soho, the financial ruin of Dr. Roebuck brought matters to a crisis. He was now in the hands of his creditors, who found his affairs in inextricable confusion. He owed some 1200*l.* to Boulton, who, rather than claim against the estate, offered to take Roebuck's two-thirds share in the engine patent in lieu of the debt. The creditors did not value the engine as worth one farthing, and were but too glad to agree to the proposal. As Watt himself said, it was only "paying one bad debt with another." Boulton wrote to Watt requesting him to act as his attorney in the matter. He confessed that he was by no means sanguine as to the success of the engine, but, being an assayer, he was willing "to assay it and try how much gold it contains." "The thing," he added, "is now a shadow; 'tis merely ideal, and will cost time and money to realise it. We have made no experiment yet that answers my purpose, and the times are so horrible throughout the mercantile part of Europe, that I have not had my thoughts sufficiently disengaged to think of new schemes."[21]

So soon as the arrangement for the transfer of Roebuck's share to Boulton was concluded, Watt ordered the engine in the outhouse at Kinneil to be taken to pieces, packed up, and sent to Birmingham.[22] Small again pressed him to come and superintend the work in person. But before he could leave Scotland it was necessary that he should complete the survey of the Caledonian Canal, which was still unfinished. This done, he promised at once to set out for Soho. In any case, he had made up his mind to leave his own country, of which he declared himself "heart-sick."[23] He hated its harsh climate, so trying to his fragile constitution. Moreover, he disliked the people he had to deal with. He was also badly paid for his work, a whole year's surveying having brought him in only about 200*l.* Out of this he had paid some portion to Dr. Roebuck to help him in his necessity, "so that," he said, "I can barely support myself and keep untouched the small sum I have allotted for my visit to you."[24]

Watt's intention was either to try to find employment as a surveyor or engineer in England, or obtain a situation of some kind abroad. He was, however, naturally desirous of ascertaining whether it was yet possible to do anything with the materials which now lay at Soho; and with the object of visiting his friends there and superintending the erection of the trial-engine, he at length made his final arrangements to leave Glasgow. We find him arrived in Birmingham in May, 1774, where he at once entered on a new and important phase of his professional career.

NOTES

1   On the 22nd May, 1765, Franklin writes Boulton, – "Mr. Baskerville informs me that you have lately had a considerable addition to your fortune, on which I sincerely congratulate you. I beg leave to introduce my friend Doctor Small to your acquaintance, and to recommend him to your civilities. I would not take this freedom, if I were not sure it would be agreeable to you; and that you will thank me for adding to the number of those who from their knowledge of you must respect you, one who is both an ingenious philosopher and a most worthy honest man. If anything new in magnetism or electricity, or any other branch of natural knowledge, has occurred to your fruitful genius since I last had the pleasure of seeing you, you will by communicating it greatly oblige me."

2   Franklin to Boulton, March 19, 1766. Boulton MSS.

3   Darwin to Boulton, March 11, 1766. Boulton MSS.

4   The following passage occurs in his letter: – "Suppose one piston up, and the vacuum made under it by the jet d'eau froid. That piston cannot yet descend, because the cock is not yet opened which admits the steam into its antagonist cylinder. Hence the two pistons are in equilibrio, being either of them pressed by the atmosphere. Then, I say, if the cock which admits the steam into the antagonist cylinder be opened gradually and not with a jerk, that the first mentioned [piston in the] cylinder will descend gradually and yet not less forcibly. Hence by the management of the steam cocks the motion may be accelerated, retarded, destroyed, revived, instantly and easily. And if this answers in practice as it does in theory, the machine cannot fail of success! Eureka!"

5   Small wrote Watt from Birmingham, on 7th January, 1768: – "Our friend Boulton will by this post send letters both to you and Dr. Roebuck. I know not well how to resolve without seeing you. I have not the pleasure of being enough acquainted with Dr. R. to judge whether we should all suit one another. His integrity and generosity everybody agrees are great. You certainly know the proposal he has made to Boulton, who will tell you his determination about it. Before I knew of your connexion with Dr. R. my idea was that you should settle here, and that Boulton and I should assist you as much as we could, which in any case we will most certainly do. I have no kind of doubt of your success, nor of your acquiring fortune, if you proceed upon a proper plan as to the manner of doing business: which, if you do, you will be sole possessor of the affair even

after your patent has expired. I had not thoroughly considered this part of the matter when you left me. In a partnership that I liked, I should not hesitate to employ any sum of money I can command on your scheme, and I am certain it may be managed with only moderate capital. Whether it would be possible to manage the wheel and reciprocating engines by separate partnerships without their interfering I am not certain. If it is, Boulton and I would engage with you in either, *provided you will live here*" – Boulton MSS.

6   Watt to Small, January 28, 1769. Boulton MSS.

7   Small to Watt, 18th April, 1769. Boulton MSS.

8   Roebuck was at this time willing to admit Boulton as a partner in the patent, but only as respected the profits of engines sold in the counties of Warwick, Stafford, and Derby. This Boulton declined, saying, "It would not be worth my while to make engines for three counties only; but it might be worth my while to make for all the world."

9   Watt to Small, 28th April, 1769. Boulton MSS.

10   Watt to Small, 20th September, 1769. Boulton MSS.

11   "I am really very sorry on my own account," he wrote, "that your engagements hinder you from entering into our scheme, for that ought to be the result of your deliberation. Though there are few things I have wished more that being connected with you on many accounts, yet I should be very loath to purchase that pleasure at the expense of your quiet, which might be the case if you involved yourself in more business than you could easily manage, or, what is worse, find money for. Besides, this is not a trade, but a project; and no man should risk more money on a project than he can afford to lose." – Watt to Small, 21st October, 1769. Boulton MSS.

12   Watt to Small, 20th September, 1769.

13   Small informed Watt that it was intended to make an engine for the purpose of drawing canal boats. "What Mr. Boulton and I", he wrote, "are very desirous of is, to move canal boats by this engine; so we have made this model of a size sufficient for that purpose. We propose first to operate without any condenser, because coals are here exceedingly cheap, and because you can, more commodiously than we, make experiments on condensers, having several already by you. Above 150 boats are now employed on these new waveless canals, so if we succeed, the field is not narrow." This suggestion of working canal boats by steam immediately elicited a reply from Watt on the subject. Invention was so habitual to him that a new method of employing power was no sooner hinted than

his active mind at once set to work to solve the problem. "Have you ever," he wrote Small, "considered a spiral oar for that purpose, or are you for two wheels?" And to make his meaning clear, he sketched out a rough but graphic outline of a screw propeller. Small's reply was unfavourable: he replied, "I have tried models of spiral oars, and have found them all inferior to oars of either of the other forms; I believe because a cylinder of water immersed in water can easily be turned round its own axis. We propose to try gun-lock springs with the fixed part longer than the moving. If we cannot succeed, we will have recourse to what you have so obligingly and clearly described." Finally Watt writes a fortnight later, "concerning spirals, I do not continue fond of them."

14 Roebuck to Boulton, February 12, 1770.

15 Small to Watt, 17th September, 1770. Boulton MSS.

16 Watt to Small, 20th October, 1770. Boulton MSS.

17 He then held an eighth share in the pottery, which brought him in about 70l. a year clear.

18 Watt to Small, 30th August, 1772. Boulton MSS.

19 Small to Watt, 16th November, 1772. Boulton MSS.

20 About this time, in order to bring himself and his engine into notice, Watt contemplated writing a treatise on steam and its applications. "I have some thoughts," he wrote to Small, "of writing a book on the elements of the theory of steam – engines, in which, however, I shall only give the enunciation of the perfect engine. This book might do me and the scheme good. It would still leave the world in the dark as to the true construction of the engine. Something of this kind is necessary, as Smeaton is labouriug hard at the subject, and if I can make no profit, at least I ought not to lose the honour of my experiments." – Watt to Small, 17th August, 1773. Boulton MSS. To this letter Small replied, "The more I consider the propriety of your publishing about steam, the more I wish you to publish. Smeaton has only trifled hitherto, though he may perhaps discover something. He told Boulton some time ago that the circular engine would not do. He said he had considered it, and was sure of this. As B. does not much respect his genius, this had no effect." Watt's treatise was, however, never written; his attention being shortly after fully occupied by other and more engrossing subjects.

21 Boulton to Watt, 29th March, 1773. Boulton MSS.

22 "As I found the engine at Kinneil perishing, and as it is from circumstances highly improper that it should continue there longer, and as I have nowhere else to put it, I have this week taken it to pieces and packed up

the ironwork, cylinder, and pump, ready to be shipped for London on its way to Birmingham, as the only place where the experiments can be completed with propriety. I suppose the whole will not weigh above four tons. I have left the whole of the woodwork until we see what we are to do." – Watt to Small, 20th May, 1773. Boulton MSS.

23   In a letter to Small, Watt wrote, "I begin to see daylight through the affairs that have detained me so long, and think of setting out for you in a fortnight at furthest. I am monstrously plagued with my headaches, and not a little with unprofitable business. I don't mean my own whims: these I never work at when I can do any other thing; but I have got too many acquaintances; and there are too many beggars in this country, which I am afraid is going to the devil altogether. Provisions continue excessively dear, and laws are made to keep them so. But luckily the spirit of emigrating rises high, and the people seem disposed to show their oppressive masters that they can live without them. By the time some twenty or thirty thousand more leave the country, matters will turn not much to the profit of the landholders." – Watt to Small, 29th April, 1774. Boulton MSS.

24   Watt to Small, 25th July, 1773. Boulton MSS.

XI

Boulton and Watt – Their Partnership

Watt had now been occupied for about nine years in working out the details of his invention. Five of these had passed since he had taken out his patent, and he was still struggling with difficulty. Several thousand pounds had been expended on the engine, besides much study, labour, and ingenuity; yet it was still, as Boulton expressed it, "a shadow, as regarded its practical utility and value." So long as Watt's connexion with Roebuck continued, there was indeed very little chance of getting it favourably introduced to public notice. What it was yet to become as a working power depended in no small degree upon the business ability, the strength of purpose, and the length of purse of his new partner.

Had Watt searched Europe through, probably he could not have found a man better fitted than Matthew Boulton for bringing his invention fairly before the world. Many would have thought it rash on the part of the latter, burdened as he was with heavy liabilities, to engage in a new undertaking of so speculative a character. Feasible though the scheme might be, it was an admitted fact that nearly all the experiments with the models heretofore made had proved failures. It is true Watt firmly believed that he had hit upon the right principle, and he was as sanguine as ever of the eventual success of his engine. But though inventors are usually sanguine, men of capital do not take up their schemes on that account. Capitalists are rather disposed to regard sanguine inventors as visionaries, full of theories of what is possible rather than of well-defined plans of what is practicable and useful.

Boulton, however, amongst his many other gifts possessed an admirable knowledge of character. His judgment of men was almost unerring. In Watt he had recognised at his first visit to Soho, not only a man of original inven-

tive genius, but a plodding, earnest, intent, and withal an exceedingly modest
man; not given to puff, but on the contrary rather disposed to underrate
the merit of his inventions. Different though their characters were in most
respects, Boulton at once conceived a hearty liking for him. The one displayed
in perfection precisely those qualities which the other wanted. Boulton was a
man of ardent and generous temperament, bold and enterprising, undaunted
by difficulty, and possessing an almost boundless capacity for work. He was
a man of great tact, clear perception, and sound judgment. Moreover, he
possessed that indispensable quality of perseverance, without which the best
talents are of comparatively little avail in the conduct of important affairs.
While Watt hated bussiness, Boulton loved it. He had, indeed, a genius for
business, – a gift almost as rare as that for poetry, for art, or for war. He possessed a marvellous power of organisation. With a keen eye for details he
combined a comprehensive grasp of intellect. While his senses were so acute,
that when sitting in his office at Soho he could detect the slightest stoppage or
derangement in the machinery of that vast establishment, and send his mes-
sage direct to the spot where it had occurred, his power of imagination was
such as enabled him to look clearly along extensive lines of possible action in
Europe, America, and the East. For there is a poetic as well as a commonplace
side to business; and the man of business genius lights up the humdrum routine of daily life by exploring the boundless region of possibility wherever it
may lie open before him.

Boulton had already won his way to the very front rank in his calling,
honestly and honourably; and he was proud of it. He had created many new
branches of industry, which gave regular employment to hundreds of families.
He had erected and organised a manufactory which was looked upon as one of
the most complete of its kind in England, and was resorted to by visitors from
all parts of the world. But Boulton was more than a man of business: he was
a man of culture, and the friend of cultivated men. His hospitable mansion
at Soho was the resort of persons eminent in art, in literature, and in science;
and the love and admiration with which he inspired such men affords one of
the best proofs of his own elevation of character. Among the most intimate
of his friends and associates were Richard Lovell Edgeworth,[1] a gentleman of
fortune, enthusiastically devoted to his long-conceived design of moving land
carriages by steam; Captain Keir, an excellent practical chemist, a wit and a
man of learning; Dr. Small, the accomplished physician, chemist, and mecha-
nist; Josiah Wedgwood, the practical philosopher and manufacturer, founder
of a new and important branch of skilled industry; Thomas Day, the ingenious author of 'Sandford and Merton;' Dr. Darwin, the poet-physician; Dr.

Withering, the botanist; besides others who afterwards joined the Soho circle, – not the least distinguished of whom were Joseph Priestley and James Watt.[2]

Boulton could not have been very sanguine at first as to the success of Watt's engine. There were a thousand difficulties in the way of getting it introduced to general use. The principal one was the difficulty of finding workmen capable of making it. Watt had been constantly worried by "villanous bad workmen," who failed to make any model that would go properly. It mattered not that the principle of the engine was right; if its construction was beyond the skill of ordinary handicraftsmen, the invention was practically worthless. The great Smeaton was of this opinion. When he saw the first model working at Soho, he admitted the excellence of the contrivance, but predicted its failure, on the ground that it was too complicated, and that workmen were not to be found capable of manufacturing it on any large scale for general uses.

Watt himself felt that, if the engine was ever to have a fair chance, it was now; and that if Boulton, with his staff of skilled workmen at command, could not make it go, the scheme must be abandoned henceforward as impracticable. Boulton must, however, have seen the elements of success in the invention, otherwise he would not have taken up with it. He knew the difficulties Watt had encountered in designing it, and he could well appreciate the skill with which he had overcome them; for Boulton himself, as we have seen, had for some time been occupied with the study of the subject. But the views of Boulton on entering into his new branch of business, cannot be better expressed than in his own words, as stated in a letter written by him to Watt in 1769, when then invited to join the Roebuck partnership:

"The plan proposed to me,"[3] said he, "is so very different from that which I had conceived at the time I talked with you upon the subject, that I cannot think it a proper one for me to meddle with, as I do not intend turning engineer. I was excited by two motives to offer you my assistance – which were, love of you, and love of a money-getting ingenious project. I presumed that your engine would require money, very accurate workmanship, and extensive correspondence, to make it turn out to the best advantage; and that the best means of keeping up our reputation and doing the invention justice, would be to keep the executive part out of the hands of the multitude of empirical engineers, who, from ignorance, want of experience, and want of necessary convenience, would be very liable to produce bad and inaccurate workmanship; all which deficiencies would affect the reputation of the invention. To remedy which, and to produce the most profit, my idea was to settle a manufactory near my own, by the side of our canal, where I would erect all the conveniences necessary for the completion of engines, and from which manufactory we would serve the world with engines of all sizes. By these means and your assistance we could engage and instruct some excellent workmen, who (with more excellent tools than would be worth any man's while to procure for one single engine) could execute the invention 20 per cent. cheaper than it would be otherwise executed, and with as great a difference of accuracy as there is between the blacksmith and the mathematical instrument maker."

He went on to state that he was willing to enter upon the speculation with these views, considering it well worth his while "to make engines for all the world," though it would not be worth his while "to make for three counties only;" besides, he declared himself averse to embark in any trade that he had not the inspection of himself. He concluded by saying, "Although there seem to be some obstructions to our partnership in the engine trade, yet I live in hopes that you or I may hit upon some scheme or other that may associate us in this part of the world, which would render it still more agreeable to me than it is, by the acquisition of such a neighbour."[4]

Five years had passed since this letter was written, during which the engine had made no way in the world. The partnership of Roebuck and Watt had yielded nothing but vexation and debt; until at last, fortunately for Watt – though at the time he regarded it as a terrible calamity – Roebuck broke down, and the obstruction was removed which had prevented Watt and Boulton from coming together. The latter at once reverted to the plan of action which he had with so much sagacity laid down in 1769; and he invited Watt to take up his abode at Soho until the necessary preliminary arrangements could be made. He thought it desirable, in the first place, to erect the engine, of which the several parts had been sent to Soho from Kinneil, in order, if possible, to exhibit a specimen of the invention in actual work. Boulton undertook to defray all the necessary expenses, and to find competent workmen to carry out the instructions of Watt, whom Boulton was also to maintain until the engine business had become productive.[5]

The materials brought from Kinneil were accordingly put together with as little delay as possible; and, thanks to the greater skill of the workmen who assisted in its erection, the engine, when finished, worked in a more satisfactory manner than it had ever done before. In November, 1774, Watt wrote Dr. Roebuck, informing him of the success of his trials; on which the Dr. expressed his surprise that the engine should have worked at all, "considering the slightness of the materials and its long exposure to the injuries of the weather." Watt also wrote to his father at Greenock.

"The business I am here about has turned out rather successful; that is to say, the fire-engine I have invented is now going, and answers much better than any other that has yet been made; and I expect that the invention will be very beneficial to me."[6] Such was Watt's modest announcement of the successful working of the engine on which such great results depended.

Much, however, remained to be done before either Watt or Boulton could reap any benefit from the invention. Six years out of the fourteen for which the patent was originally taken had already expired; and all that had been accomplished was the erection of this experimental engine at Soho. What further period might elapse before capitalists could be brought to recognise the practical uses of the invention could only be guessed at; but the probability was that the patent right would expire long before such a demand for the engines arose as should remunerate Boulton and Watt for their investment of time, labour, and capital. And the patent once expired, the world at large would be free to make the engines, though Watt himself had not recovered one farthing towards repaying him for the long years of experiment, study, and ingenuity bestowed by him in bringing his invention to perfection. These considerations made Boulton hesitate before launching out the money necessary to provide the tools, machinery, and buildings, for carrying on the intended manufacture on a large scale and in the best style.

When it became known that Boulton had taken an interest in a new engine for pumping water, he had many inquiries about it from the mining districts. The need of a more effective engine than any then in use was every year becoming more urgent. The powers of Newcomen's engine had been tried to the utmost. So long as the surface-lodes were worked, its power was sufficient to clear the mines of water; but as they were carried deeper, it was found totally inadequate for the work, and many mines were consequently becoming gradually drowned out and abandoned. The excessive consumption of coals by the Newcomen engines was another serious objection to their use, especially in districts such as Cornwall, where coal was very dear. When Small was urging Watt to come to Birmingham and make engines, he wrote: "A friend of Boulton's, in Cornwall, sent us word a few days ago that four or five copper-mines are just going to be abandoned because of the high price of coals, and begs us to apply to them instantly. The York Buildings Company delay rebuilding their engine, with great inconvenience to themselves, waiting for yours. Yesterday application was made to me by a Mining Company in Derbyshire to know when you are to be in England about the engines, because they must quit their mine if you cannot relieve them." The necessity for an improved pumping power had set many inventors to work besides Watt, and some of the less scrupulous of them were already trying to adopt his principle in such a way as to evade his patent. Moore, the London linendraper, and Hatley, one of Watt's Carron workmen, had brought out and were pushing engines similar to Watt's; the latter having stolen and sold for a considerable sum working drawings of the Kinneil engine.

From these signs Boulton saw that, in the event of the engine proving successful, he and his partner would have to defend the invention against a host of pirates; and he became persuaded that he would not be justified in risking his capital in the establishment of a steam-engine manufactory unless a considerable extension of the patent-right could be secured. To ascertain whether this was practicable, Watt proceeded to London in the beginning of 1775, to confer with his patent agent and take the opinion of counsel on the subject. Mr. Wedderburn, who was advised with, recommended that the existing patent should be surrendered, and in that case he did not doubt that a new one would be granted. While in London, Watt looked out for possible orders for his engine: "I have," he wrote Boulton, "a prospect of two orders for fire-engines here, one to water Piccadilly, and the other to serve the south end of Blackfriars Bridge with water. I have taken advice of several people whom I could trust about the patent. They all agree that an Act would be much better and cheaper, a patent being now 130*l.*, the Act, if obtainable, 110*l.* The present patent has eight years still to run, bearing date January, 1769. I understand there will be an almost unlimited sale for wheel-engines to the West Indies, at the rate of 100*l.* for each horse's power.'[7]

Watt also occupied some of his time in London in superintending the adjustment of weights manufactured by Boulton and Fothergill, then sold in considerable quantities through their London agent. That he continued to take an interest in his old business of mathematical instrument making is apparent from the visits which he made to several well-known shops. One of the articles which he examined with most interest was Short's Gregorian telescope. At other times, by Boulton's request, he went to see the few steam-engines then at work in London and the neighbourhood, and make inquiries as to their performances. With that object he examined the engines at the New River, Hungerford, and Chelsea. At the latter place, he said, "it was impossible to try the quantity of injection, and the fellow told me lies about the height of the column of water." But Watt soon grew tired of London, "running from street to street all day about gilding," inquiring after metal-rollers, silver-platers, and button-makers. He did his best, however, to execute the commissions which Boulton from time to time sent him; and when these were executed, he returned to Birmingham to confer with his friends as to the steps to be taken with respect to the patent. The result of his conferences with Boulton and Small was, that it was determined to take steps to apply for an Act for its extension in the ensuing session of Parliament.

Watt went up to London a second time for the purpose of having the Bill drawn. He had scarcely arrived there when the sad intelligence reached him of the death of Dr. Small. He had long been ailing, yet the event was a shock alike to himself and Boulton. The latter wrote Watt in the bitterness of his grief, "If there were not a few other objects yet remaining for me to settle my affections upon, I should wish also to take up my abode in the mansions of the dead." Watt replied, rewinding him of the sentiments of their departed friend, as to the impropriety of indulging in unavailing sorrow, the best refuge from which was the more sedulous performance of duty. "Come, my dear sir," said he, "and immerse yourself in this sea of business as soon as possible. Pay a proper respect to your friend by obeying his precepts. I wait for you with impatience, and assure yourself no endeavour of mine shall be wanting to render life agreeable to you"

It had been intended to include Small in the steam-engine partnership on the renewal of the patent. He had been consulted in all the stages of the proceedings, and one of the last things he did was to draw up Watt's petition for the Bill. No settled arrangement had yet been made – not even between Boulton and Watt. Everything depended upon the success of the application for the extension of the patent.

Meanwhile, through the recommendation of his old friend Dr. Robison, then in Russia officiating as Mathematical Professor at the Government Naval School at Cronstadt, Watt was offered an appointment under the Russian Government, at a salary of about 1000*l.* a year. He was thus presented with a means of escape from his dependence upon Boulton, and for the first time in his life had the prospect before him of an income that to him would have been affluence. But he entertained strong objections to settling in Russia: he objected to its climate, its comparative barbarism, and, notwithstanding the society of his friend Robison, to the limited social resources of St. Petersburg. Besides, Boulton's favours were so gracefully conferred, that the dependence on him was not felt; for he made the recipient of his favours feel as if the obligation were entirely on the side of the giver. "Your going to Russia staggers me," he wrote to Watt; "the precariousness of your health, the dangers of so long a journey or voyage, and my own deprivation of consolation render me a little uncomfortable; but I wish to assist and advise you for the best, without regard to self." The, result was, that Watt determined to wait the issue of the application for the extension of his patent.

The Bill was introduced to Parliament on the 28th of February, 1775, and it was obvious from the first that it would have considerable opposition to encounter. The mining interest had looked forward to Watt's invention as a means of helping them out of their difficulties and giving a new value to their property by clearing the drowned mines of water. They therefore desired to have the free use of the engine at the earliest possible period; and when it was proposed to extend the patent by Act of Parliament, they set up with one accord the cry of "No monopoly." Up to the present time, as we have seen, the invention had been productive to Watt of nothing but loss, labour, anxiety, and headaches; and it was only just that a reasonable period should be allowed to enable him to derive some advantage from the results of his application and ingenuity. But the mining interest took a different view of the matter. They did not see the necessity of recognising the rights of the inventor beyond the term of his existing patent, and they held that the public interests would suffer if the proposed "monopoly" were granted. Nor were they without supporters in Parliament, for among the most strenuous we find the name of Edmund Burke, – influenced, it is supposed, by certain mining interests in the neighbourhood of Bristol, which city he then represented.

There is no doubt that the public would have benefited by Watt's invention having been made free to all. But it was not for the public merely that Watt had been working at his engine for fifteen long years. He was a man of comparatively small means, and had been buoyed up and stimulated to renewed exertion during that time by the hope of ultimate reward in the event of its success. If labour could give a man a title to property in his invention, Watt's claim was clear. The condensing-engine had been the product of his own skill, contrivance, and brain-work. But there has always been a difficulty in getting the claims of mere brain-work recognised. Had he expended his labour in building a house instead of in contriving a machine, his right of property would at once have been acknowledged. As it was, he had to contend for justice and persuade the legislature of the reasonableness of granting his application for an extension of the patent. In the "Case" which he drew up for distribution amongst the members of the Lower House, on the motion being carried for the recommittal of the Bill, he set forth that having, after great labour and expense extending over many years, succeeded in completing working engines of each of the two kinds he had invented, he found that they could not be carried into profitable execution without the further expenditure of large sums of money in erecting mills, and purchasing the various materials and utensils necessary for making them; and from the reluctance with which the public generally adopt new inventions, he was afraid that the whole term granted by his patent would expire before the engines should have come into general use and any portion of his expenses be repaid.

"The inventor of these new engines," said he, "is sorry that gentlemen of knowledge, and avowed admirers of his invention, should oppose the Bill by putting it in the light of a monopoly. He never had any intention of circumscribing or claiming the inventions of others; and the Bill is now drawn up in such a manner as sufficiently guards those rights, and must oblige him to prove his own right to every part of his invention which may at any time be disputed … If the invention be valuable, it has been made so by his industry, and at his expense; he has struggled with bad health, and many other inconveniences, to bring it to perfection, and all he wishes is to be secured in the profits which he may reasonably expect from it, – profits which he cannot obtain without an exertion of his abilities to bring it into practice, by which the public must be the greatest gainers, and which are limited by the performance of the common engines; for he cannot expect that any person will make use of his contrivance, unless he can prove to them that savings will take place, and that his demand for the privilege of using the invention will amount only to a reasonable part of them. No man will lay aside a known engine, and stop his work to erect one of a new contrivance, unless he is certain to be a very great gainer by the exchange; and if any contrivance shall so far excel others as to enforce the use of it, it is reasonable that the author of such a contrivance should be rewarded."

These weighty arguments could not fail to produce an impression on the minds of all reasonable men, and the result was, that Parliament passed an Act extending Watt's patent right for the further term of twenty-four years. Watt wrote Boulton on the 27th May, – "I hope to be clear to come away by Wednesday or Thursday. I am heartily sick of this town and *fort ennuyée* since you left it. Dr. Roebuck is likely to get an order, out of Smeaton's hands, for an engine in Yorkshire that, according to Smeaton's calculation, will burn 1200*l*. per annum in coals. But this has had one bad effect. It has made the Doctor repent of his bargain and wish again to be upon the 1-10th [profits]; but we must see to keep him right if possible, so don't vex yourself about it." Dr. Roebuck had been finally settled with before the passing of the Act. It had been arranged that Boulton should pay him 1000*l*. out of the first profits aris-

ing from his share in the engine, making about 2200*l.* in all paid by Boulton
to Roebuck for his two-thirds of the patent.[8]

Watt returned to Birmingham to set about the making of the engines
for which orders had already been received. Boulton had been busily
occupied during his absence in experimenting on the Soho engine. A new
18-inch cylinder had been cast for it at Bersham by John Wilkinson, the
great ironfounder,[9] who had contrived a machine for boring it with accuracy. This cylinder was substituted for the tin one brought from Kinneil,
and other improvements having been introduced, the engine was again
set to work with very satisfactory results. Watt found his partner in good
spirits; not less elated by the performances of the model than by the passing of the Act; and arrangements were at once set on foot for carrying
on the manufacture of engines upon an extensive scale. Applications for
terms, followed by orders, shortly came in from the mining districts; and
before long the works at Soho were resounding with the clang of hammers and machinery employed in manufacturing steam-engines for all
parts of the civilized world.

NOTES

1   Mr. Edgeworth was first introduced to the notice of Mr. Boulton in the
    following letter from Dr. Darwin (1767): – "Dear Boulton, I have got
    with me a mechanical friend, Mr. Edgeworth, from Oxfordshire, – the
    greatest conjurer I ever saw. God send fine weather, and pray come to my
    assistance, and prevail on Dr. Small and Mrs. Boulton to attend you to-
    morrow morning, and we will reconvey you to Birmingham if the devil
    permit. E. has the principles of nature in his palm, and moulds them as
    he pleases, – can take away polarity, or give it to the needle by rubbing it
    thrice on the palm of his hand! And can see through two solid oak boards
    without glasses! Wonderful! Astonishing!! Diabolical!!! Pray tell Dr. Small
    he must come to see these miracles. Adieu, E. Darwin."

2   Richard Lovell Edgeworth says of this distinguished coterie, – "By
    means of Mr. Keir I became acquainted with Dr. Small of Birmingham,
    a man esteemed by all who knew him, and by all who were admitted
    to his friendship beloved with no common enthusiasm. Dr. Small
    formed a link which combined Mr. Boulton, Mr. Watt, Dr. Darwin,
    Mr. Wedgewood, Mr. Day, and myself together – men of very different
    characters, but all devoted to literature and science. This mutual

intimacy has never been broken but by death, nor have any of the number failed to distinguish themselves in science or literature. Some may think that I ought with due modesty to except myself. Mr. Keir with his knowledge of the world and good sense; Dr. Small, with his benevolence and profound sagacity; Wedgewood, with his increasing industry, experimental variety, and calm investigation; Boulton, with his mobility, quick perception, and bold adventure; Watt, with his strong inventive faculty, undeviating steadiness, and bold resources; Darwin, with his imagination, science, and poetical excellence; and Day, with his unwearied research after truth, his integrity and eloquence; – proved altogether such a society as few men have had the good fortune to live with; such an assemblage of friends, as fewer still have had the happiness to possess, and keep through life." – Memoirs, i. 186.

3   Dr. Roebock proposed to confine Boulton's profits to the engine business done only in three counties. It will be observed that Boulton declined to negotiate on such a basis.

4   Boulton to Watt, 7th February, 1769. Boulton MSS.

5   In a statement prepared by Mr. Boulton for the consideration of the arbitrators between himself and Fothergill as to the affairs of that firm, the following passage occurs: – "The first engine that was erected at Soho I purchased of Mr. Watt and Dr. Roebuck. The cylinder was cast of solid grain tin, which engine, with the boiler, the valves, the condenser, and the pumps, were all sent from Scotland to Soho. This engine was erected for the use of the Soho manufactory, and for the purpose of making experiments upon by Mr. Watt, who occupied two years of his time at Soho with that object: and lived there at Mr. Boulton's expense. Nevertheless Mr. Watt often assisted Boulton and Fothergill in anything in his power, and made one journey to London upon their business, when he worked at adjusting and marking weights manufactured by Boulton and Fothergill." In another statement of similar kind, Mr. Boulton says, – "The only fire-engine that was erected at Soho prior to Boulton and Watt obtaining the Act of Parliament, was entirely made and erected in Scotland, and was removed here by sea, being a part of my bargain with Roebuck. All that were afterwards erected were for persons that ordered them, and were at the expense of erecting them." – Boulton MSS.

6   Quoted in Muirhead's 'Mechanical Inventions of James Watt,' ii. 79.

7   Watt to Boulton, 31st January, 1775. Boulton MSS.

8   Bonds were given for the 1000*l.*, but the assignees of Roebuck becoming

impatient for the money, Boulton discharged them to get rid of
their importunity, long before any profits had been derived from the
manufacture of the engines.

9   John Wilkinson, the "father of the iron-trade" as he styled himself,
was a man of extraordinary energy of character. He was strong-headed
and strong-tempered and of inflexible determination. His father, Isaac
Wilkinson, who originally started the iron trade at Wrexham, was a
man possessed of quick discernment and versatile talents, though he
wanted that firmness and constancy of purpose which so eminently
distinguished his son. Isaac Williamson used thus to tell his own
history: – "I worked," said he, "at a forge in the north. My masters
gave me 12s. a week: I was content. They raised me to 14s.: I did not
ask them for it. They went on to 16s., 18s.: I never asked them for
the advances. They gave me a guinea a week! Said I to myself, if I
am worth a guinea a week to you, I am worth more to myself! I left
them, and began business on my own account – at first in a small
way. I prospered. I grew tired of my leathern bellows, and determined
to make iron ones. Everybody laughed at me. I did it, and applied
the steam-engine to blow them; and they all cried, 'Who would have
thought it!'" His son John carried on the operations connected with
the iron manufacture on a far more extensive scale than his father at
Bradley, Willey, Snedshill, and Bersham. His castings were the largest
until then attempted, and the boring machinery which he invented
was the best of its kind. All the castings for Boulton and Watt's large
Cornish engines were manufactured by him, previous to the erection of
the Soho foundry. He also bored cannon for the government on a large
scale. Amongst his other merits, John Wilkinson is clearly entitled
to that of having built the first iron vessel. It was made to bring
peatmoss to his iron furnace at Wilson House, near Castle Head, in
Cartmel, in order to smelt the hematite iron-ore of Furness. This was
followed by other larger vessels, one of which was of 40 tons burden,
and used to carry iron down the Severn. Before Wilkinson's first iron
boat was launched, people laughed at the idea of its *floating*, – as it
was so well known that iron immediately sank in water! In a letter to
Mr. Stockdale, of Clarke, Cartmel, the original of which is before us,
dated Broseley, 14th July, 1787, Mr. Wilkinson says, "Yesterday week
my iron boat was launched, – answers all my expectations, and has
convinced the unbelievers, who were 999 in 1000. It will be only a
nine days' wonder, and afterwards a Columbus's egg." In another letter,

dated Bradley Iron Works, 24th October, 1788, he writes to the same,
– "There have been two iron vessels lauched in my service since 1st
September. One is a canal-boat for this navigation, the other a barge of
40 tons, for the river Severn. The last was floated on Monday, and is, I
expect, now at Stourport, a-lading with bar-iron. My clerk at Broseley
advises me that she swims remarkably light, and exceeds even my own
expectations." For further notice of John Wilkinson, see 'Lives of the
Engineers,' ii. 337, 356

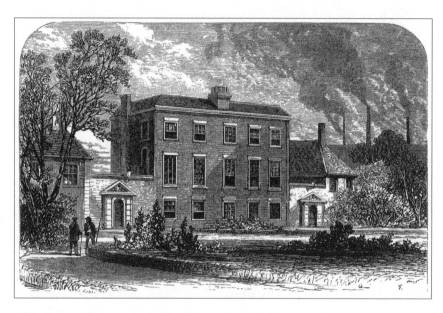

Watt's House, Harper's Hill, Birmingham

XII

Boulton and Watt begin the Manufacture of Steam-engines

Watt now arranged to take up his residence in Birmingham until the issue of the steam-engine enterprise could be ascertained, and he went down to Glasgow to bring up his two children, whom he had left in charge of their relatives. Boulton had taken a house on Harper's Hill, which was in readiness for the reception of the family on their arrival about the end of August, 1775. Regent's-place, Harper's Hill, was then the nearest house to Soho on that side of Birmingham. It was a double house, substantially built in brick, with stone facings, standing on the outskirts of the town, surrounded by fields and gardens. St. Paul's, the nearest church, was not built until four years after Watt took up his abode there. But the house at Harper's Hill is in the country no longer: it is now surrounded in all directions by dense masses of buildings, and is itself inhabited by working people.

The first engine made at Soho was one ordered by John Wilkinson to blow the bellows of his ironworks at Broseley. Great interest was, of course, felt in the success of this engine. Watt took great pains with the drawings; the workmen did their best to execute the several parts accurately, for it was understood that many orders depended upon whether it worked satisfactorily or not. Wilkinson's iron-manufacturing neighbours, who were contemplating the erection of Newcomen engines, suspended their operations until they had an opportunity of seeing what Boulton and Watt's engine could do; and all looked forward to its completion with the most eager interest. When all was ready at Soho, the materials were packed up and sent to Broseley, Watt accompanying them to superintend the erection. He had as yet no assistant to whom he could intrust such a piece of work, on which so much depended. The engine was erected and ready for use about the beginning of 1776.

As it approached completion Watt became increasingly anxious to make a trial of its powers. But Boulton wrote to him not to hurry – not to let the engine make a stroke until every possible hinderance to its successful action had been removed; "and then," said he, "in the name of God, fall to and do your best." The result of the extreme care taken with the construction and erection of the engine was entirely satisfactory. It worked to the admiration of all who saw it, and the fame of Boulton and Watt became great in the midland counties.

While Watt was thus occupied, Boulton was pushing on the new buildings at Soho. He kept his partner fully advised of all that was going on. "The new forging-shop," he wrote, "looks very formidable: the roof is nearly put on, and the hearths are both built." Tools and machinery were being prepared, and all looked hopeful for the future. Orders were coming in for engines. One in hand for Bloomfield Colliery was well advanced. Many inquiries had come from Cornwall. Mr. Papps, of Truro, was anxious to introduce the engine in that county. Out of forty engines there, only eighteen were in work; so that there was a fine field for future operations. "Pray tell Mr. Wilkinson," Boulton added, "to get a dozen cylinders cast and bored, from 12 to 50 inches diameter, and as many condensers of suitable sizes. The latter must be sent here, as we will keep them ready fitted up, and then an engine can be turned out of hand in two or three weeks. I have fixed my mind upon making from twelve to fifteen reciprocating and fifty rotative engines per annum. I assure you that of all the toys and trinkets which we manufacture at Soho, none shall take the place of fire-engines in respect of my attention."[1]

Boulton was not, however, exclusively engrossed by engine affairs. Among other things he informed Watt that he had put his little boy Jamie to a good school, and that he was very much occupied, as usual, in entertaining visitors. "The Empress of Russia," he wrote, "is now at my house, and a charming woman she is." The Empress afterwards sent Boulton her portrait, and it was long one of the ornaments of Soho. Amidst his various occupations he contrived to find leisure for experiments on minerals, having received from a correspondent in Wales a large assortment of iron-ores to assay. He was also trying experiments on the model engine, the results of which were duly communicated to his partner.[2]

On Watt's return to Soho, Boulton proceeded to London on financial affairs, as well as to look after engine orders. He there found reports in circulation among the engineering class that the new engine had proved a failure. The Society of Engineers in Holborn, of which Smeaton was the great luminary, had settled it that neither the tools nor the workmen existed that could manufacture so complex a machine with sufficient precision, and it was asserted that all the ingenuity and skill of Soho had been unable to conquer the defects of the piston. "So said Holmes, the clockmaker," wrote Boulton, being the intimate friend of Smeaton; "but no language will be sufficiently persuasive on that head except the good performance of the engines themselves."[3] Boulton, therefore, urged the completion of the engine then in hand for Cooke and Company's distillery at Stratford-le-Bow, near London. "Wilby," [managing partner] said he, "seems very impatient, and so am I, both for the sake of reputation as well as to begin to turn the tide of money," – the current of which had as yet been all outwards. Boulton went to see the York Buildings engine, which had been reconstructed by Smeaton, and was then reckoned one of the best on the Newcomen plan. The old man who tended it lauded the engine to the skies, and notwithstanding Boulton's description of the new engines at work in Staffordshire, he would not believe that any engine in existence could excel his own.

In the course of the summer Watt again visited Glasgow, – this time for the purpose of bringing back a wife. The lady he proposed to marry was Miss Anne Macgregor, daughter of a respectable dyer. The young lady's consent was obtained, as well as her father's, to the proposed union; but the latter, before making any settlement on his daughter, intimated to Watt that he desired to see the partnership agreement between him and Boulton. Now, although the terms of partnership had been generally arranged, they had not yet been put into legal form, and Watt asked that this should be done for the cautious old gentleman's satisfaction without delay.[4] About his love affair Watt wrote:

> Whether a man of the world, such as you, look upon my present love as the folly of youth or the dotage of age [Watt was then in his fortieth year], I find myself in no humour to lay it aside, or to look upon it in either of these lights, but consider it as one of the wisest of my actions, and should look upon a disappointment in it as one of the greatest of my misfortunes … I have had better health since I left you than has been my lot for years, and my spirits have borne me through my vexations wonderfully. I have lost all dread of any future connexion with Monsieur la Verole, and, if I carry my point in this matter, I hope to be very much more useful to you than has hitherto been in my power. The spur will be greater.[5]

While in Scotland Watt obtained orders for several engines; amongst others, he undertook to supply one for the Torryburn Colliery, in Fife, on the terms of receiving one-third of the savings effected by it compared with the engine then at work, with such further sum as might be judged fair. Another was ordered by Sir Archibald Hope for his colliery near Edinburgh, on similar terms. At the same time Watt proceeded with the collection of his old outstanding debts, though these did not amount to much. "I believe," he wrote to Boulton, "I shall have no occasion to draw on you for any money, having got in some of my old scraps, which will serve, or nearly serve, my occasions here."

The deed of partnership not arriving, Watt wrote again, pressing Boulton for some communication from him to satisfy the old gentleman as to his situation.

"Don't let me be detected in a falsehood," said he, "or accused of imprudence. The thing which sticks most in his [Mr. Macgregor's] stomach is, that somehow or other, in case of the failure of success, I may be brought into a load of debt which may totally ruin me. I hope you will excuse his caution in this matter, as I do, when you consider that he is disposing of a favourite child, and consequently must expect all the security possible for her wellbeing. I must also do him the justice to say that he has behaved to me in a very open and friendly manner; and, when he found that his daughter's affections were engaged beyond recall, gave his consent with a good grace … I have nothing to write you in the way of news. I am bandied about like a football, and perfectly impatient to leave this country, but do not care to come away without my errand. I long vastly to hear from you, how you all are, and how matters go on. I hope Jemmy is minding his school and is well: you need not tell him nor anybody else that I am going to bring him home a mamma."[6]

Boulton's reply was perfectly satisfactory. He confirmed the heads of the agreement, as sketched out by Watt himself, adopting his own words. He warmly congratulated him on his approaching marriage, being convinced that it was the goddess of wisdom that had led him to the altar of love. But he thought Watt might be over delicate as to money matters.

"You certainly," said he, "have a right to expect from the lady's father a child's share, both present and reversionary; and you certainly have a right to expect some ready money, as a small sum may be of more importance to you in the meridian of life than a large one at the close of it. I have always heard you speak of the old gentleman as a man of exceeding good sound sense, and therefore I should think you will have the less difficulty in settling matters with him. No doubt he will expect some settlement to be made upon his daughter, and all that I advise is, that you do not undervalue (according to your custom) your own abilities or your property. It may be difficult to say what is the value of your property in partnership with me. However, I will give it a name, and I do say that I would willingly give you two or perhaps three thousand pounds for the assignment of your third part of the Act of Parliament; but I should be sorry to make you so bad a bargain, or to make any bargain at all that tended to deprive me of your friendship, acquaintance, and assistance, – hoping, as I do, that we shall harmoniously live to wear out the twenty-five years together ... I wish I had more time to tell you all the circumstances that have occurred in the engine trade; but that shall be the subject of my next. All is well, and when you return you'll be quite charmed at the simplicity and quietness of the Soho engine."[7]

With his usual want of confidence in himself, Watt urged Boulton to come down to Glasgow and assist him in concluding matters with the old gentleman.

"I am afraid," he wrote, "that I shall otherwise make a very bad bargain in money matters, which wise men like you esteem the most essential part, and I myself, although I be an enamoured swain, do not altogether despise. You may perhaps think it odd that in the midst of my friends here I should call for your help; but the fact is, that from several reasons I do not choose to place that confidence in any of my friends here that would be necessary in such a case, and I do not know any of them that have more to say with the gentleman in question than I have myself. Besides, you are the only person who can give him satisfactory information concerning my situation."

But Boulton was too busy at the time to go down to Glasgow to the help of his partner. He was full of work, full of orders, full of Soho. He replied:

Although I have added to the list of my bad habits by joking upon matrimony, yet my disposition and my judgment would lead me to marry again were I in your case. I know you will be happier as a married man than as a single one, and therefore it is wisdom in you to wed; and if that could not be done without my coming to Scotland, I certainly would come if it were as far again; but I am so beset with difficulties, that nothing less than the absolute loss of your life, or wife – which is virtually the same thing – could bring me.

He further explained that a good deal of extra work had fallen upon him, through the absence of some of his most important assistants. Mr. Matthews, his London financial agent, like Watt, was about to be married, and would be absent abroad for a tour on a wedding trip, in which he was to be accompanied by Fothergill, Boulton's partner in the toy and button trade. Mr. Scale, the manager, was also absent, added to which the button orders were in arrear some 16,000 gross; so that, said Boulton, "I have more real difficulties to grapple with than I hope ever to have in any other year in my life."

There were also constant visitors arriving at Soho: among others the Duke of Buccleuch, who had called to see the works and inquire after Mr. Watt; and Mr. Moor, of the Society of Engineers in the Adelphi, who had come to see with his own eyes whether the reports in circulation against the new engine were true or false. The perfecting of the details of the engine also required constant attention.

> "Our copper bottom," said Boulton, "hath plagued us very much by steam leaks, and therefore I have had one cast (with its conducting pipe) all in one piece; since which the engine doth not take more than 10 feet of steam, and I hope to reduce that quantity, as we have just received the new piston, which shall be put in and at work to-morrow. Our Soho engine never was in such good order as at present. Bloomfield and Willey [engines] are both well, and I doubt not but Bow engine will be better than any of 'em."

Boulton was almost as full of speculation as Watt himself as to the means of improving the engine. "I did not sleep last night," he wrote, "my mind being absorbed by steam." One of his speculations was as to the means of increasing the heating surface, and with that object he proposed to apply the fire "in copper spheres within the water." His mind was also running on economising power by working steam expansively, "being clear that the principle is sound."

Later, he wrote Watt that he had an application from a distiller at Bristol for an engine to raise 15,000 gallons of ale per hour 15 feet high; another for a coal mine in Wales, and two others for London distilleries. To add to his anxieties, one Humphry Gainsborough, a dissenting minister at Henley-on-Thames, had instituted proceedings against Watt for an alleged piracy of his invention! On this Boulton wrote to his partner, – "I have just received a summons to attend the Solicitor-General next week in opposition to Gainsborough, otherwise the solicitor will make his report. This is a disagreeable circumstance, particularly at this season, when you are absent. Joseph [Harrison] is in London, and idleness is in our engine-shop." There was therefore every reason why Watt should make haste to get married, and return to Soho as speedily as possible. On the 28th July, 1776, Watt wrote to apologise for his long absence, and to say that the event was to come off on the following Monday, after which he would set out immediately for Liverpool, where he proposed to meet Boulton, unless countermanded. He also intimated that he had got another order for an engine at Leadhills.[8] Arrived at Liverpool, a letter from Boulton met him, saying he had been under the necessity of proceeding to London.

> "Gainsborough," said he, "hath appointed to meet me at Holt's, his attorney, on Monday, when I shall say little besides learning his principles and invention. If we had a hundred wheels [engines] ready made, and a hundred small engines, like Bow engine, and twenty large ones executed, we could readily dispose of them. Therefore let us make hay while the sun shines, and gather our barns full before the dark cloud of age lowers upon us, and before any more Tubal Cains, Watts, Dr. Faustuses, or Gainsboroughs, arise with serpents like Moses's to devour all others ... As to your absence, say nothing about it. I will forgive it this time, provided you promise me never to marry again."[9]

Watt hastened back to Birmingham, and after settling his wife in her new home, proceeded with the execution of the orders for engines which had come in during his two months' absence. Mr. Wilby was impatient for the delivery of the Bow engine, and as soon as it was ready, which was early in September, the materials were forwarded to London with Joseph Harrison, to be fitted and set to work. Besides careful verbal instructions, Watt supplied Joseph with full particulars in writing of the measures he was to adopt in putting the engine together. Not a point in detail was neglected, and if any difficulty arose, Joseph was directed at once to communicate with him by letter. When the engine was set to work, it was found that the steam could not be kept up, on which Watt suggested that as it had been calculated to make only ten strokes per minute – that being enough to raise the quantity of water desired – the reason of the defect must be that, as it was going at fourteen or fifteen strokes the minute, it must be going too fast. He also pointed out that probably the piston was not quite good, and perhaps there was some steam-leak into the inner cylinder, or by the regulators into the condenser; or it was possible that the injection might spout too far up the horizontal steam-pipe and throw water into the inner nozzle. All these points Joseph must carefully look to.

On further trials the engine improved; still its performances did not come up to Watt's expectations, and there were consequently more directions from him as to the packing of the pistons and measures for the prevention of leaks. But to see that his suggestions were properly carried out, Watt himself went up to town in November, and had the machine put in complete working trim. His partner, however, could not spare him long, as other orders were coming in. "We have a positive order," wrote Boulton, "for an engine for Tingtang mine, and, from what I heard this day from Mr. Glover, we may soon expect other orders from Cornwall. Our plot begins to thicken apace, and if Mr. Wilkinson don't bustle a little, as well as ourselves, we shall not gather our harvest before sunset." ... "I hope to hear," he added, "that Joseph hath made a finish, for he is much wanted here ... I perceive we shall be hard pushed in engine-work; but I have no fears of being distanced when once the exact course or best track is determined on."[10] Joseph Harrison got quite knocked up and ill through his anxiety about the Bow engine, on which Boulton wrote Watt to send at once for Dr. Fordyce to attend him, "let the expense be what it will, until you think him safe landed."

A letter reached Soho from the Shadwell Waterworks Company relative to a pumping-engine, and Boulton asked Watt, while in town, to wait upon them on the subject; but he cautioned Watt that he "never knew a Committee but, in its corporate capacity, was both rogue and fool, and that the Shadwell Committee were rich rogues." Watt, by his own account, treated them very cavalierly. "Yesterday," said he, "I went again to Shadwell to meet the deputies of the Committee, and to examine their engines when going. We came to no terms further than what we wrote them before, which I confirmed, and offered moreover to keep the engine in order for one year. They modestly insisted that we should do so for the whole twenty-five years, which I firmly refused. They seemed to doubt the reality of the performances of the Bow engine; so I told them we did not solicit their orders and would wait patiently until they were convinced, – moreover, that while they had any doubts remaining, we would not undertake their business on any terms. I should not have been so sharp with them had they not begun with bullying me, *selon la mode de Londres*. But the course I took was not without its effect, for in proportion as they found I despised their job, they grew more civil. After parting with these heroes I went down to Stratford, where I found that the engine had gone very well. I caused it to be kept going all the afternoon, and this morning I new-heat the piston and kept it going till dinner time at about fifteen strokes per minute, with a steam of one inch or at most two inches strong, and the longer it went the better it grew … I propose that Joseph should not leave it for a few days, until both his health and that of the engine be confirmed. A relapse of the engine would ruin our reputation here, and indeed elsewhere."[11]

The Bow engine had, however, a serious relapse in the following spring, and it happened in this way: – Mr. Smeaton, the engineer, having heard of its success, which he doubted, requested Hadley, Boulton's agent, to go down with him to Stratford-le-Bow to witness its performances. He carefully examined the engine, and watched it while at work, and the conclusion he arrived at was, that it was a pretty engine, but much too complex for practical uses. On leaving the place Smeaton gave the engineman some money to drink, and he drank so much that next day he let the engine run quite wild, and it was thrown completely out of order. Mr. Wilby, the manager, was very wroth at the circumstance. He discharged the engineman and called upon Hadley to replace the valves, which had been broken, and make good the other damage that had been done to the engine. When the repairs were made, everything went satisfactorily as before.

Watt had many annoyances of this sort to encounter, and one of his greatest difficulties was the incapacity and unsteadiness of his workmen. Although the original Soho men were among the best of their kind, the increasing business of the firm necessarily led to the introduction of a large number of new hands, who represented merely the average workmen of the day. They were for the most part poor mechanics, very inexpert at working in metal, and greatly given to drink.[12]

In organising the works at Soho, Boulton and Watt found it necessary to carry division of labour to the farthest practicable point. There were no slide-lathes, planing-machines, or boring-tools, such as now render mechanical accuracy of construction almost a matter of certainty. Everything depended upon the individual mechanic's accuracy of hand and eye; and yet mechanics generally were then much less skilled than they are now. The way in which Boulton and Watt contrived partially to get over the difficulty was, to confine their workmen to special classes of work, and make them as expert in them as possible. By continued practice in handling the same tools and fabricating the same articles, they thus acquired great individual proficiency. "Without our tools and our workmen," said Watt, "very little could be done."

But when the men got well trained, the difficulty was to keep them. Foreign tempters were constantly trying to pick up Boulton and Watt's men, and induce them by offers of larger wages to take service abroad. The two fitters sent up to London to erect the Bow engine were strongly pressed to go out to Russia.[13] There were also French agents in England at the same time, who tried to induce certain of Boulton and Watt's men to go over to Paris and communicate the secret of making the new engines to M. Perrier, who had undertaken to pump water from the Seine for the supply of Paris. The German States also sent over emissaries with a like object, Baron Stein having been specially commissioned by his Government to master the secret of Watt's engine – to obtain working plans of it and bring away workmen capable of making it, – the first step taken being to obtain access to the engine-rooms by bribing the work men.

Besides the difficulties Boulton and Watt had to encounter in training and disciplining their own workmen, they had also to deal with the want of skill on the part of those to whom the working of their engines was intrusted after they had been delivered and fixed complete. They occasionally supplied trustworthy men of their own; but they could not educate mechanics fast enough, and needed all the best men for their own work. They were therefore compelled to rely on the average mechanics of the day, the greater part of whom were comparatively unskilled and knew nothing of the steam-engine. Hence such mishaps as those which befell the Bow engine, through the engineman getting drunk and reckless, as above described. To provide for this contingency Watt endeavoured to simplify the engine as much as possible, so as to bring its working and repair within the capacity of the average workman.

At a very early period, while experimenting at Kinneil, he had formed the idea of working steam expansively, and altered his model from time to time with that object. Boulton had taken up and continued the experiments at Soho, believing the principle to be sound and that great economy would attend its adoption. The early engines were accordingly made so that the steam might be cut off before the piston had made its full stroke, and expand within the cylinder, the heat outside it being maintained by the expedient of the steam-case. But it was shortly found that this method of working was beyond the capacity of the average engineman of that day, and it was consequently given up for a time.

> "We used to send out," said Watt to Robert Hart, "a cylinder of double the size
> wanted, and cut off the steam at half stroke. This was great saving of steam so
> long as the valves remained as at first; but when our men left her to the charge of
> the person who was to keep her, he began to make or try to make improvements,
> often by giving more steam. The engine did more work while the steam lasted,
> but the boiler could not keep up the demand. Then complaints came of want
> of steam, and we had to send a man down to see what was wrong. This was so
> expensive that we resolved to give up the expansion of the steam until we could

get men that could work it, as a few tons of coal per year was less expensive than having the work stopped. In some of the mines a few hours' stoppage was a serious matter, as it would cost the proprietor as much as 70*l.* per hour."[14]

The principle was not, however, abandoned. It was of great value and importance in an economical point of view, and was again taken up by Watt and embodied in a more complete form in a subsequent invention. Since his time, indeed, expansive working has been carried to a much farther extent than he probably ever dreamt of; and has more than realised the beneficial results which his sagacious insight so early anticipated.

NOTES

1   Boulton to Watt, 24th February, 1776. Boulton MSS.

2   Watt was himself occupied, during his temporary residence at Broseley, in devising improvements in the details of his engine. Boulton says – "I observe you are thinking of making an inverted cylinder. Pray how are you to counterbalance the descent of the piston and pump rods, which will be vast in weight? If by a counterweight you gain nothing. But if you can employ the power that arises from the descent of that vast weight to strain a spring that will repay its debts – if by it you can compress air in an iron cylinder which in its return will contribute to overcome the vis inertiae of the column of water to be raised, you will thereby get rid of that unmechanical tax, and very much improve the reciprocating engine." – Boulton to Watt, 24th February, 1776. Boulton MSS.

3   Boulton to Watt, 23rd April, 1776. Boulton MSS.

4   The arrangement between the partners is indicated by the following passage of Watt's letter to Boulton: –
"As you may have possibly mislaid my missive to you concerning the contract, I beg just to mention what I remember of the terms.

1. I to assign to you two-thirds of the property of the invention.

2. You to pay all expenses of the Act or others incurred before June, 1775 (the date of the Act), and also the expense of future experiments, which money is to be sunk without interest by you, being the consideration you pay for your share.

3. You to advance stock in trade bearing interest, but having no claim on me for any part of that, further than my intromissions; the stock itself to be your security and property.

4. I to draw one-third of the profits so soon as any arise from the business, after paying the workmen's wages and goods furnished, but abstract from the stock in trade, excepting the interest thereof, which is to be deducted before a balance is struck.

5. I to make drawings, give directions, and make surveys, the company paying the travelling expenses to either of us when upon engine business.

6. You to keep the books and balance them once a year.

7. A book to be kept wherein to be marked such transactions as are worthy of record, which, when signed by both, to have the force of the contract.

8. Neither of us to alienate our share without consent of the other, and if either of us by death or otherwise shall be incapacitated from acting for ourselves, the other of us to be the sole manager without contradiction or interference of heirs, executors, as signees, or others; but the books to be subject to their inspection, and the acting partner of us to be allowed a reasonable commission for extra trouble.

9. The contract to continue in force for twenty-five years, from the 1st of June, 1775, when the partnership commenced, notwithstanding the contract being of later date.

10. Our heirs, executors, and assignees, bound to observance.

11. In case of demise of both parties, our heirs, &c., to succeed in same manner, and if they all please, they may burn the contract.

If anything be very disagreeable in these terms, you will find me disposed to do everything reasonable for your satisfaction." – Boulton MSS.

5   Watt to Boulton, 3rd July, 1776. Boulton MSS.

6   Watt to Boulton, 8th July, 1776. Boulton MSS.

7   Boulton to Watt, 15th July, 1776. Boulton MSS.

8   During his Scotch visit, Watt spent much of his time in arranging his father's affairs, which had got into confusion. He was now seventy-five years old, and grown very infirm. "He is perfectly incapable," wrote his son, "of giving himself the least help, and the seeing him in such a situation has much hurt my spirits." – Watt to Boulton, 28th July, 1766. Boulton MSS.

9   Boulton to Watt (without date) 1776. Boulton MSS. In this letter, Boulton throws out a suggestion for Watt's consideration – "When," he says, "we have got our two-foot pumps up, I think it would be right to try our Soho engine with a steam strong enough to work the pumps with the axis in the centre of the beam, which will be almost 19lb. upon the inch."

10 Boulton to Watt, 3rd November, 1776. In the same letter Boulton informs
    Watt that Perrins, another fireman, had returned from Bedworth, and had
    not a stroke to do, the fittings for the second engine not having arrived.
    The first engine was working twenty-four hours a day, but the pit was so
    full of water that the owners feared they would before long be drowned
    out; and if the work was stopped, the loss would be far greater than the
    whole value of the engine. But the sales of coal, though large, were but
    "a small consideration in comparison with the starving to death of the
    poor ribbon-weavers of Coventry and a great part of Oxfordshire ...
    Coals are 9d. and 10d. per cwt., and 'tis said that they will be a shilling at
    Birmingham on Monday.

11 Watt to Boulton, 3rd December, 1776. Boulton MSS.

12 Fire-engines at work were objects of curiosity in those days, and had many
    visitors. The engineman at the York Buildings reminded those who went
    to see his engine that something was expected, placing over the entrance to
    the engine room the following distich: –
    "Whoever wants to see the engine here,
    Must give the engine-man a drop of beer."

13 "Mr. White told me this morning as a great secret," wrote Boulton's
    London agent, "that he has reason to believe that Carless and Webb were
    going beyond sea, for Carless had told him he had 1000l. offered for six
    years, and he overheard Webb say that he was ready at an hour's warning."
    Carless and Webb were immediately ordered back to Soho, and the firm
    obtained warrants for the apprehension of the men as well as the person
    who had bribed them, if they attempted to abscond "even theough," said
    Watt to Boulton, "Carless be a drunken and comparatively useless fellow."
    Later he wrote, "I think there is no risk of Webb's leaving us soon, and he
    offers to re-engage. Carless has been working very diligently this week, and
    is well on with his nozzle patterns. I mentioned to William the story of Sir
    John Fielding's warrant, to show him that we are determined to act with
    spirit in case of interlopers." – Watt to Boulton, May 3, 1777.

14 Robert Hart's 'Reminiscences of James Watt,' cited above.

XIII

Watt in Cornwall – Introduction of his Pumping-engines

The Cornish miners continued baffled by their attempts to get rid of the water which hindered the working of their mines. The Newcomen engines had been taxed to the utmost, but were unable to send them deeper into the ground, and they were accordingly ready to welcome any invention that promised to relieve them of their difficulty. Among the various new contrivances for pumping water, that of Watt seemed to offer the greatest advantages; and if what was alleged of it proved true – that it was of greater power than the Newcomen engine, while its consumption of fuel was much less, – then it could not fail to prove of the greatest advantage to Cornish industry.

Long before Watt's arrival in Birmingham, the Cornishmen had been in correspondence with Boulton, making inquiries about the new Scotch invention, of which they had heard; and Dr. Small, in his letters to Watt, repeatedly urged him to perfect his engine, with a view to its being employed in the drainage of the Cornish mines. Now that the engine was at work in several places, Boulton invited his correspondents in Cornwall to inquire as to its performances, at Soho, or Bedworth, or Bow, or any other place where it had been erected. The result of the inquiry and inspection was satisfactory, and several orders for engines for Cornwall were received at Soho by the end of 1776. The two first that were ready for erection were those ordered for Wheal Busy, near Chacewater, and for Tingtang, near Redruth. The materials for the former were shipped by the middle of 1777; and, as much would necessarily depend upon the successful working of the first engines put up in Cornwall, Watt himself went to superintend their erection in person.

Watt reached his destination after a long and tedious journey over bad roads. He rode by stage as far as Exeter, and posted the rest of the way.

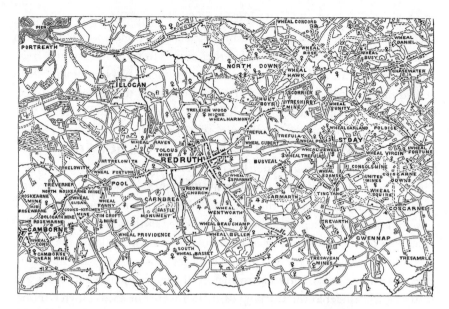

Map of United Mines District

At Chacewater he found himself in the midst of perhaps the richest mining district in the world. From thence to Camborne, which lies to the west, and Gwennap to the south, is a constant succession of mines. The earth has been burrowed in all directions for many miles in search of ore, principally copper – the surface presenting an unnaturally blasted and scarified appearance by reason of the "deads" or refuse run out in heaps from the mine-heads. Engine-houses and chimneys are the most prominent features in the landscape, and dot the horizon as far as the eye can reach.

When Watt arrived at Chacewater he found the materials for the Wheal Busy engine had come to hand, and that some progress had been made with its erection. The materials for the Tingtang engine, however, had not yet been received from Soho, and the owners of the mine were becoming very impatient for it. Watt wrote to his partner urging despatch, otherwise the engine might be thrown on their hands, especially if the Chacewater engine, now nearly ready for work, did not give satisfaction. From Watt's account, it would appear that the Cornish mines were in a very bad way. "The Tingtang people," he said, "are now fairly put out by water, and the works are quite at a stand." The other mines in the neighbourhood were in no better plight. The pumping-engines could not keep down the water. "Poldice has grown worse than Wheal Virgin was: they have sunk 400*l*. a month for some months past, and

700*l.* the last month; they will probably soon give up. North Downs seems to be our next card."[1] The owners of the Wheal Virgin mine, though drowned out, like many others, could not bring their minds to try Watt's engine. They had no faith in it, and stuck by the old atmospheric of Newcomen. They accordingly erected an additional engine of this kind to enable them to go about eight fathoms deeper, "and they have bought," wrote Watt, "an old boiler of monstrous size at the Briggin, which they have offered 50*l.* to get carried to its place."

At Chacewater Watt first met Jonathan Hornblower, son of the Joseph Hornblower who had come into Cornwall from Staffordshire, some fifty years before, to erect one of the early Newcomen engines. The son had followed in his father's steps, and become celebrated in the Chacewater district as an engineer. It was natural that he should regard with jealousy the patentees of the new engine; for if it proved a success, his vocation as a maker of atmospheric engines would be at an end. Watt thus referred to him in a letter to Boulton: "Hornblower seems a very pleasant sort of old Presbyterian: he carries himself very fair, though I hear that he is an unbelieving Thomas." His unbelief strongly showed itself on the starting of the Wheal Busy engine shortly after, when he exclaimed, "Pshaw! it's but a bauble: I wouldn't give twopence halfpenny for her." There were others beside Hornblower who disliked and resented what they regarded as the intrusion of Boulton and Watt in their district, and indeed never became wholly reconciled to the new engine, though they were compelled to admit the inefficiency of the old one. Among these was old Bonze, the engineer, a very clever mechanic, who positively refused to undertake the erection of the proposed new engine at Wheal Union if Boulton and Watt were to be in any way concerned with it. But the mine-owners had to study their own interest rather than the humour of their former engineers, and Watt secured the order for the Wheal Union engine. Several other orders were promised, conditional on the performances of the Wheal Busy engine proving satisfactory. "Ale and Cakes,"[2] wrote Watt, "must wait the result of Chacewater: several new engines will be erected next year, for almost all the old mines are exhausted, or have got to the full power of the present engines, which are clumsy and nasty, the houses cracked, and everything dropping with water from their cisterns."[3]

Watt liked the people as little as he did their engines. He thought them ungenerous, jealous, and treacherous. "Certainly," said he, "they have the most ungracious manners of any people I have ever yet been amongst." At the first monthly meeting of the Wheal Virgin adventurers, which he attended, he found a few gentlemen, but "the bulk of them would not be disgraced by being classed with Wednesbury colliers." What annoyed him most was, that the miners invented and propagated all sorts of rumours to his preju-dice. "We have been accused," said he, "of working without leather upon our buckets, and making holes in the clacks in order to deceive strangers ... I choose to keep out of their company, as every word spoken by me would be bandied about and misrepresented. I have already been accused of mak-ing several speeches at Wheal Virgin, where, to the best of my memory, I have only talked about eating, drinking, and the weather. The greater part of the adventurers at Wheal Virgin are a mean dirty pack, preying upon one another, and striving who shall impose most upon the mine."[4] Watt was of too sensitive and shrinking a nature to feel himself at home amongst such people. Besides, he was disposed to be peevish and irritable, easily cast down, and ready to anticipate the worst. It had been the same with him when employed amongst the rough labourers on the Monkland Canal, where he had declared himself as ready to face a loaded cannon as to encounter the altercations of bargain-making. But Watt must needs reconcile himself to his post as he best could; for none but himself could see to the proper erection of the Wheal Busy engine and get it set to work with any chance of success. Meanwhile, the native engineers were stimulated by his presence, and by the reputed power of the new engine, to exert themselves in improving the old one. Bonze was especially active in contriving new boilers and new arrangements, by which be promised to outstrip all that Watt could possibly accomplish.[5]

A letter from Mrs. Watt to Mrs. Boulton, dated Chacewater, September 1st, 1777, throws a little light on Watt's private life during his stay in Cornwall. She describes the difficulty they had in obtaining accommodation on their arrival, "no such thing as a house or lodging to be had for any money within some miles of the place where the engine was to be erected;" hence they had been glad to accept of the hospitality of Mr. Wilson, the superintendent of the mine.

> I scarcely knew what to say to you of the country. The spot we are at is the most disagreeable in the whole county. The face of the earth is broken up in ten thousand heaps of rubbish, and there is scarce a tree to be seen. But don't think that all Cornwall is like Chacewater. I have been at some places that are very pleasant, nay beautiful. The sea-coast to me is charming, but not easy to be got at. In some cases my poor husband has been obliged to mount me behind him to go to some of the places we have been at. I assure you I was not a little perplexed at first to be set on a great tall horse with a high pillion. At one of our jaunts we wero only charged twopence a piece for our dinner. You may guess

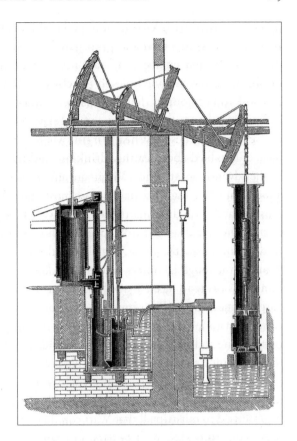

Watt's single-acting
Pumping-engine for mines

what our fare would be from the cost of it; but I assure you I never ate a dinner with more relish in my life, nor was I ever happier at a feast, than I was that day at Portreath ... One thing I *must* tell you of is, to take care Mr. Boulton's principles are well fixed before you trust him here. Poor Mr. Watt is turned Anabaptist, and duly attends their meeting; he is, indeed, and goes to chapel most devoutly.

At last the Chacewater engine was finished and ready for work. Great curiosity was felt about its performances, and mining men and engineers came from all quarters to see it start. "All the world are agape," said Watt, "to see what it can do." It would not have displeased some of the spectators if it had failed. But to their astonishment it succeeded. At starting, it made eleven eight-feet strokes per minute; and it worked with greater power, went more steadily, and "forked" more water than any of the ordinary engines, with only about one-third the consumption of coal. "We have had many spectators," wrote Watt, "and several have already become converts. I understand all the west country captains are to be here to-morrow to see the prodigy."[6] Even Bonze, his rival, called to see it, and promised not only to read his recantation as soon as convinced but never to touch a common engine again. "The velocity, violence, magnitude, and horrible noise of the engine," Watt added, "give universal satisfaction to all beholders, believers or not. I have once or twice trimmed the engine to end its stroke gently, and to make less noise; but Mr. Wilson cannot sleep without it seems quite furious, so I have left it to the engine-men; and, by the by, the noise seems to convey great ideas of its power to the ignorant, who seem to be no more taken with modest merit in an engine than in a man." In a later letter he wrote, "The voice of the country seems to be at present in our favour; and I hope will be much more so when the engine gets on its whole load, which will be by Tuesday next. So soon as that is done, I shall set out for home."

A number of orders for engines bad come in at Soho during Watt's absence; and it became necessary for him to return there as speedily as possible, to prepare the plans and drawings, and put the work in hand. There was no person yet attached to the concern who was capable of relieving him of this part of his duties; while Boulton was fully occupied with conducting the commercial part of the business. By the end of autumn he was again at home; and for a week after his return he kept so close to his desk in his house on Harper's Hill, that he could not even find time enough to go out to Soho and see what had been doing in his absence. At length he felt so exhausted by the brain-work and confinement that he wrote to his partner, "a very little more of this hurrying and vexation will knock me up altogether." To add to his troubles, letters arrived from Tingtang, urging his return to Cornwall, to erect the engine, the materials for which had at last arrived. "I fancy," said Watt, "that I must be cut in pieces, and a portion sent to every tribe in Israel."

After four month's labour of this sort, during which seven out of the ten engines then in hand were finished and erected, and the others well advanced, Watt again set out for Cornwall, which he reached by the beginning of June, 1778. He took up his residence at Redruth, as being more convenient for Tingtang than Chacewater, hiring a house at Plengwarry, a hamlet on the outskirts of the town. Redruth is the capital of the mining districts of Camborne, Redruth, and Gwennap. It is an ancient town, consisting for the most part of a long street, which runs down one hill and up another.

All round it the country seems to have been disembowelled; and heaps of scoriæ, "deads," rubbish, and granite blocks cover the surface. The view from the lofty eminence of Carn Brea, a little to the south of Redruth, strik-

Redruth High Street
(by R. P. Leitch)

ingly shows the scarified and apparently blasted character of the district, and
affords a prospect the like of which is rarely to be seen.

On making inquiry as to the materials which had arrived during his
absence, Watt was much mortified to find that the Soho workmen had made
many mistakes. "Forbes's eduction-pipe," he wrote, "is a most vile job, and
full of holes. The cylinder they have cast for Chacewater is still worse, for it
will hardly do at all. The Soho people have sent here Chacewater eduction-
pipe instead of Wheal Union; and the gudgeon pipe has not arrived with the
nozzles. These repeated disappointments," said he, "will undoubtedly ruin
our credit in the country; and I cannot stay here to bear the shame of such
failures of promise."

Watt had a hard time of it while in Cornwall, what with riding and
walking from mine to mine, listening to complaints of delay in the arrival
of the engines from Soho, and detecting and remedying the blunders and
bad workmanship of his mechanics. Added to which, everybody was low-

spirited and almost in despair at the bad times, – ores falling in price, mines filled with water, engine-men standing idle, and adventurers bemoaning their losses. Another source of anxiety was the serious pecuniary embarrassments in which the Soho firm had become involved. Boulton had so many concerns going that a vast capital was required for the purpose of meeting current engagements; and the engine business, instead of relieving him, had hitherto only proved a source of additional outlay, and increased his difficulties at a time of general commercial depression. He wrote Watt, urging him to send remittances for the Cornish engines; but the materials, though partly delivered, were not erected; and the miners demurred to paying on account until they were fixed complete and at work. Boulton then suggested to Watt that he should try to obtain an advance from the Truro bankers, on security of the engine materials. "No," replied Watt, "that cannot be done, as the knowledge of our difficulties would damage our position in Cornwall, and hurt our credit. Besides," said he, "no one can be more cautious than a Cornish banker; and the principal of the firm you name is himself exceedingly distressed for money."[7] Nor was there the least chance, in Watt's opinion, even if they had the money to advance, of their accepting any security that Boulton and Watt had to offer. "Such is the nature of the people here," said he, "and so little faith have they in our engine, that very few of them believe it to be materially better than the ordinary one, and so far as I can judge, no one I have conversed with would advance us 500*l.* on a mortgage of it."[8]

All that Watt could do was to recommend that the evil day should be staved off as long as possible, or at all events until the large engines he was then erecting were at work, when he believed their performances would effect a complete change in the views of the adventurers. The only suggestion he could offer was to invite John Wilkinson, or some other moneyed man, to join them as partner and relieve them of their difficulties; for "rather than founder at sea," said he, "we had better run ashore."[9] Meanwhile, he urged Boulton to apply the pruning-knife and cut down expenses, assuring him that he himself was practising all the frugality in his power. But as Watt's personal expenses at the time did not amount to 2*l.* a week, it is clear that any savings he could effect, however justifiable and laudable, were but a drop in the ocean compared with the liabilities to be met, and which must be provided without delay to avoid insolvency and ruin.

Fothergill, Boulton's other partner, was even more desponding than Watt. When Boulton left Soho on his journeys to raise ways and means, Fothergill pursued him with dolorous letters, telling him of mails that had arrived without remittances, of bills that must be met, of wages that must be paid on Saturday night, and of the impending bankruptcy of the firm, which he again and again declared to be "inevitable." "Better stop payment at once," said he, "call our creditors together, and face the worst, than go on in this neck-and-neck race with ruin." Boulton would hurry back to Soho, to quiet Fothergill, and keep the concern going; on which another series of letters would pour in upon him from Mr. Matthews, the London financial agent, pressing for remittances, and reporting the increasingly gloomy and desperate state of affairs.

Boulton himself was, as usual, equal to the occasion. His courage and determination rose in proportion to the difficulties to be overcome. He was borne up by his invincible hope, by his unswerving purpose, and above all by his unshaken belief in the commercial value of the condensing engine. If they could only weather the storm until its working powers could be fully demonstrated, all would yet be well.

In illustration of his hopefulness, we may mention that in the midst of his troubles a fire took place in the engine-room at Soho, which was happily extinguished, but not before it had destroyed the roof and done serious damage to the engine, which was brought to a stand-still. Boulton had long been desirous of rebuilding the engine-house in a proper manner, but had been hindered by Watt, who was satisfied with alterations merely sufficient to accommodate the place to the changes made from time to time in the engine which he called "Beelzebub."[10] On hearing of the damage done by the fire, Boulton, instead of lamenting over it, exclaimed, "*Now* I shall be able at last to have the engine-house built as it should be."

After many negotiations, Boulton at length succeeded in raising a sum of 7000*l.* by granting a Mr. Wiss security for the payment of an annuity, while the London bankers, Lowe, Vere, and Williams, allowed an advance of 14,000*l.* on security of a mortgage granted by Boulton and Watt on the royalties derived from the engine patent, and of all their rights and privileges therein. Though the credit of the house was thus saved, the liabilities of Boulton and his partners continued to press heavily upon them for a long time to come. Meanwhile, however, a gleam of light came from Cornwall. Watt sent the good news to Soho that "both Chacewater and Tingtang engines go on exceedingly well, and give great satisfaction. Chacewater goes 14 strokes of 9 foot long per minute, and burns about 128 bushels per 24 hours. The water has sunk 12 fathoms in the mine, and the engine will fork [i.e. pump out] the first lift this night. No cross nor accident of any note has happened, except the bursting of a pump at Tingtang, which was soon repaired." Four days later Watt wrote, "The engines are both going very well, and Chacewater has got the water down 18½ fathoms; but after this depth it must make slower progress, as a very large house of water begins there, and the feeders grow stronger as we go deeper."[11]

Watt looked upon the Chacewater trial as the *experimentum crucis*, and continued to keep his partner duly informed of every circumstance connected with it. "They say," he wrote, "that if the new engine can fork the water from Chacewater, it can fork anything, as that is the heaviest to fork in the whole county." On the 15th of August he wrote, "Chacewater is now down to 10 fathoms of the second lift, and works steady and well; it sinks 9 feet per day. Chacewater people in high spirits: Captain Mayor furiously in love with the engine." On the 29th he wrote again, "Chacewater engine is our capital card, for should it succeed in forking this mine all doubts will then be removed." The adventurers of the great Poldice mine watched the operations at Chacewater with much interest. Two common engines, pumping night and day for months, had failed to clear their mine of water; and now they thought of ordering one of the new engines to take their place; "but all this," said Watt, "depends on the success of Chacewater, which God protect: it is now down 31½ fathoms, and will be in fork of this lift to-morrow, when it is to be put down three fathoms lower, and fixed there." On the 17th he wrote, "I have been at Chacewater to-day, where they are in fork of the second lift 34½ fathoms. The great connexion-rod still unbalanced. The engine went yesterday 14 strokes per minute. Tomorrow I go to Wheal Union, and on Saturday to Truro, to meet Poldice adventurers … By attending to the business of this county alone," said he, "we may at least live comfortably; for I cannot suppose that less than twelve engines will be wanted in two or three years, but after that very few more, as these will be sufficient to get ore enough; though you cannot reckon the average profits to us at above 200*l.* per engine."

When Boulton and Watt first started the manufacture of steam-engines, they were mainly concerned to get orders, and were not very particular as to the terms on which they were obtained. But when the orders increased, and the merits of the invention gradually became recognised, they found it necessary to require preliminary agreements to be entered into as to the terms on which the patent was to he used. It occurred to them, that as one of its principal merits consisted in the saving of fuel, it would be a fair arrangement to take one-third of the value of such saving by way of royalty, leaving the owners of the engines to take the benefit of the remaining two- thirds. Nothing could be fairer than the spirit of this arrangement, which, it will be seen, was of even more advantage to the owners of the engines than to the patentees themselves. The first Cornish engines were, however, erected without any condition as to terms; and it was only after they had proved their power by "forking" the water, and sending the miners twenty fathoms deeper into the ground, that the question of terms was raised. Watt proposed that agreements should be entered into on the basis above indicated. But the Cornishmen did not see the use of agreements. They had paid for the engines, which were theirs, and Boulton and Watt could not take them away. Here was the beginning of a long series of altercations, which ended only with the patent right itself. The miners could not do without the engine. It was admitted to be of immense value to them, rendering many of their mines workable that would otherwise have been valueless. But why should they have to pay for the use of such an invention? This was what they never could clearly understand.

To prevent misunderstandings in future, Watt wrote to Boulton, recommending that no further orders for engines should be taken unless the terms for using them were definitely settled beforehand. "You must excuse me," he added, "when I tell you that, for my part, I will not put pen to paper [i.e. make the requisite drawings] on a new subject until that is done. Until an engine is ordered, our power is greater than that of the Lord Chancellor; as I believe even he cannot compel us to make it unless we choose. Let our terms be moderate, and, if possible, consolidated into money *à priori*, and it is certain we shall get *some* money, enough to keep us out of jail, in continual apprehension of which I live at present."[12]

To meet the case, a form of agreement was drawn up and required to be executed before any future engine was commenced. It usually provided that an engine of certain given dimensions and power was to be erected at the expense of the owners of the mine; and that the patentees were to take as their recompense for the use of their invention, one-third of the value of the fuel saved by it compared with the consumption of the ordinary engine. It came to be understood that the saving of fuel was to be estimated according to the number of strokes made. To ascertain this, Watt contrived an ingenious piece of clockwork, termed the Counter, which, being attached to the main beam, accurately marked and registered, under lock and key, the number of its vibrations. Thus the work done was calculated, and the comparative saving of fuel was ascertained.

Though the Cornish miners had been full of doubts as to the successful working of Watt's engine, they could not dispute the evidence of their senses after it had been erected and was fairly at work. There it was, "forking water" as never engine before had been known to "fork." It had completely mastered the water at Wheal Busy; and if it could send the workmen down that mine, it could in like manner send them down elsewhere. Wheal Virgin was on the point of stopping work, in which case some two thousand persons would be thrown out of bread. Bonze's new atmospheric engine had proved a failure, and the mine continued flooded. It had also failed at Poldice, which was drowned out. "Notwithstanding the violence and prejudice against us," wrote Watt, "nothing can save the mines but our engines … *Even the infidels of Dalcoath* are now obliquely inquiring after our terms! Cook's Kitchen, which communicates with it, has been drowned out some time." Watt, accordingly, had many applications about engines; and on that account he entreated his partner to come to his help. He continued to hate all negotiating about terms, and it did not seem as if he would ever learn to like it. He had neither the patience to endure, nor the business tact to conduct a negotiation. He wanted confidence in himself, and did not feel equal to make a bargain. He would almost as soon have wrestled with the Cornish miners as higgled with them. They were shrewd, practical men, rough in manner and speech, yet honest withal;[13] but Watt would not encounter them when he could avoid it. Hence his repeated calls to Boulton to come and help him. Writing to him about the proposed Wheal Virgin engine, be said, "Before I make any bargain with these people, I must have you here." A few days after, when communicating the probability of obtaining an order for the Poldice engine, he wrote, – "I wish you would dispose yourself for a journey here, and strike while this iron is hot." A fortnight later he said, "Poldice people are now welding hot, and must not be suffered to cool. They are exceedingly impatient, as they lose 150*l.* a month until our engine is going … I hope this will find you ready to come away. At Redruth, inquire for Plengwarry Green, where you will find me."

At length, about the beginning of October, 1778, Boulton contrived to make his long-promised journey into Cornwall.[14] He went round among the mines, and had many friendly conferences with the managers. He found the engine had grown in public favour, and that the impression prevailed throughout the mining districts that it would before long become generally adopted. Encouraged by his London financial agent, he took steps to turn this favourable impression to account.[15] Before he left Cornwall, where he remained until the end of the year, he succeeded in borrowing a sum of 2000*l.* from Elliot and Praed, the Truro bankers, on security of the engines erected in the county; and the money was at once forwarded to the London agents for the relief of the Birmingham firm. He also succeeded in getting the terms definitely arranged for the use of several of the more important engines erected and at work. It was agreed that 700*l.* a year should be paid as royalty in respect of the Chacewater engine, – an arrangement even more advantageous to the owners of the mine than to the patentees, as it was understood that the saving of coals amounted to upwards of 2400*l.* a year. Other agreements were entered into for the use of the engines erected at Wheal Union and Tingtang, which brought in about 400*l.* per annum more, so that the harvest of profits seemed at length fairly begun.

Watt remained at Cornwall for another month, plodding at Poldice and Wheal Virgin engines, and returned to Birmingham early in January, 1779. Though the pumping-engine had thus far proved remarkably successful, and accomplished all that Watt had promised, he was in no better spirits than before. "Though we have, in general, succeeded in our undertak-ings," he wrote Dr. Black, "yet that success has, from various unavoidable circumstances, produced small profits to us; the struggles we have had with natural difficulties, and with the ignorance, prejudices, and villanies of mankind, have been very great, but I hope are now nearly come to an end, or vanquished."[16] His difficulties were not, however, nearly at an end, as the heavy liabilities of the firm had still to be met. More money had to be borrowed; and Watt continued to groan under his intolerable burden. "The thought of the debt to Lowe, Vere, and Co.," he wrote to his partner, "lies too heavy on my mind to leave me the proper employment of my faculties in the prosecution of our business; and, besides, common honesty will prevent me from loading the scheme with debts which might be more than it could pay."[17]

A more hopeful man would have borne up under these difficulties; for the reputation of the engine was increasing, and orders were coming in from various quarters. Soho was full of work; and, provided their credit could be maintained, it was clear that the undertaking on which the firm had entered could not fail to prove remunerative. Watt could not see this, but his partner did; and Boulton accordingly strained every nerve to keep up the character of the concern. While Watt was urging upon him to curtail the business, Boulton sought in all ways to extend it. He sent accounts of his marvellous engines abroad, and orders for them came in from France[18] and Holland. Watt was more alarmed than gratified by the foreign orders, fearing that the engine would be copied and extensively manufactured abroad, where patents had not yet been secured. He did not see that the best protection of all was in the superiority of his tools and mechanics, enabling first-class work to be turned out, – important advantages, in which the Soho firm had the start of the world. It is true his mechanics were liable to be bribed, and foreigners were constantly haunting Soho for the purpose of worming out the secrets of the manufacture, and decoying away the best men. Against this every precaution was taken, though sometimes in vain. Two Prussian engineers came over from Berlin in 1779, to whom Watt showed every attention; after which, in his absence, they got into the engine-room, and carefully examined all the details of "Old Bess," making notes. When Watt returned, he was in high dudgeon, and wrote to his partner that he "could not help it unless by discountenancing every foreigner who does not come avowedly to have an engine."[19]

Their principal reliance, however, was necessarily on home orders, and these came in satisfactorily. Eight more engines were wanted for Cornwall, those already at work continuing to give satisfaction. Inquiries were also made about pumping engines for collieries in different parts of England. But where coals were cheap, and the saving of fuel was of less consequence, the patentees were not solicitous for orders unless the purchasers would fix a fair sum for the patent right, or rate the coals used at a price that would be remunerative in proportion to the savings effected. The orders were indeed becoming so numerous, that the firm, beginning to feel their power, themselves fixed the annual royalty, though it was not always so easy to get it paid.

The working power of Watt himself was but limited. He still continued to suffer from intense headaches; and, as all the drawings of new engines were made by his own hands, it was necessary in some measure to limit the amount of work undertaken. "I beg," he wrote to his partner in May, 1779, relative to proposals made for two new engines, "that you will not undertake to do anything for them before Christmas. It is, in fact, impossible, at least on my part; I am quite crushed." But he was not always so dispirited, for in the following month we find him writing Boulton an exultant letter, announcing orders for three new engines from Cornwall.[20]

Watt continued for some time longer to suffer great annoyance from the shortcomings of his workmen. He was himself most particular in giving his instructions, verbally, in writing, and in drawings. When he sent a workman to erect an engine, he sent with him a carefully drawn up detail of the step by step proceedings he was to adopt in fitting the parts together. Where there was a difficulty, and likely to be a hitch, he added a pen and ink drawing, rapid but graphic, and pointed out how the difficulty was to he avoided. It was not so easy, however, to find workmen capable of intelligently fitting together the parts of a machine so complicated and of so novel a construction. Moreover, the first engines were in a great measure experimental, and to have erected them perfectly, and provided by anticipation for their various defects, would have argued a knowledge of the principles of their construction almost as complete as that of Watt himself. He was not sufficiently disposed to make allowances for the workmen's want of knowledge and want of experience, and his letters were accordingly full of complaints of their shortcomings. He was especially annoyed with the mistakes of a foreman, named Hall, who had sent the wrong articles to Cornwall, and he urged Boulton to dismiss him at once. But Boulton knew better. Though Watt understood engines, he did not so well understand men. Had Boulton dismissed such as Hall because they made mistakes, the shop would soon have been empty. The men were as yet but at school, learning experience, and Boulton knew that in course of time they would acquire dexterity. He was ready to make allowance for their imperfections, but at the same time he did not abate in his endeavours to find out and engage the best hands, wherever they were to be found – in Wales, in Cornwall, or in Scotland. He therefore kept on Hall, notwithstanding Watt's protest, and the latter submitted.[21]

Watt was equally wroth with the enginemen at Bedworth. "I beg and expect," he wrote Boulton, "that so soon as everything is done to that engine, you will instantly proceed to trial before creditable witnesses, and if possible have the whole brood of these enginemen displaced, if any others can be procured; for nothing but slovenliness, if not malice, is to be expected of them." It must, however, be acknowledged that the Bedworth engine was at first very imperfect, having been made of bad iron, in consequence of which it frequently broke down. In Cornwall the men were no better. Dudley, Watt's erector at Wheal Chance and Hallamanin, was pronounced incapable and a blunderer. "If something be not very bad in London, I wish you would employ Hadley to finish those engines, and send Joseph here to receive his instructions and proceed to Cornwall, otherwise Dudley will ruin us."[22]

The trusty "Joseph" was accordingly despatched to Cornwall to look after Dudley and remedy the defects in Wheal Chance and Hallamanin engines; but when Watt arrived at Chacewater shortly after, he found that Joseph, too, had proved faithless. He wrote to Boulton, "Joseph has pursued his old practice of drinking in the neighbourhood in a scandalous manner, until the very enginemen turned him into ridicule. I have not heard how he behaved in the west; but that he gave the ale there a bad character."[23] Notwithstanding, however, his love of strong potations, Joseph was a first-rate workman. Two days later, Watt wrote, "Though Joseph has attended to his drinking, he has done much good at his leisure hours, and has certainly prevented much mischief at Hallamanin and some at Wheal Union. He has had some hard and long jobs, and consequently merits some indulgence for his foibles." By the end of the month "Joseph had conquered Hallamanin engine, all but the boiler," but Watt added, "His indulgence has brought on a slight fit of the jaundice, and as soon as the engine is finished, he must be sent home."[24]

By this time Watt had called to his aid two other skilled workmen, Law and Murdock, who arrived in Cornwall in the beginning of September, 1779. In Watt's letters we find frequent allusions to Murdock. Wherever any work had to be done requiring more than ordinary attention, Watt specially directed that "William" should he put to it. "Let William be sent for from Bedworth," he wrote from Cornwall in 1778, " to set the patterns for nozzles quite right for Poldice." Boulton wished to send him into Scotland to erect the engine at Wenlockhead, but Watt would not hear of it. "William" was the only man he could trust with the nozzles. Then William was sent to London to take the charge of Chelsea engine; next to Bedworth, to see to the completion of the repairs previous to the final trial; then to Birmingham again to attend to some further special instructions of Watt; and now we find him in Cornwall, to take charge of the principal engines erecting there.

William Murdock was not only a most excellent and steady workman, but a man of eminent mechanical genius. He was the first maker of a model locomotive in this country; he was the introducer of lighting by gas, and the inventor of many valuable parts of the working steam-engine, hereafter to be described. His father was a millwright and miller, at Bellow Mill, near Old Cumnock, in Ayrshire, and was much esteemed for his probity and industry, as well as for his mechanical skill. He was the inventor of bevelled cast-iron gear for mills, and his son was proud to exhibit, on the lawn in front of his house at Sycamore Hill, Handsworth, a piece of the first work of the kind executed in Britain. It was cast for him at Carron Ironworks, after the pattern furnished by him, in 1766. William was born in 1754, and brought up to his father's trade. On arriving at manhood, he became desirous of obtaining a larger experience of mill-work and mechanics than he could acquire in his father's little mill. Hearing of the fame of Boulton and Watt, and the success of their new engine, he determined to travel south, and seek for a job at Soho. Many Scotchmen were accustomed to call there on the same errand, probably relying on the known clanship of their countrymen, and thinking that they would find a friend and advocate in Watt. But strange to say, Watt did not think Scotchmnen capable of becoming first-class mechanics.[25]

When Murdock called at Soho, in the year 1777, to ask for a job, Watt was from home, but he saw Boulton, who was usually accessible to callers of every rank. In answer to Murdock's inquiry whether he could have a job, Boulton replied that work was rather slack with them then, and that every place was filled up. During the brief conversation that ensued, the blate young Scotchman, like most country lads in the presence of strangers, had some difficulty in knowing what to do with his hands, and unconsciously kept twirling his hat with them. Boulton's attention was directed to the twirling hat, which seemed to be of a peculiar make. It was not a felt hat, nor a cloth hat, nor a glazed hat; but it seemed to be painted, and composed of some unnusual material. "That seems to be a curious sort of hat," said Boulton, looking at it more closely; "why, what is it made of?" "Timmer, sir," said Murdock, modestly. "Timmer! Do you mean to say that it is made of wood ?" "Yes, sir." "Pray, *how* was it made?" "I turned it mysel', sir, in a bit lathey of my own making." Boulton looked at the young man again. He had risen a hundred degrees in his estimation. He was tall, good-looking, and of open and ingenuous countenance; and that he had been able to turn a wooden hat for himself in a lathe of his own making was proof enough that he was a mechanic of no mean skill. "You may call again, my man," said Boulton. "Thank you, sir," said Murdock, giving his hat a final twirl.

When Murdock called again, he was at once put upon a trial job, after which he was entered as a regular hand. We learn from Boulton's memorandum-book that he was engaged for two years, at 15s. a week when at home, 17s. when from home, and 18s. when in London. Boulton's engagement of Murdock was amply justified by the result. Beginning as a common mechanic, he applied himself diligently and conscientiously to his work, and became trusted. More responsible duties were confided to him, and he strove to perform them to the best of his power. His industry and his skilfulness soon marked him for promotion, and he rose from grade to grade until he became Boulton and Watt's most trusted co-worker and adviser in all their mechanical undertakings of importance.

When Murdock went into Cornwall to take charge of the engines, he gave himself no rest until he had conquered their defects and put them in thorough working order. He devoted himself to his duties with a zeal and ability that completely won Watt's heart. He was so filled with his work, that when he had an important job in hand, he could scarcely sleep at nights for thinking of it. When the engine at Wheal Union was ready for starting, the people of the house at Redruth, in which Murdock lodged, were greatly disturbed one night by a strange noise in his room. Several heavy blows on the floor made them start from their beds, thinking the house was coming down. They rushed to Murdock's room, and there was he in his shirt, heaving away at the bedpost in his sleep, calling out, "Now she goes, lads! now she goes."

Murdock was not less successful in making his way with the Cornishmen with whom he was brought into daily contact; indeed, he fought his way to their affections. One day at Chacewater, some half-dozen of the mining captains came into the engine-room and began bullying him. This he could not stand, and adopted a bold expedient. He locked the door, and said, "Now, then, you shall not leave this place until I have it fairly out with you." He selected the biggest, and put himself in a fighting attitude. The Cornishmen love fair play, and while the two engaged in battle, the others, without, interfering, looked on. The contest was soon over; for Murdock was a tall, powerful fellow, and speedily vanquished his opponent. The others, seeing the kind of man they had to deal with, made overtures of reconciliation; and they shook hands all round, and parted the best of friends.[26]

Watt continued to have his differences and altercations with the Cornishmen, but he had no such way of settling them. Indeed, he was almost helpless when he came in contact with rough men of business. Most of the mines were then paying very badly, and the adventurers raised all sorts of objections to making the stipulated payment of the engine dues. Under such circumstances, altercations with them took place for which Watt was altogether unprepared. He was under the apprehension that they were constantly laying their heads together for the purpose of taking advantage of him and his partner. He never looked on the bright side of things, but always on the darkest. "The rascality of mankind," said he to Dr. Black, "is almost beyond belief." Though his views of science were large, his views of men were narrow. Much of this may have been the result of his recluse habits and closet life, as well as of his constant ill-health. With his racking headaches, it was indeed difficult for him to be cheerful. But no one could be more conscious of his own defects – of his want of tact, his want of business qualities, and his want of temper – than he was himself. He knew his besetting infirmities, from which even the best and wisest are not exempt. His greatness was mingled with imperfections, and his strength with weakness, else had he been more than human. It is not in the order of Providence that the gifts and graces of life should be concentrated in any one perfectly adjusted character. Even when we inquire into the "Admirable Crichton" of biography, and seek to trace his life, it vanishes almost into a myth.

In the midst of his many troubles and difficulties, Watt's invariable practice was to call upon Boulton for help. Boulton was satisfied to take men as he found them, and try to make the best of them. Watt was a man of the study; Boulton a man of the world. Watt was a master of machines; but Boulton, of men. Though Watt might be the brain, Boulton was the heart of the concern. "If you had been here," wrote Watt to Boulton, after one of his disagreeable meetings with the adventurers, "If you had been here, and gone to that meeting with your cheerful countenance and brave heart, perhaps they would not have been so obstinate." The scene referred to by Watt occurred at a meeting of the Wheal Union Adventurers, at which the savings effected by the new engine were to be calculated and settled. Here is Watt's own description of the affair, and his feelings on the occasion, which will give a good idea of the irksomeness of his position, and the disagreeable people he had occasionally to encounter: –

At Wheal Union account our savings were ordered to be charged to the interest of Messrs. Edwards and Phillips; but when to be paid, God knows ! Bevan said in a month. After all this was settled, in came Capt. Trevithick, I believe on purpose, as he came late and might have heard that I was gone there. He immediately fell foul of our account, in a manner peculiar to himself ... laboured to demonstrate that Dalcoath engines not only surpassed the table, but even did more work with the coals than Wheal Union did, and concluded with saying that we had taken or got the advantage of the adventurers. I think he first said the former and then hedged off by the latter statement. Mr. Phillips defended, and Mr. Edwards, I thought, seemed staggered, though candid. Mr. Phillips desired the data that he might calculate it over in his way. Mr. Edwards slipped away, but I found afterwards that he was in another room with Capt. Gundry (who, and Hodge also, behaved exceedingly well – I believe Gundry to be a very sincere, honest man). I went out to speak to Joseph, and on my return found only Trevithick, Bevan, Hodge, and some others. Soon after, Mr. Edwards called out Trevithick to him and Gundry. I heard them very loud, and waited their return for an hour; but they not seeming ready to return, night coming on, and feeling myself very uncomfortable, I came away – so know not what passed further. During all this time, I was so confounded with the impudence, ignorance, and overbearing manner of the man that I could make no adequate defence, and indeed could scarcely keep my temper; which however I did, perhaps to a fault; for nothing can be more grievous to an ingenuous mind than the being sus-

Cardozos Pumping-engine,
United Mines

pected or accused of deceit. To mend the matter, it had been an exceedingly
rainy morning, and I had got a little wet going thither, which had rather hurt
my spirits. Yesterday I had a violent headache and could do nothing ... Some
means must be taken to satisfy the country, otherwise this malicious man will
hurt us exceedingly. The point on which Mr. Edwards seemed to lay the most
stress was the comparing with a 77 ^{1}/10 cylinder, as he alleged they would
not have put in so large an engine; and in this there is some reason, as I do
not think they believed that the engine would be so powerful as it is. Add to
this, that the mine barely pays its way. Trevithick made a great noise about
short strokes at setting on, &c. The Captains seemed to laugh at that; and I
can demonstrate that, were it allowed for, it would not come to 2s. 6d. per
month. I believe they can be brought to allow that they would have put in a
70-inch. Now, query if we ought to allow this to be calculated from a 70 (at
which it will come to near 400l. a year), and on making this concession insist
on our having a good pay master to pay regularly once a month, and not be
obliged to go like beggars to their accounts to seek our due and be insulted by
such scoundrels into the bargain. As to Hallamanin, they have not met yet,
and when they do meet, I shall not go to them. I cannot bear such treatment,

but it is not prudent to resent it too warmly just now. I believe you *must* come here. I think fourteen days would settle matters. Besides my inability to battle such people, I really have not time to bestow on them.[27]

In subsequent letters Watt continued to urge Boulton to come to him. His headaches were constant, unfitting him for work. Besides, he could scarcely stir out of doors for the rain. "It rains here," said he, "prodigiously. When you come, bring with you a waxed linen cloak for yourself, and another for me, as there is no going out now for a few miles without getting wet to the skin. When it rains in Cornwall, and it rains often, it rains solid."

NOTES

1   Watt to Boulton, 4th August, 1777.

2   A mine so-called. Many of the Cornish mines have very odd names. "Cook's Kitchen," near Camborne, is one of the oldest and richest. Another is called "Cupboard." There are also Wheal Fannys and Wheal Abrahams; and Wheal Fortunes and Wheal Virgins in great numbers.

3   Watt to Boulton, 14th August, 1777.

4   Watt to Boulton, 25th August, 1777. Boulton MSS.

5   "I have seen five of Bonze's engines," wrote Watt, "but was far from seeing the wonders promised. They were 60, 63, and 70 inch cylinders. At Dalcoath and Wheal Chance they are said to use each about 130 bushels of coal in the 24 hours, and to make about 6 or 7 strokes per minute, the strokes being under 6 feet each. They are burdened to 6, 6½, and 7 lbs. per inch. One of the 60 inches threw out about two cubic feet of hot water per stroke, heated from 60° to 165°. The 63 inches, with a 5 feet stroke, threw out 1½ cubic foot, heated from 60° to 159°," and so on with the others. – Watt to Boulton, 25th August, 1777. Boulton MSS.

6   Watt to Boulton, 13th September, 1777.

7   Watt to Boulton, 2nd July, 1778. Boulton MSS.

8   Watt to Boulton, 8th July, 1778, Boulton MSS.

9   Watt to Boulton, 8th July 1778. Boulton MSS

10 While in Cornwall in the previous year, Watt wrote long letters to his partner as to certain experimental alterations of "Beelzebub." This was

the original engine brought from Kinneil, which continued to he the subject of constant changes. "I send a drawing," he wrote on the 4th August, 1777, "of the best scheme I can at present devise for equalising the power of Beelzebub, and obliging him to save part of his youthful strength to help him forward in his old age ... As the head of one of the levers will rise higher than the roof, a hole must be cut for it, which may after trial be covered over. If the new beam answer to be centred upon the end wall and to go out at a window, it will make the execution easy ... I long (he concluded) to have some particulars of Beelzebub's doings, and to learn whether he has got on his jockey coat yet [i.e. an outer cylinder], for till that be done, you can form no idea of his perfection." The engine continued to be the subject of repeated alterations, and was renewed, as Watt observed, like the Highlandman's gun, in stock, lock, and barrel After the occurrence of the above fire, we learn from Watt's MS Memoir of Boulton, that "Beelzebub" was replaced by a larger engine, the first on the expensive principle, afterwards known by the name of "Old Bess." This engine continued in its place long after the career of Boulton and Watt had come to an end; and in the year 1857, the present writer saw "Old Bess" working as steadily as ever, though eighty years had passed over her head. The old engine has since found an honourable asylum in the Museum of Patents at South Kensington.

11 Watt to Boulton, 8th August, 1778. Boulton MSS.

12 Watt to Boulton, 29th August, 1778. Later, Watt wrote from Redruth, "Captain Paul desires me to attend at Wheal Virgin meeting on Thursday, where several Tingtang people will be; but I shall only write, as I know they will be just in the worst of humours about Wheal Virgin affairs, and they are very disagreeable at best. Every article must be settled and sealed with Cornish adventurers before we begin, otherwise never ... Do not let Chelsea begin until signed and sealed. I hope you will not take amiss my writing so positively on this subject of agreements; but really my faith in mankind will carry me no further, and if I can't get money, I'm resolved to save my bacon and to live in hunger and ease. As it is, we don't get such a share of reputation as our works deserve, for every man who cheats us defames us in order to justify himself." – Watt to Boulton, 6th September, 1778. Boulton MSS.

13 With all the faults of the Cornish people, I think we have better chance for tolerable honesty here than elsewhere, as, their meetings being public, they will choose not to expose themselves any further that strict dealing

may justify; and besides, there are generally too many to cabal." – Watt to Boulton, 29th August, 1778. Boulton MSS.

14   During his absence Mr. Keir took charge of the works at Soho. It had been intended to introduce him as a partner, and he left the glass-making concern at Stourbridge, into which he had entered, for the purpose; but when he came to look into the books of the Soho firm, he was so appalled by their liabilities that he eventually declined the connexion.

15   Matthews wrote him on the 8th October, 1778, that he had met Mr. Boldero at the Goldsmiths' Hall, who had much influence in Cornwall, and that he expressed the opinion that, if the engines could do what Boulton and Watt promised, they might soon get from 40,000*l.* to 80,000*l.* for them in Cornwall. Matthews accordingly recommended to Boulton to apply to Elliot and Praed, the Cornish bankers, for an advance on security of the engine contracts. – It would appear from a letter written to Boulton a few days later, by Mr. Barton, Matthews's partner, that Boulton was, amidst his many speculations, engaged in privateering adventure during the war of the American Revolution: – "It may give you some pleasure," wrote Barton, "to hear we are likely to receive some produce from our adventures to New York. One of our vessels our little brig took last year was fitted out at New York, and in a cruise of 13 weeks has taken 13 prizes, 12 of which are carried safe in, and we have advice of 200 hogsheads of tobacco being shipped as part of the prizes, which, if now here, would fetch 10,000*l.* But while the embargo on shipping at New York continues, they cannot stir out of port. However, *I think we shall see them before you raise that sum from your entire engine concern, and yet I hope that is not very far off.*"

16   Watt to Black, 12th December, 1778.

17   Watt to Boulton, 15th Jan., 1779.

18   M. Perrier, of Paris, ordered an engine early in 1779, and the materials were despatched to Nantes by the end of May in the same year. The engine was erected by M. Jary at a colliery near Nantes, but the fitting was so bad – the steam-case having been forgotten – that it went only four strokes per minute. As Boulton and Watt sought a patent for France, it was necessary in the first place that Commissioners should certify that the new engine was superior to the common engine. This they could not do, and the patent was not secured. Watt feared that there was "a plot" against him; as Perrier immediately proceeded with a manufacture of steam-engines after the alleged invention of M. Betancourt, though this "invention" turned

out to be a close copy of the engine M. Betancourt himself had imported
from Soho.

19 Watt to Boulton, 27th January, 1779. Boulton MSS.

20 The following is Watt's letter, written in a very unusual style: –
    "Birmingham, June 30th, 1779.
    Hallelujah! Hallelujee!
    We have oncluded with Hawkesbury,
    217*l*. per annum from Lady-day last;
    275*l*. 5*s*. for time past; 157*l*. on account.
    We make them a present of 100 guineas –
    Peace and good-fellowship on earth –
    Perrins and Evans to be dismissed –
    3 more engines wanted in Cornwall –
    Dudley repentant and amendant –
    Yours rejoicing,
    James Watt."

21 Watt wrote Boulton, 2nd July 1778, – "On the subject of Mr. Hall
    I should not have been so earnest had I not been urged on by the
    prospect of impending ruin which may be much accelerated by a
    wicked or careless servant in his place." Later on the 6th August, Watt
    wrote, "I look upon Hall as a very great blunderer, and very inattentive
    to everything that has hitherto been committed to his care; but I think
    that our present necessities will oblige us to employ him." – Boulton
    MSS.

22 Watt to Boulton, 11th August, 1779.

23 Watt to Boulton, 4th October, 1779.

24 Watt to Boulton, 28th October, 1779.

25 Watt told Sir Walter Scott that though hundreds probably of his
    northern countrymen had sought employment at his establishment, he
    never could get one of them to become a first-rate mechanic. "Many of
    them," said he, "were too good for that, and rose to be valuable clerks
    and book-keepers; but those incapable of this sort of advancement
    had always the same insuperable aversion to toiling so long at any one
    point of mechanism as to gain the highest wages among the workmen."
    – Note to Lockhart's 'Life of Scott.' The fact, we suppose was, that
    the Scotch mechanics were only as yet in the course of training, – the
    English having had a long start of them. Though Watt's statement that
    Scotchmen were incapable of being first-class mechanics may have been
    true in his day, it is no longer, as the workshops of the Clyde can prove;

some of the most highly finished steam-engines of modern times having been turned out of Glasgow workshops.

26 The above anecdotes, of Mudock's introduction to Soho, and the fight with the captains, were communicated by his son, the late Mr. Murdock of Sycamore Hill near Birmingham. He also informed us that Murdock fought a duel with Captain Trevithick (father of the Trevithick of locomotive celebrity), in consequence of a quarrel between him and Watt, in which Murdock conceived his master to have been unfairly and harshly treated.

27 Watt to Boulton, from Chacewater, 16th October, 1779. Boulton MSS.

United Mines district—St. Day in the middle distance (by R.P. Leitch)

XIV

Financial Difficulties – Boulton in Cornwall – Attack and Defence of the Engine Patent

Boulton again went to Watt's help in Cornwall at the end of autumn, 1779. He could not afford to make a long stay, but left so soon as he had settled several long-pending agreements with the mine proprietors. The partners then returned to Birmingham together. Before leaving, they installed Lieutenant Henderson as their representative, to watch over their interests in their absence. Henderson was a sort of Jack-of-all-trades and master of none. He had been an officer of marines, and afterwards a West India sugar-planter. He lost all that he possessed in Jamaica, but gained some knowledge of levelling, draining, and machinery. He was also a bit of an inventor, and first introduced himself to Boulton's notice by offering to sell him a circular motion by steam which he alleged he had discovered. This led to a correspondence, which resulted in his engagement to travel for the firm, and to superintend the erection of engines when necessary.

Henderson experienced the same difficulty that Watt had done in managing the adventurers, and during his stay in Cornwall he was never done calling upon Boulton to hasten to his assistance and help him, as he said, "to put them in good spirits and good temper." As the annual meetings drew near, Henderson anticipated a stormy time of it, and pleaded harder than ever for Boulton to come to him. It seemed as if it would be necessary for Boulton to take up his residence in Cornwall; and as the interests at stake were great, it might be worth his while to do so. By the summer of 1780 Boulton and Watt had made and sold forty pumping-engines, of which number twenty were erected and at work in different parts of Cornwall; and it was generally expected that before long there would scarcely be an engine of the old construction at work in the county. This was, in fact, the only branch of Boulton's extensive concerns that promised to be remunerative.[1] He had become loaded with a burden of debt, from which the success of the engine-business seemed to offer the only prospect of relief.

Boulton's affairs seemed indeed fast approaching to a crisis. He had raised money in all directions to carry on his extensive concerns. He had sold the Patkington estate, which came to him by his wife, to Lord Donegal, for 15,000l.; he had sold the greater part of his father's property, and raised further sums by mortgaging the remainder; he had borrowed largely from Day,[2] Wedgwood, and others of his personal friends, and obtained heavy advances from his bankers; but all this was found insufficient, and his embarrassments seemed only to increase. Watt could do nothing to help him with money, though he had consented to the mortgage of the steam-engine royalties to Mr. Wiss, by which the sum of 7000l. had been raised. This liability lay heavy on the mind of Watt, who could never shake himself free of the horror of having incurred such a debt; and many were the imploring letters that he addressed to Boulton on the subject. "I beg of you," said he, "to attend to these money affairs. I cannot rest in my bed until they [i.e. the mortgage and banker's advance] have some determinate form. I beg you will pardon my importunity, but I cannot bear the uneasiness of my own mind, and it is as much your interest as mine to have them settled."[3]

The other partner, Fothergill, was quite as downhearted. He urged that the firm of Boulton and Fothergill should at once stop payment and wind up; but as this would have seriously hurt the credit of the engine firm, Boulton would not listen to the suggestion. They must hold on as they had done before, until better days came round. Fothergill recommended that at least the unremunerative branches of the business should be brought to a close. The heaviest losses had indeed been sustained through Fothergill himself, whose foreign connexions, instead of being of advantage to the firm, had proved the reverse; and Mr. Matthews, the London agent, repeatedly pressed Boulton to decline further transactions with foreigners.

There was one branch of the Boulton and Fothergill business which Boulton at once agreed to give up. This was the painting and japanning business; by which, as appears from a statement prepared by Mr. Walker, now before us, the firm were losing at the rate of 500l. a year.

The picture-painting business seems to have been begun in 1777, and was carried on for some years under the direction of Mr. Eginton, who afterwards achieved considerable reputation at Birmingham as a manufacturer of painted glass. A degree of interest has been recently raised on the subject of the Soho pictures, in consequence of the statements hazarded as to the method by which they are supposed to have been produced. It has been surmised that they were taken by some process resembling photography. We have, however, been unable to find anything in the correspondence of the firm calculated to support this view. On the contrary, they are invariably spoken of as "mechanical paintings," "pictures," or "prints," produced by means of "paints" or "colours." Though the precise process by which they were produced is not now known, there seems reason to believe that they were impressions from plates prepared in a peculiar manner. The impressions were taken "mechanically" on paper; and both oil and water colours[4] were made use of. Some of the pictures were of large size – 40 by 50 inches – the subjects being chiefly classical. This branch of the business being found unproductive, was brought to a close in 1780, when the partnership with Eginton was at the same time dissolved.

Another and more fortunate branch of business into which Boulton entered with Watt and Keir, about the same time, was the manufacture of letter-copying machines. Watt made the invention, Boulton found the money for taking out the patent, and Keir conducted the business. Watt was a very voluminous correspondent, and the time occupied by him in copying letters, the contents of which he desired to keep secret from third parties, was such that in order to economise it he invented the method of letter-copying in such common use. The invention consisted in the transfer, by pressure, of the writing made with mucilaginous ink, to damped and unsized transparent copying-paper, by means either of a rolling press or a screw press. Though Watt himself preferred the rollers, the screw press is now generally adopted as the more simple and efficacious process.

This invention was made by Watt in the summer of 1778. In June we find him busy experimenting on copying-papers of different kinds, requesting Boulton to send him specimens of "the most even and whitest unsized paper;" and in the following month he wrote Dr. Black, "I have lately discovered a method of copying writing instantaneously, provided it has been written the same day, or within twenty-four hours. I send you a specimen, and will impart the secret if it will be of any use to you. It enables me to copy all my business letters."[5] For two years Watt kept his method of copying a secret; but hearing that certain persons were prying into it with the view of turning it to account, he determined to anticipate them by taking out a patent, which was secured in May, 1780. By that time Watt had completed the details of the press and the copying-ink. Sufficient mahogany and lignum had been ordered for making 500 machines, and Boulton went up to London to try and get the press introduced in the public offices. He first waited upon several noblemen to interest them in the machine, amongst others on Lord Dartmouth, who proposed to show it to George III. "The King," said Boulton, in a letter to Watt, "writes a great deal, and takes copies of all he writes with his own hand, so that Lord Dartmouth thinks it will be a very desirable thing for His Majesty." Several of those to whom the machine was first shown, apprehended that it would lead to increase of forgery – then a great source of terror to commercial men. The bankers concurred in this view, and strongly denounced the invention; and they expostulated with Boulton and Watt's agent for offering the presses for sale. "Mr. Woodmason," wrote Boulton, "says the bankers mob him for having anything to do with it; they say that it ought to be suppressed." Boulton was not dismayed by this opposition, but proceeded to issue circulars to the members of the Houses of Lords and Commons, descriptive of the machine, inviting them to an inspection of it, after which he communicated the results to his partner:

On Tuesday morning last I waited on some particular noblemen, according to promise, at their own houses, with the press, and at one o'clock I took possession of a private room adjoining the Court of Requests, Westminster Hall, where I was visited by several members of both Houses, who in general were well pleased with the invention; but all expressed their fears of forgery, which occasioned and obliged me to exercise my lungs very much. Many of the members tried to copy bank notes, but in vain. I had a full audience till half-past eight o'clock … I had quite a mob of members next day; some of them mobbed me for introducing such wicked arts; however, upon the whole, I had a greater majority than Lord North hath had this year.

On Thursday … at half-past two … I had a tolerable good House, even a better than the Speaker, who was often obliged to send his proper officer to fetch away from me the members to vote, and sometimes to make a House. As soon as the House formed into a Committee upon the Malt-tax, the Speaker left the chair and sent for me and the machine, which was carried through the gallery in face of the whole House into the Speaker's Chamber. I found him full of fears about the dreadful consequences, which I quieted before I left him, and he with his two friends subscribed. I attended again on Friday, but, from a very thin House and curiosity abating, I had very few [subscriptions]. Mr. Banks came to see the machine on Thursday. I thought it might be of service to show it to the Royal Society that evening … After the business of the Society was over, he announced Mr. Watt's invention, and my readiness to show it, and it was accordingly brought in and afforded much satisfaction to a crowded audience. I did not show the list of subscribers and the proposals, nor dishonour philosophy by trade in that room ... I spent Friday evening with Smeaton and other engineers at a coffee-house, when a gentleman (not knowing me) exclaimed against the copying-machine, and wished the inventor was hanged and the machines all burnt, which brought on a laugh, as I was known to most present ... There are great names enough already among the subscribers to give a sanction and authority to it, as well as to make it fashionable, which has more influence upon the minds of three-fourths of the Londoners than the intrinsic merit of the thing, and without which it would have been some years in making its way.[6]

By the end of the year, the 150 machines first made were sold off, and more orders were coming in. Thirty were wanted for exportation abroad, and a still greater number were wanted at home. The letter-copying machine gradually and steadily made its way, until at length there was scarcely a house of any extensive business transactions in which it was not to be found. Watt himself, writing of the invention some thirty years later, observed that it had proved so useful to himself that it had been worth all the trouble of inventing it, even had it been attended with no pecuniary profit whatever.

Boulton's principal business, however, while in town, was not so much to push the letter-copying machine, but to set straight the bankers' account, which had been overdrawn to the amount of 17,000*l*. He was able to satisfy them to a certain extent by granting mortgages on the engine royalties payable in Cornwall, besides giving personal bonds for repayment of the advances within a given time. It was necessary to obtain Watt's consent to both these measures; but, though Watt was willing to agree to the former expedient, he positively refused to be a party to the personal bonds.[7] Boulton was therefore under the necessity of arranging the matter himself. He was thereby enabled to meet the more pressing claims upon the firm, and to make arrangements for pushing on the engine business with renewed vigour. Watt was, however, by no means so anxious on this score as Boulton was. He was even desirous of retiring from the concern, and going abroad in search of health. "Without I can spare time this next summer," he wrote, "to go to some more healthy climate to procure a little health, if climate will do, I must give up business and the world too. My head is good for nothing."[8] While Boulton was earnestly pressing the invention on the mining interest, and pushing for orders, Watt shuddered at the prospect of one. He saw in increase of business only increase of headaches. "The care and attention which our business requires," said he, "make me at present dread a fresh order with as much horror as other people with joy receive one. What signifies it to a man though he gain the whole world, if he lose his health and his life? The first of these losses has already befallen me, and the second will probably be the consequence of it, without some favourable circumstances which at present I cannot foresee should prevent it."

Judging by the correspondence of Watt, his sufferings of mind and body at this time must have been excessive; and the wonder is how he lived through it. But "the creaking gate hangs long on its hinges," and he lived to the age of eighty-three, long surviving his stronger and more courageous partner. Intense headache seemed to be his normal state, and his only tolerable moments were those in which the headache was less violent than usual. His son has since described how he remembered seeing his father about this time, sitting by the fireside for hours together, with his head leaning on his elbow, suffering from most acute sick-headaches, and scarcely able to give utterance to his thoughts. "My headache," he would write to Boulton, "keeps its week-aversary to-day." At another time, "I am plagued with the blues; my head is too much confused to do any brain-work." Once, when he had engaged to accompany his wife to an evening concert, he wrote, "I am quite eat up with the mulligrubs, and to complete the matter I am obliged to go to an oratorio, or serenata, or some other nonsense, to-night." Mrs. Watt tried her best to draw him out of himself, but it was not often that she could divert him from his misery. What relieved him most was sleep, when he could obtain it; and, to recruit his powers, he was accustomed to take from nine to eleven hours sleep at night, besides naps during the day. When Boulton had erysipelas, in Cornwall, and could not stir abroad, he wrote to his partner complaining of an unusual lowness of spirits, on which Watt undertook to be his comforter in his own peculiar way. "There is no pitch of low spirits," said he, "that I have not a perfect notion of, from hanging melancholy to peevish melancholy: conquer the devil when he is young." Watt experienced all the tortures of confirmed dyspepsia, which cast its dark shadow over the life of every day. His condition was often most pitiable. It is true, many of the troubles which beset him were imaginary, but he suffered from them in idea as much as if they had been real. Small evils fretted him, and great ones overwhelmed him. He met them all more than halfway, and usually anticipated the worst. He had few moments of cheerfulness, hopefulness, or repose. Speaking of one of his violent headaches, he said, "I believe it was caused by something making my stomach very acid;" and, unhappily, as in the case of most dyspeptics, the acidity communicated itself to his temper. When these fits came upon him, and the world was going against him, and ruin seemed about to swallow him up quick, he would sit down and pen a long gloomy letter to his partner, full of agony and despair. His mental condition at the time shows at what expense of suffering in mind and body the triumphs of genius are sometimes achieved.

In the autumn of 1780, Boulton went into Cornwall for a time to look after the business there. Several new engines had been ordered, and were either erected or in progress, at Wheal Treasury, Tresavean, Penrydee, Dalcoath, Wheal Chance, Wheal Crenver, and the United Mines. One of the principal objects of his visit was to settle the agreements with the mining companies for the use of these engines.

It had been found difficult to estimate the actual savings of fuel, and the settlement of the accounts was a constant source of cavil. There was so much temptation on the one side to evade the payments according to the tables prepared by Watt, and so much occasion for suspicion on the other that they had been evaded by unfair means, that it appeared to Boulton that the only practicable method was to agree to a fixed annual payment for each engine erected, according to its power and the work it performed. Watt was very averse to giving up the tables which had cost him so much labour to pre-pare; but Boulton more wisely urged the adoption of the plan that would work most smoothly, and get rid of the heartburnings on both sides. Boulton accordingly sent down to Watt a draft agreement with the Wheal Virgin adventurers, who were prepared to pay the large sum of 2500*l.* a year in respect of five new engines erected for their firm; and urged him to agree to the terms. "You must not be too rigid," said he, "in fixing the dates of pay-ment. A hard bargain is a bad bargain." Watt replied in a long letter, urging the accuracy of his tables, and intimating his reluctance to depart from them. To this Boulton responded, "Now, my dear Sir, the way to do justice to our own characters, and to trample under our feet envy, hatred, and malice, is to dispel the doubts, and to clear up the minds of the gentlemanly part of this our best of all kingdoms; for if they think we do wrong, it operates against us although we do none, just as much as if we really did the wrong. Patience and candour should mark all our actions, as well as firmness in being just to our-selves and others. A fair character and standing with the people is attended with great advantage as well as satisfaction, of which you are fully sensible, so I need say no more."[9]

Watt did not give up his favourite tables without further expostulation and argument, but at length he reluctantly gave his assent to the Wheal Virgin agreement, by which the annual payment of 2500*l.* was secured. Though this was really an excellent bargain, Watt seemed to regard it in the light of a calamity. In the letter intimating his reluctant concurrence, he observed:

Cosgarne House

"These disputes are so very disagreeable to me, that I am very sorry I ever bestowed so great a part of my time and money on the steam-engine. I can bear with the artifices of the designing part of mankind, but having myself no intention to deceive others, I cannot brook the suspicions of the honest part, which I am conscious I never merited even in intention, far less by any actual attempt to deceive."[10] Two days later Watt again wrote, urging the superiority of his tables, concluding thus: "I have been so much molested with headaches this week, that I have perhaps written in a more peevish strain than I should have done if I had been in better health, which I hope you will excuse." Boulton replied, expressing regret at his lowness of spirits and bad health, advising him to cheer up. "At your leisure," said be, "you may amuse yourself with a calculation of what all the engines we shall have in eighteen months erected in Cornwall will amount to; you will find it good for low spirits." "I assure you," he said at another time, "you have no cause for apprehension as to anything in this country; all is going on well." Boulton seemed to regard his partner in the light of a permanent invalid, which he was; and on writing to his various correspondents on matters of business at Soho, he would abjure them not to cross Mr. Watt. To Fothergill he wrote respecting the execution of an order, "the matter must be managed with some delicacy respecting Mr. Watt, as you know that when he is low-spirited he is vexed at trifles."

Another important part of Boulton's business in Cornwall, besides settling the engine agreement, was to watch the mining adventures themselves, in which by this time Boulton and Watt had become largely interested. In the then depressed state of the mining interest, it was in many cases found difficult to raise the requisite money to pay for the new engines; and the engineers must either go without orders or become shareholders to prevent the undertakings dropping through altogether. Watt's caution impelled him at first to decline entering into such speculations. He was already in despair at what he considered the bad fortunes of the firm, and the load of debts they had incurred in carrying on the manufacture of engines. But there seemed to be no alternative, and he at length came to the conclusion with Boulton, that it was better "not to lose a sheep for a ha'porth of tar."[11]

Rather than lose the orders, therefore, or risk the losses involved by the closing of the mines worked by their engines, the partners resolved to incur the risk of joining in the adventures, and in course of time they became largely interested in them. They also induced friends in the North to join them, more particularly Josiah Wedgwood and John Wilkinson, who took shares to a large amount.

Boulton now made it his business to attend the meetings of the adventurers, in the hope of improving their working arrangements, which he believed were very imperfect. He was convinced of this after his first meeting with the adventurers of the Wheal Virgin mine. He found their proceedings conducted without regard to order. The principal attention was paid to the dining, and after dinner and drink little real business could be done. No minutes were made of the proceedings; half the company were talking at the same time on different subjects; no one took the lead in conducting the discussions, which were disorderly and anarchical in the extreme. Boulton immediately addressed himself to the work of introducing order and despatch. He called upon his brother adventurers to do their business first, and dine and talk afterwards. He advised them to procure a minute-book in which to enter the resolutions and proceedings. His clear-headed suggestions were at once agreed to; and the next meeting, for which he prepared the agenda, was so entirely different from all that had preceded it, in respect of order, regularity, and the business transacted, that his influence with the adventurers was at once established. "The business," he wrote to Watt, "was conducted with more regularity, and more of it was done, than was ever known at any previous meeting." He perceived, however, that there was still room for great improvements, and added, "somebody must be here all next summer ... I shall be here myself the greater part of it for there will want more kicking than you can do ... *Grace au Dieu!* I neither want health, nor spirits, nor even flesh, for I grow fat."[12]

To increase his influence among the adventurers, and secure the advantages of a local habitation among them, Boulton deemed it necessary to take a mansion capable of accommodating his family, and which should serve the same purpose for his partner when sojourning in the neighbourhood. Boulton's first idea was to have a portable wooden house built and fitted up in the manner of a ship's cabin, which might readily be taken to pieces and moved from place to place as business required. This plan was, however, eventually abandoned in favour of a residence of a more fixed kind. After much searching, a house was found which promised to answer the intended purpose, – an old-fashioned, roomy mansion, with a good-sized garden full of fruit trees, prettily situated at Cosgarne, in the Gwennap valley. Though the United Mines district was close at hand, and fourteen of Boulton and Watt's engines were at work in the immediate neighbourhood, not an engine chimney was to be seen from the house, which overlooked Tresamble Common, then an unenclosed moor. Here the partners by turns spend much of their time for several successive years, travelling about from thence on horseback from mine to mine to superintend the erection and working of their engines.

By this time the old Newcomen engines had been almost completely superseded, only one of that construction remaining at work in the whole county of Cornwall. The prospects of the engine business were, indeed, so promising, that Boulton even contemplated retiring altogether from his other branches of business at Soho, and settling himself permanently in Cornwall.[13]

Notwithstanding the great demand for engines, the firm continued for some time in serious straits for money, and Boulton was under the necessity of resorting to all manner of expedients to raise it, sometimes with Watt's concurrence, but oftener without. Watt's inexperience in money matters, conjoined with his extreme timidity and nervousness, made him apprehend ruin and bankruptcy from every fresh proposition made to him on the subject of raising money. He was kept so utterly wretched by his fears as to be on occasions quite unmanned, and he would brood for days together on the accumulation of misery and anxiety which his great invention had brought upon him. His wife was kept almost as miserable as himself, and as Matthew Boulton was the only person, in her opinion, who could help him out of his troubles, she privately appealed to him in the most pathetic terms: –

"I know," she wrote, "the goodness of your heart will readily forgive me for this freedom, and your friendship for Mr. Watt will, I am sure, excuse me for pointing out a few things that press upon his mind. I am very sorry to tell you that both his health and spirits have been much worse since you left Soho. It is all that I can do to keep him from sinking under that fatal depression. Whether the badness of his health is owing to the lowness of his spirits, or the lowness of his spirits to his bad health, I cannot pretend to tell. But this I know, that there are several things that prey so upon his mind as to render him perfectly miserable. You know the bond that he is engaged in to Vere's house has been the source of great uneasiness to him. It is still so, and the thought of it bows him down to the very ground. He thinks that company has used both you and him very ill in refusing to release him, when you can give them security for a vast deal more than you are bound for. Forgive me, dear Sir, if I express myself wrong. It is a subject I am not used to write on. I know if you can you will set his mind at rest on this affair. I need not tell you that the seeing him so very unhappy must of consequence make me so. There is another affair that sits very heavy on his mind; that is, some old accounts that have remained unsettled since the commencement of the business. They never come across his mind but he is rendered unfit for doing anything for a long time. A thousand times have I begged him to mention them to you ... I am sure he would suffer every kind of anxiety rather than ask you to do a thing you seemed not to approve of. I know the humanity of your nature would make you cheerfully give relief to any of the human race that was in distress, as far as was within your power. The knowledge of this makes me happy in the thought that you will exert every nerve to give ease to the mind of your friend. Believe me, there is not on earth a person who is dearer to him than you are. It causes him pain to give you trouble. The badness of his constitution, and his natural dislike to business, make him leave many things undone that he knows ought to be done, and, when it is perhaps too late, to make himself unhappy at their being neglected ... In his present state of weakness, every ill, however trifling, appears of a gigantic size, while on the other hand every good is diminished. Again, I repeat, that from the certain knowledge I have of his temper, nothing could contribute more to his happiness and make him go on cheerfully with business than having everything finished as he goes along, and have no unsettled scores to look back to and brood over in his mind."[14]

Mrs. Watt concluded by entreating that no mention would be made to her husband of her having written this letter, as it would only give him pain, and explaining that she had adopted the expedient merely in the hope that something might be done to alleviate his sufferings. This, however, was a very difficult thing to do. Boulton could remind his hopeless partner of the orders coming in for engines, and that such orders meant prosperity, not ruin; but he could not alter the condition of a mind essentially morbid. Boulton was himself really in far greater straits than Watt. He had risked his whole fortune on the enterprise; and besides finding money for buildings, plant, wages, materials, and credits, he was maintaining Watt until the engine business became productive. We find from the annual balance-sheets that Watt was regularly paid 330*l.* a year, which was charged upon the hardware business; and that this continued down to the year 1785. Till then everything had been out-go; the profits were all to come. It was estimated that upwards of 40,000*l.* were invested in the engine business before it began to yield profits; and all this was found by Boulton. In one of his letters to Matthews he wrote, "I find myself in the character of P, pay for all," but so long as his credit held good, Watt's maintenance was secure.

So soon, however, as it became clear that the enterprise would be a success, and that the demand for engines must shortly become national, the firm was threatened with a danger of another kind, which occasioned almost as much alarm to Boulton as it did to Watt. This was the movement set on foot in Cornwall and elsewhere with the object of upsetting their patent. Had the engine been a useless invention, no one could have questioned their right of property in it; but, being recognised as of boundless utility, it began to be urged that the public ought to be free to use it without paying for it. It was alleged that it had become indispensable for the proper working of the mines, and that the abolition of the patent right would be an immense boon to the mining interest, and enable them to work the ores at a much reduced cost, while the general industry of the country would also be greatly benefited.

When Boulton wrote Watt from Cornwall, informing him that the Cornishmen were agitating the repeal of the special Act by which their patent had been extended, and getting up petitions with that object, Watt replied, "I suspected some such move as this; and you may depend upon it they will never be easy while they pay us anything. This is a match of all Cornwall against Boulton and Watt; and though we may be the better players, yet they can hold longer out. However, if we do die, let us die hard."[15]

But would Parliament really take away that right of property in the invention which they had granted, and deprive Watt and his partner of the fruits of their long labour and anxiety, and their heavy outlay, now that the superiority of the engine had become established? Would the legislature consign them to certain ruin because it would be for the advantage of the Cornish miners to have the use of the invention without paying for it? Watt would not for a moment believe this, and both he and Boulton felt strong in the conviction that their patent right would be maintained.

Time was, when Watt would have gladly parted with his invention for a very small sum, and made the engine free to all, so far as he was concerned. Even after it had been perfected at Soho, after repeated and costly experiments, he declared his willingness to sell all his interest in it for 7000*l.*, which would have barely remunerated him for the time and labour he had bestowed upon it, then extending over nearly twenty years of the best period of his life. And now, after six years of the partnership had run, and the heavy expenditure incurred by Boulton in introducing the engine was still unproductive, he regarded it as cruel in the extreme to attempt to deprive him of his just reward. To Boulton he disburdened himself fully, in strong and sometimes bitter terms. "They charge us," he said, "with establishing a monopoly, but if a monopoly, it is one by means of which their mines are made more productive than ever they were before. Have we not given over to them two-thirds of the advantages derivable from its use in the saving of fuel, and reserved only one-third to ourselves, though even that has been still further reduced to meet the pressure of the times? They say it is inconvenient for the mining interest to be burdened with the payment of engine dues; just as it is inconvenient for the person who wishes to get at my purse that I should keep my breeches-pocket buttoned. It is doubtless also very inconvenient for the man who wishes to get a slice of the squire's land, that there should be a law tying it up by an entail. Yet the squire's land has not been of his own making, as the condensing engine has been of mine. He has only passively inherited his property, while this invention has been the product of my own labour, and of God knows how much anguish of mind and body;" –

"Why don't they," he asked, "petition Parliament to take Sir Francis Bassett's mines from him? He acknowledges that he has derived great profits from using our engines, which is more than we can say of our invention; for it appears by our books that Cornwall has hitherto eaten up all the profits we have drawn from it, as well as all that we have got from other places, and a good sum of our own money into the bargain. We have no power to compel anybody to erect our engines. What, then, will Parliament say to any man who comes there to complain of a grievance he can avoid, and which does not exist but in his own imagination? Will Parliament give away our property without an equivalent? Will they not collect that equivalent from the county of Cornwall? Will they adjudge them to pay us any less sum than it has cost ourselves? Will they not further add some reward for the quantity of life that has been devoted to the pursuit of what is evidently for the advantage of others, but hitherto has not been for our own? Lastly, will Parliament compel us to work for anybody without a remuneration adequate to our experience, or will they oblige us to labour for any one without our consent? We are in the state of the old Roman who was found guilty of raising better crops than his neighbours, and was therefore ordered to bring before the assembly of the people his instruments of husbandry, and to tell them of his art. He complied, and when he had done said, 'These O Romans, are the instruments of our art; but I cannot bring into the forum the labours, the sweats, the watchings, the anxieties, the cares, which produced these crops.' So, every one sees the reward which we may yet probably receive from *our* labours; but few consider the price we have paid for that reward, which is by no means a certain annuity, but a return of the most precarious sort. To put an end, as far as lies in my power, to all disputes with the people of Cornwall, let them pay my debts and give me a reasonable sum for the time I have lost, and I will resign my part in their favour, and think myself well off by the bargain. Or, if you can find any man who is agreeable to yourself, I'll sell him my share on reasonable terms, and, like the sailor, I will promise to contrive no more fire-engines. In short, my dear Sir, with a good cause in hand, I do not fear going before Parliament or anywhere. I am sure that if they did anything they would put us in a better position than we are in now."[16]

The petition to Parliament, though much talked about, was not, however, presented; and the schemers who envied Boulton and Watt the gains which they had now the prospect of deriving from the use of their engine, shortly after resorted to other means of participating in them, to which we shall hereafter refer. In the mean time Boulton, at the urgent entreaty of Watt, who described himself as "loaded to 12 lbs. on the inch," returned to Birmingham; though he had scarcely left before urgent entreaties were sent after him that he must come back again to Cornwall.[17]

While Boulton was in Cornwall, the principal manufacturers of Birmingham, dissatisfied with the bad and dear supply of copper, resolved to form themselves into a company for the purpose of making brass and spelter; and they wrote to Boulton offering to raise the requisite means, provided he would take the lead in the management of the concern. He could not but feel gratified at this best of all proofs of the esteem in which his townsmen held him, and of their confidence in his business qualities. Boulton, however, declined to undertake so large an addition to his labours. He felt that he would soon be an old man, and that it would be necessary for him to contract rather than extend the field of his operations; besides, the engine business was already sufficiently prosperous to induce him to devote to it the chief share of his attention. But he promised to his Birmingham friends

Entrance to Cosgarne House

that he would always be glad to give them his best advice and assistance. He accordingly furnished them with a plan of operations, and drew up a scheme for their consideration, which was unanimously adopted, and the whole of the share capital was at once subscribed for. He also made arrangements with his Cornish friends for a regular supply of copper direct from the mines on the best terms. On his return to Birmingham, we find him entering upon an elaborate series of experiments, to determine the best constituents of brass; in the course of which he personally visited the principal calamine works in Wales and Derbyshire, for the purpose of testing their different produce. He diligently read all the treatises on the subject, and made inquiries as to the practice adopted in foreign countries. Finding, however, that the continuance of his connexion with the brass company was absorbing more of his time than he could afford to bestow upon it, he shortly withdrew from the concern, – partly also, because he was dissatisfied with what he considered the illiberal manner in which the managing committee were conducting its affairs.

Another subject which occupied much of Boulton's attention about the same time was the improvement of engine boilers. At an early period he introduced tubes in them, through which the heated air of the furnace passed, thereby greatly increasing the heating surface and enabling steam to be raised more easily and rapidly. We find him in correspondence with Watt on the subject, while residing at Redruth in the autumn of 1780. He first suggested iron tubes; but Watt wrote, "I cannot advise iron for the tubes of boilers, but they may be thought of."[18] Next Boulton suggested the employment of copper tubes;

to which Watt replied, "I approve of what you observe about making copper flanches to the boiler pipes in future, and Ale and Cakes can easily be converted to that way whenever they put up a second boiler." We find Boulton introducing four copper tubes 20 inches in diameter into the Wheal Busy boiler, which was 28 feet in length, – the fire passing through two of the tubes, and returning through the other two. Here, therefore, we have Boulton anticipating the invention of the tubular boiler, and clearly adopting it in practice, before the existence of the locomotive, for which it was afterwards re-invented. In fact, the multitubular boiler is but a modification and extension of Boulton's principle, as applied by him at so early a period in the Cornish boilers.

The numerous MS. books left by Boulton show the care with which he made his experiments, and the scrupulousness with which he recorded the results. Copies of his observations and experiments on boilers were sent to Watt, to be entered by him in "the calculation book," in which was recorded the tabulated experience of the firm. Boulton was also an excellent mechanical draughtsman, as appears from his tablets, which contain a number of beautifully executed drawings of engines and machinery, with very copious and minutely written instructions for erecting them. Some of the drawings of sugar-mills are especially well executed, and delicately coloured. A rough sketch is given in one of the books, with a written explanation in Boulton's hand, of a mode of applying power in taking canal-boats through tunnels. It consists of an engine-boat, with toothed claws attached to it for the purpose of catching metal racks fastened along the sides of the tunnel, such being his design for working boats upon canals. While in Cornwall, he occupied his evenings in drawing sections of various mines, showing the adits, and the method of applying the pumping machinery, to which were also added numerous elaborate calculations of the results of engine working. He also continued to devise improvements in the construction and working of the steam-engine, on which subject he exchanged his views with Watt at great length. In one of his letters he says: "I like your plan of making all the principal wearing parts of tempered steel, and the racks of best Swedish iron, with the teeth cut out. Query: Would it not be worth while to make a *machine* for dividing and cutting the teeth in good form out of sectors? The iron would be less strained by that mode of cutting." At other times, when the steam-engine subject seemed exhausted, he proceeded with the designing of road-carriages, in which he was an adept, filling a quarto drawing-book, entitled 'Thoughts on Carriages,' with sketches of different kinds of vehicles, some in pencil and Indian ink, and others in colours, beautifully finished. Such were the leisure employments of this indefatigably industrious man.

NOTES

1   It appears from a statement prepared by Zaccheus Walker, the accountant of Boulton and Fothergill, that on an invested capital of about 20,000*l.*, the excess of losses over profits during the eighteen years ending 1780, had been upwards of 11,000*l.*; and that but for the capital and credit of Matthew Boulton, that concern must have broken down.

2   Thomas Day, the eccentric but kindly author of 'Sandford and Merton,' lent Boulton 3000*l.* at 4 per cent. When Boulton came to pay a higher rate of interest on the other loans, he wrote Day proposing to pay him the same rate; but Day refused to accept the advance, as he could not make more money elsewhere. Day, however, offered him some good advice. "Give me leave," said he, "with the real interest of a sincere friend, to express my wishes that now at last when a fortune is within your power, you will contract that wide sphere of business in which your ingenuity has so long kept you engaged, and which has prevented you hitherto, if I may believe the words of one of your sincerest friends, the late Dr. Small, from acquiring that independence which you ought to have had long ago. I should think that now, like a good Christian, thoroughly convinced of the inutility of other works, you ought to attach yourself to the one thing needful, and determine to be saved 'even as by fire.' You are now, dear Sir, not of an age to sport any longer with fortune. Forgive the freedom of these sentiments, and believe me, with the greatest sincerity and regard, Yours, &c.,
Thomas Day."

3   Watt to Boulton, 20th January, 1779.

4   Some of the specimens in water colour are to be seen at the Museum of Patents, South Kensington. When the paper is moistened with the finger, the colour easily rubs off. The whole subject of these pictures has recently been thoroughly sifted by M.P.W. Boulton, Esq., in his 'Remarks on some Evidence recently communicated to the Photographic Society' (Bradbury and Evans, 1864), apropos of the Papers of Mr. W.P. Smith on the same subject, in which it was surmised that they were the result of some photographic process. Mr. Boulton clearly shows, from the original correspondence, that the process was mechanical colour-printing. He also adds, – "From the brief statements which I remember to have heard from my father concerning the polygraphic process, my impression of it was that it copied colour *mechanically*, not merely chiaro-scuro. And I agree

with the opinion which has been expressed to other persons, that in the coloured specimens in the Museum, there are indications that the colour was laid on mechanically, – not by head or brush." As the process of "dead-colouring" the pictures is occasionally referred to, it is probable that the pictures passed through more stages than one, as in the case of modern colour-printing. In one of Eginton's letters, three plates were spoken of as necessary for taking impressions of one of the pictures.

5   Watt to Dr. Black, 24th July, 1778.

6   Boulton to Watt, 14th May, 1780. Boulton MSS.

7   On 18th May, 1780, Watt wrote Boulton, then in London, as follows: – "I am sorry, my dear Sir, to prove in any shape refractory to what you desire, but my quiet, my peace of mind, perhaps my very existence, depend on what I have told you. I am unhappy in not having any person I can advise with on this subject; and my knowledge of it is insufficient. Therefore, if I appear too rigid, do not blame me, but my ignorance and timidity." And again, on the 19th, on returning the draft mortgage, he wrote: – "If my executing this deed cannot be dispensed with, I will do it, but will not execute any personal bond for the money. I would rather assign you all Cornwall on proper conditions than execute this."

8   Watt to Boulton, 11th April, 1780.

9   Boulton, at Plengwarry, to Watt, at Birmingham, 14 th September, 1780. This day was Boulton's birthday, and alluding to the circumstance he wrote, – "As sure as there are 1728 inches in a cubic foot, so sure was I born in that year; and as sure as there are 52 weeks in the year and 52 weeks in the year and 52 cards in the pack, so surely am I 52 years old this very day. May you and Mrs. Watt live very long and be very happy."

10   Watt to Boulton, 10th October, 1780. Boulton MSS.

11   Watt to Boulton, 20th April, 1780.

12   Boulton to Watt, 25th and 30th September, 1780. Boulton MSS

13   His partner Fothergill would not, however, consent to let Boulton go, and the Soho business continued until the death of Fothergill (bankrupt) in 1782, after which it was continued for some time longer under the firm of Boulton and Scale.

14   Mrs. Watt to Mr. Boulton, then in London, 15th April, 1781. Boulton MSS.

15   In another letter Watt described himself as "worried by the Wheal Chanceians ... In short," says he, "I am at this moment so provoked at the undeserved rancour with which we are persecuted in Cornwall, that, were it not on account of the deplorable state of debt I find myself in, I would

live on bread and cheese, and suffer the water to run out at their adits, before I would relax the slightest iota of what I thought my right in their favour." – Watt to Boulton, 17th October, 1780. Boulton MSS.

16   Watt to Boulton, 31st October, 1780. Boulton MSS.

17   "Though your long stay, when you were last here," wrote Henderson, the resident agent, "must have been attended with great inconveniences, yet you are now very much wanted in Wheal Virgin affairs. Different interests have produced a sort of anarchy ... Were Mr. Watt here now, I don't think his health would allow him to stand the battles with the different people. I have not written to him freely on his subject, as I am afraid it would hurt him ... Your authority here as an adventurer has much greater weight than anything I can propose." – Henderson to Boulton, 4th February, 1781. Boulton MSS.

18   Watt to Boulton, 17th October, 1780.

The "Waggon and Horses," Handsworth

XV

Watt again visits Cornwall – Invention of the Rotary Motion – The Patent Right again Assailed

Watt's presence being much wanted in Cornwall, he again proceeded thither, accompanied by his wife and family, and arrived at Cosgarne towards the end of June, 1781. He found that many things had gone wrong for want of the master's eye, and it was some time before he succeeded in putting affairs in order. The men had been neglecting their work, "going a-drinking." Cartwright had "contracted a fever in his working arm, and been swallowing ale for a cure," until he heard Watt had come, when the fever left him. Mrs. Watt also found occasion to complain of sundry little grievances, and favoured Boulton with a long catalogue of them. Gregory and Jessy had caught cold on the journey, and workmen were hammering about the house making repairs. There was, however, one gleam of brightness in her letter: "James's spirits were surprisingly mended since his arrival."

Watt was a most voluminous correspondent. He wrote Boulton several times a week great folio sheets, written close, in small hand. The letters must have occupied much of his time to write, and of Boulton's to read. The latter, seeing his partner's tendency to indulge in "worrit" about petty troubles, advised him in a kindly spirit not to vex himself so much about such matters, but to call philosophy to his aid. Why should he not occupy some of his spare time in writing out a history of all his steam-engine contrivances, to be dedicated to Sir Joseph Banks, and published in the 'Transactions of the Royal Society'? But Watt was extremely averse to writing anything for publication, and the suggestion was not acted on. Then, knowing Watt's greatest pleasure to be in inventing, Boulton in a subsequent letter advised him to take up afresh, and complete a plan which they had often discussed, of producing rotary motion, by which the engine might be applied to work mills and drive machinery.

Watt had from the first regarded the employment of the steam-engine in producing continuous rotary motion as one of its most useful applications, and with this object he invented his original wheel-engine. No steps were taken to introduce the invention to practical use; but it occurred to Watt that the same object might be better effected by employing the ordinary engine for the purpose, with certain modifications.[1] The subject had partially occupied his attention during his first visit to Cornwall; for we find him writing Boulton from Chacewater, in 1779, "As to the circular motion, I will apply it as soon as I can, but foresee that I shall be very busy shortly, and much out of doors." On his subsequent return to Birmingham, after frequent conferences with his partner on the subject, he proceeded to prepare a model, in which he made use of a crank connected with the working beam of the engine to produce the rotary motion. There was no originality in the employment of the crank, which was an expedient that Watt had long before made use of.[2] The crank was, indeed, one of the most common of mechancal appliances. It was in daily use in every spinning-wheel, in every grindstone turned by hand, in every turner's and knife-grinder's foot-lathe, and in every potter's wheel. It was one of the commonest, as it must have been one of the oldest, of mechanical expedients. "The true inventor of the crank rotative motion," said Watt, "was the man who first contrived the common foot-lathe: applying it to the engine was like taking a knife to cut cheese which had been made to cut bread."

Though Watt had become very reserved, especially to strangers, about his inventions, he could not altogether keep from the knowledge of his workmen the contrivances on which his thoughts were occupied. He was under the necessity of employing them to make patterns after his drawings, from which any ingenious man might readily apprehend what he was aiming at. The Soho workmen were naturally curious about the new inventions and adaptations which Watt was constantly producing, and these usually formed the subject of conversation at their by-hours. While the model of the crank engine was under construction at Soho in the summer of 1780, a number of the workmen met one Saturday evening, according to custom, to drink together at the "Waggon and Horses," a little old-fashioned, low-roofed, roadside public-house, still standing in the village of Handsworth. The men were seated round the little kitchen-parlour, talking about their work, and boasting, as men will do over their beer, of the new and wonderful things which they were carrying forward in the shops. Dick Cartwright, the pattern maker, was one of the loudest of the party. He was occupied upon a model for the purpose of producing rotary motion, which he declared would prove one of the best

The crank as applied in the foot-lathe

things Mr. Watt had ever brought out. The other men were curious to know all about it, and to illustrate the action of the machine, Cartwright proceeded to make a rude sketch of the crank upon the wooden table with a bit of chalk. A person who sat in the kitchen corner in the assumed garb of a workman, drank in greedily all that the men had been saying; for there were many eaves-droppers constantly hanging about Soho, some for the purpose of picking up surreptitious information, and others to decoy away skilled workmen who were in the secrets of the manufacture. Watt himself had never thought of taking out a patent for the crank, not believing it to be patentable; but the stranger aforesaid had no such hesitation, and it is said he posted straight to London and anticipated Watt by securing a protection for the contrivance.[3]

Watt was exceedingly wroth when he discovered the trick which had been played him, and he suspected that Matthew Washborough was at the bottom of it. Washborough was a Bristol mechanic, who carried on several branches of mechanical trade, amongst others that of clock-making on a large scale. Watt had employed Washborough to make nozzles for several of the Cornish engines, but was not satisfied with his work; for we find him writ-

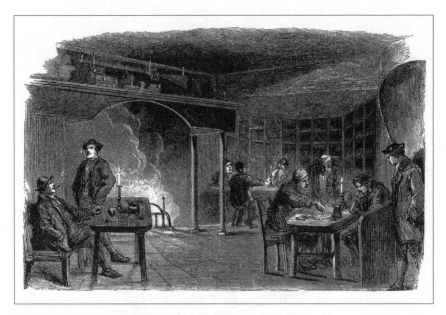

Interior of the "Waggon and Horses." (By Percival Skelton)

ing to his partner, "If Washborough makes no better engines than he does eduction-pipes, he will soon be blown: the Wheal Union pipe is the worst job you ever saw, being worse than Forbes's, which was very bad; I scarce know what to do with it." It would appear from this that Washborough had begun to make engines, thereby turning to account the knowledge he had acquired in Cornwall. One of the first he made was for the purpose of driving the lathes of his own manufactory at Bristol; and it affords a clear proof of Washborough's ingenuity that in this engine he employed both the fly-wheel and the crank. He has been styled the inventor of the fly-wheel, but he was no more its inventor than he was of the crank; the Irish Professor Fitzgerald having proposed to employ it as part of a Papin's engine as early as the year 1757. Washborough shortly after erected an engine after the same plan for a manufacturer on Snow Hill, Birmingham; and then it was that Watt learned that he had been "bolted out," as he termed it, from making use of the crank.

At first he was puzzled what to do to overcome the difficulty, but his prolific mind was rarely at a loss, and before many months were over he had contrived several other methods for effecting rotary motion. "I dare not, however," he wrote to Boulton, "*make* my new scheme, lest we be betrayed again; I believe we had best take the patent first." At the same time Watt was persuaded that no contrivance could surpass the crank[4] for directness, simplicity, and efficiency. He was therefore desirous, if possible, of making use of it in his rotative engine, as originally proposed; and he wrote to Boulton, then at Redruth, "I think you ought to call upon Washborough as you return, and let him know that we will dispute his having an exclusive right to those cranks."[5] Boulton called upon Washborough accordingly, and gave him notice to this effect. But Watt hesitated to use the crank after all. Although the contrivance was by no means new, its application to the steam-engine was new; and, notwithstanding the unfair way in which Pickard had antici-pated him, Watt did not like to set the example of assailing a patent, however disputable, as it might furnish a handle to those who were at the time seek-ing to attack his own. The proposal was made to him that he should allow the Washborough Company to use his steam-engine in exchange for their allowing him to use the crank; but this he positively refused to agree to, as he felt confident in yet being able to produce a circular motion without employing the crank at all.

Thus matters stood until the beginning of the year 1781, when Washborough, having entered into an arrangement with the Commissioners of the Navy to erect an engine for grinding flour at the Deptford Victualling Yard,[6] a formal application was made to Boulton and Watt to apply their engine for the pur-pose. Watt protested that he could not bring himself to submit to such an indignity. If the Commissioners thought proper to employ him to erect the necessary engine, rotative motion, and machinery, he would exert every fac-ulty which God had given him in doing so, but he "would never consent to hold the candle to Washborough."

"Had I esteemed him," he wrote to Boulton, "a man of ingenuity and the real inventor of the thing in question, I should not have made any objection; but, when I know that the contrivance is my own, and has been stolen from me by the most infamous means, and, to add to the provocation, a patent been sur-reptitiously obtained for it, I think it would be descending below the character of a *man* to be found in any way aiding or assisting him in his pretended inven-tion ... I think, therefore, that you should propose to the Honourable Board to undertake the direction of the whole; and, provided you can agree with them about the customary premium for the savings by our engine, you should do the whirligig part [rotative motion] for love. If this proposal should not be accepted, I beg of you to decline having any concern with it, and leave the field clear to Washborough. We may perhaps gain more by so doing than we can lose, as I assure you I have a very mean opinion of the mechanical abilities of our opponents. They have committed many gross errors in such of their works as I have had occasion to know about, and we may get honour by rectifying their mistakes. Perhaps this may seem to you to savour of vanity. If it does, excuse it on account of the very provoking circumstances which have extorted the confession. If these engineers had let us alone, I should not have meddled with them; but, as it is, I think we should be wanting in common prudence if we suffered a marriage between our machine and theirs, and if we did not do all we could to strip them of their borrowed feathers, which I hope there is justice enough left in England to enable us to do."[7]

Boulton acted on his partner's advice, and declined the proposed connexion. The Navy Board were placed in a dilemma by this decision. They then referred the matter to Mr. Smeaton, and requested him to report to them as to the most suitable plan of a flour-mill, and the steam-engine best calculated to drive it. To the great surprise of Watt as well as Washborough, Smeaton reported that both their engines were alike unsuited for such a purpose. "I apprehend," he said, "that no motion communicated from the reciprocating lever of a fire-engine can ever produce a perfect circular motion, like the regular efflux of water in turning a water-wheel!" This report relieved the Commissioners. They abandoned their scheme, and the order for Washborough's engine was at once countermanded.[8]

So soon as Watt had got fairly settled at Cosgarne, in the summer of 1781, he proceeded to work out the plan of a rotary-working engine. Boulton was making experiments with the same object at Soho, communicating to him the results from day to day. He was stimulated to prosecute the inquiry by the applications which he received from many quarters for steam-engines suitable for driving mills. He therefore urged Watt to complete the invention, and to prepare the drawings and specification, declaring his readiness at any time to provide the money requisite for taking out a patent. "The people in London, Manchester, and Birmingham," said he, "are *steam-mill mad*. I don't mean to hurry you, but I think that in the course of a month or two we should determine to take out a patent for certain methods of producing rotative motion from the vibrating or reciprocating motion of the fire-engine, – remembering that we have four months in which to describe the particulars of the invention."[9]

Watt proceeded to put his ideas in a definite shape as fast as his bad health and low spirits would allow. Every now and then a fit of despair came upon him about his liability to the bankers, and so long as it lasted he was unmanned, and could do nothing. At the very time that Boulton was writing the letter last quoted, Watt was thus bewailing his unhappy lot:

"When I executed the mortgage," said he, "my sensations were such as were not to be envied by any man who goes to death in a just cause; nor has time lessened the acuteness of my feelings ... I thought I was resigning in one hour the fruits of the labour of my whole life, – and that if any accident befell you or me, I should have left a wife and children destitute of the means of subsistence, by throwing away the only jewel Fortune had presented me with ... These transactions have been such a burden upon my mind that I have become in a manner indifferent to all other things, and can take pleasure in nothing until my mind is relieved from them; and perhaps, from so long a disuse of entertaining pleasing ideas, never may be capable of receiving them any more."[10]

Boulton made haste to console his partner, and promised to take immediate steps to relieve his mind of the anxiety that weighed so heavy upon it; and he was as good as his word. At the same time he told Watt that he must not suppose he was the only man in the world who had cares and troubles to endure. Boulton himself had, perhaps, more than his share, but he tried to bear them as lightly as he could. With his heavy business engagements to meet, his large concerns to keep going, he was not a man much to be envied; yet he continued to receive his visitors as usual at Soho, and to put on a cheerful countenance. "I am obliged," he wrote, "to smile, to laugh, to be good-humoured, sometimes to be merry, and even go to the play! Oh, that I were at the Land's End!" Such was his playful way of reminding Watt of the necessity of cheerfulness to enable one to get through work pleasantly.[11] But Watt's temperament was wholly different. His philosophy never rose to the height of taking things easy. He could not cast his cares behind him nor lose sight of them; but carried them about with him by day, and took them to bed with him at night; thus making life a sort of prolonged vexation – a daily and nightly misery.

But a new and still more alarming source of anxiety occurred to disturb the mind of poor Watt, and occasion him many more sleepless nights. The movement to abolish the patent by repeal of the Act of Parliament having broken down, attempts were now made in many quarters to evade it by ingenious imitations, in which the principle of Watt's engine was adopted in variously disguised forms. But to do this successfully would have required an inventive faculty almost as potent as that of Watt himself; and he had drawn the specification of his patent too carefully to be easily broken through by the clumsy imitators who made the attempt. It was, however, only natural that the success of the new engine should draw the attention of ingenious mechanics to the same subject. Watt had drawn a great prize, and why should not they?

though they little knew the burden of sorrow which his prize had brought upon him. They only knew of the large annual dues – probably exaggerated by the tongue of rumour – which were being paid to the patentees for the use of their engines; and they not unnaturally sought to share in the good fortune. There might possibly be other mechanical methods by which the same objects were to be accomplished, without borrowing from Watt; at all events it was worth trying. Hence the number of mechanical schemers who made their appearance almost simultaneously in all parts of the country, and the number of new methods of various kinds contrived by them for the production of motive power.

Watt was very soon informed of the schemes which were on foot in his immediate neighbourhood – much too soon for his peace of mind. He at once wrote to his partner: "Some Camborne gentlemen (supposed to be Bonze and Trevithick) have invented a new engine which they say beats ours two-thirds, and one of the partners has gone to London to procure a patent for it. A Mr. Vice says he has also invented a new engine, and that they have stolen his and compounded it with ours; he intends to take out a caveat against them."[12] Though Bonze was an excellent engineer, and elicited the admiration of Watt himself, it turned out that he had no concern with the new invention. Its projectors proved to be the Hornblowers, also engineers of considerable local repute. Watt had befriended the family, and employed them in erecting his engines, by which means they became perfectly familiar with their construction and mode of action. Jonathan Hornblower had a large family of sons, of whom Jabez, Jesse, Jethro, and Jonathan were engineers, like their father. Jabez, one of the cleverest, had spent some time in Holland, from whence he had returned with some grand scheme in his head for carrying out an extensive system of drainage in that country. Like his father and the other sons, he was employed in erecting Watt's engines,[13] which had the effect of directing his attention to the invention of a new power which should supersede that of his employer.

It was for some time doubtful what was the precise character of the new engine. Indeed the Hornblowers themselves long remained undecided about its actual form, being still in the throes of invention. They knew that they must copy discreetly, so as not to lay themselves too open to attack; and though they urged the superiority of their engine so strongly as to induce several of the mining companies to believe in them and even to withhold orders from Boulton and Watt, they refrained as yet from publishing their invention. Watt wrote to his partner that he understood the Hornblowers' engine was on some new principle, and the only novelty he could think of was a caloric air-engine. He therefore asked Boulton to make all the inquiries he could as to the respective bulks and prices per 1000 feet of all possible kinds of air in their most expanded states. "I am much vexed," he continued, "by this affair. Jabez does not want abilities: the rest are fools. If they have really found a prize, it will ruin us … Bankruptcy might ensue to both. But I don't fear getting my bread independent of engines, though much easier with them."[14] Watt was, however, in error as to the nature of the Hornblowers' engine, which he discovered three days later, when he wrote Boulton, –

The matter is this: Ever since the ungrateful, idle, insolent Hornblowers knew anything about our engines, they have laboured to evade our Act, and for that purpose have long been possessed of a copy of our specification. They made an attempt at Wheal Maid two years ago, by connecting two cylinders together and injecting into one of them, which did not succeed, although they had gathered together numbers of their friends in order to make a great exhibition. Since that, Jonathan the coppersmith, who, like Alexander of the like trade, hath done me much evil, has laboured close at some more successful evasion, which he says he has now completed and taken a patent for, – concerning which I hear as follows from public reports, propagated by Jethro's confidants: – 1st. That Jonathan Hornblower is the inventor and patentee; that Winwood, Jones and Company, of Bristol, are his partners and supporters with money (that Winwood was lately in this country on a sleeveless errand is certain); that they have made their model work to 14 lbs. on the inch, and expect it will work to 18 lbs. 2ndly. That they press the piston down by steam, and maintain they have a right to do so, because, say they, it can be proved that such was done before my patent. I suppose by this they allude to Gainsborough's bauble, which, by-the-by, was *after* the patent. If they do not mean this I am at a loss, as I now declare that I do not know of any one having done it before the patent except myself. However, it behoves us to inquire into this, and if the exhibition was not a public one it avails not. 3rdly. That they pretend to condense the steam in the cylinder; but I have heard that they do it in a separate vessel within the cylinder, or close to it. 4thly. That they do not use an air or water pump, from which I conjecture that they let the hot water down the shaft by a pipe more than 30 feet long, as you know I proposed but had several objections to. You will remember, and I dare say Joseph and Peploe also do, that we made the 18-inch Soho cylinder work by blowing the hot water out of the eduction-pipe and used no air-pump, but found a waste of steam by so doing. There is also some confused report about a wheel being employed on their engine, which makes me suspect that M. Washborough may be the Bristol man concerned with them.[15]

Two days later Watt wrote, – "My principal hope is that almighty Nature will prove Lord Chancellor, and put a negative on their scheme. Amen, so be it! I abhor lawsuits, and reckon a cause half lost that is litigated."

On the 23rd of July he returned to the subject: –

"The Horners," said he, "continue bragging of what they are to do, and I hear the country in general takes part with them, as even the aversion they have to the Horners does not equal the pleasure they would feel at our undoing … The Horners say they can make a common engine equal to ours, but that their new engine is one-third better. We must now attend to making use of all the elastic power of the steam, which, unless I am much deceived, will save one-half over our best engines, and at any rate it may easily be applied to work the condenser, which will save about one-eighth. I will not conceal from you that I am rendered very unhappy by one thing and another, but fight with it all I can."

In the mean time Boulton continued to urge Watt to complete the specification and drawings of his rotative engine, informing him of the success of the model which he had now completed at Soho: –

"Though you studied a thousand years," said he, "I do not think you could make one ten per cent. better than a small model with two cones which Joseph has executed after my drawings. It has little friction, goes sweeter than anything of the kind you have yet touched, and has not the least shake. It is so perfect that I don't consider it worth while even to think of any other for horizontal motions. I am therefore positively decided in my mind as to the necessity of taking out a patent and including in it all the principles and constructions you please; for if it be not secured soon we may lose it."[16]

In the same letter, Boulton communicated to Watt the rumours that had reached him from Scotland of more inventions of engines that were to beat Watt's out of the field. "The cry is still, they come!" said he. "Hatley from Scotland is going with Lord Dunmore to Virginny; says that he and somebody else in Scotland have invented an engine that is three times better than yours."

Boulton recommended that a search should be made at the Patent-Office, to ascertain what was going on in new engine patents. Watt entirely approved of this, and urged that the search should be made at once. "I do not think we are safe a day to an end," he wrote, "in this enterprising age. One's thoughts seem to be stolen before one speaks them. It looks as if Nature had taken an aversion to monopolies, and put the same thing into several people's heads at once to prevent them; and I begin to fear that she has given over inspiring me, as it is with the utmost difficulty that I can hatch anything new."

Notwithstanding this confession on the part of Watt, his inventive faculties were really never at any period of his life more vigorous than now; for he was rapidly maturing his rotative engine, with its various ingenious methods for securing circular motion; and working out the details of the double-cylinder expansion engine, with its many admirable contrivances hereafter to be described. Boulton continued to receive applications at Soho, from various quarters, for engines capable of working flour-mills and other machinery, and Watt himself was urged by like inquiries from manufacturers in Cornwall. "Mr. Edwards," he wrote Boulton, "waits impatiently the success of our rotative machine. He wants a power able to lift a hammer of 700 lbs., 2 feet high, 120 times per minute ... In relation to the circular engine, an experiment should be made on a large scale, and to work a hammer. I want your ideas on that head."[17] A fortnight later, Watt had matured his own ideas, and made the necessary declaration of his invention before a magistrate, preliminary to making the usual application for a patent.[18]

Watt was exceedingly busy about this time in superintending the erection of new engines. No fewer than twelve were in progress in different parts of the county. As he travelled about from one mine to another on horseback, and spent a good deal of his time in the open air, his mind was diverted from preying upon itself according to his ordinary habit, and his health and spirits improved accordingly. Boulton was equally busy at Soho, where he was erecting a powerful engine for blowing the furnaces at Walker's ironworks at Rotherham, and another for Wilkinson's forges at Bradley, in which he proposed to employ a double cylinder, with a double crank[19] and a pair of fly-wheels. At intervals he went into Yorkshire, Lancashire, and Shropshire, to look after various other engines in progress; writing Watt cheerful letters as to the improving prospects of the firm. He found the steam-engine everywhere gaining in public estimation. "The more it is known," he wrote, "the more it will be in demand. As to the scheme of the Hornblowers, they shall sooner press me down into the earth than they shall press down a piston with steam." And again, "Give yourself no uneasiness about the Horners' engine. Our title to the invention is as clear as can be; and it is as well secured as an Act of Parliament can make it –

Doubt that the sun is fire,
Doubt all the powers of sight,

Doubt troth to be a lyer,
But never doubt our right.

Watt's first surmise, that the Hornblowers intended to work their engine by
heated air or gas, had set Boulton upon a series of inquiries and experiments
on the subject, in which he was assisted by Dr. Priestley, who had shortly
before settled in Birmingham, and was a willing co-operator in all investigations of this nature. Their object was to ascertain whether it was practicable to
produce mechanical power by the absorption and condensation of gas on the
one hand, and by its disengagement and expansion on the other.

> "What you propose," Watt wrote, "is exceeding probable, and akin to what I
> have long contemplated – the use of mixed air and steam, which have a wonder-
> ful expansion and contraction. Nevertheless, I fear that there is in all such cases
> a proportional assumption of latent heat; but be it tried though it be beginning
> a new series of vexations and expense … I suspect that a forcible compression
> would hinder the gas from separating from the water, and on the contrary any
> tolerable degree of vacuum would hinder the water from attracting it; but per-
> haps part of both may be used… My greatest hope is in the expansive engine
> with double or single cylinder, which I consider as proved by many facts, and
> shall send you my ideas of the execution of it very soon. At the same time I am
> clear to take the air patent, which, as I have worded the petition, may include
> some other improvements on the steam engine … I hope my last letters have
> relieved you, as the knowledge of the Horners' being a steam-engine working
> on our principle relieved me. I have some trust in the judges, though I have
> little in the law; and I think impartial people will regard us as injured persons,
> and not suffer the thief of our horse to escape because he has painted him of
> another colour."[20]

Watt's fears for his patent were about this time excited anew by the great
Arkwright trial, in which Arkwright was nonsuited, and compelled to forego
the rights derived from his improvements and combinations of spinning-
machinery. The principal ground on which the patent was set aside was that
the specification was unintelligible. On this, Watt observed, –

> Though I do not love Arkwright, I don't like the precedent of setting aside
> patents through default of specification. I fear for our own. The specification is
> not perfect according to the rules lately laid down by the judges. Nevertheless,
> it cannot be said that we have hid our candle under a bushel. We have taught

all men to erect our engines, and are likely to suffer for our pains ... I begin to have little faith in patents; for, according to the enterprising genius of the present age, no man can have a profitable patent but it will be pecked at, and no man can write a specification of a fire-engine that cannot be evaded, if the words and not the true intent and meaning be attended to. As kissing goes by favour, and as, in dubious cases, men are actuated by their prejudices, so, where a blue is very like a green they may decide either way."[21]

Watt continued to be alarmed by the rumours of the forthcoming Hornblowers' engine. "I have heard," he wrote, "that a female confidant of Jonathan's has seen the engine; and says that they evaporate half a hogshead of water with *one ounce* of coals! ... that in a few days they are to publish in print what their invention is, illustrated with a copper-plate. Then we shall see and admire, if God pleaseth; I hope we shall not believe and tremble." Later he wrote, – "Our cause is good, and yet it has a bad aspect. We are called monopolists, and exactors of money from the people for nothing. Would to God the money and price of the time the engine has cost us were in our pockets again, and the devil might then have the draining of their mines in place of me. Yet all are not alike. Some are just, and I believe do not grudge us, and some are friendly. All this is to no purpose. The law must decide whether we have property in this affair or not, and we must submit to what we cannot help."[22]

At length Watt learnt the precise nature of the Hornblowers' invention. "It is no less," he wrote Boulton, "than our double-cylinder engine, worked upon our principle of expansion." This was an old idea of Watt's, which he had pursued while labouring upon his model at Kinneil. "It is fourteen years," he said, "since I thought of the double-cylinder engine, and I think that I mentioned it to Mr. Smeaton, when I explained the expansion engine to him in your parlour, some years ago. Wm. Murdock and Mr. Henderson can testify to my having mentioned it to them; but this of the Horners seems to be a different thing, being hung on the same beam."[23] As early as May, 1769, he had communicated to Dr. Small a clear and explicit description of his method of working steam expansively; and he adopted the principle in the Soho engine, in 1778, as well as in the Shadwell engine erected in the same year. He was, however, prevented carrying it out extensively in practice by the inexpertness of the workmen. "Though the effect of the steam," he explained to a correspondent, "is thereby increased 50 per cent. (by theory 100 per cent.), it cannot be done without rendering the machine more complicated than we wish; and simplicity is a most essential point in mechanics.

There are other contrivances known to us which would increase the effect in an inferior degree, say from one-fourth to one-sixth, but they are all attended with peculiar inconveniences which forbid their use until the illiterate and obstinate people who are intrusted with the care of the engines become more intelligent and better acquainted with the machine."[24]

Though suffering much from his usual headaches, which frequently disabled him from thinking, Watt finished the drawings of the rotary engine in a week, and forwarded them to Boulton at Soho. "I believe," he said in a later letter, "a well-regulated expansive-engine is the *ne plus ultra* of our art." But he intimated that a new trouble had come upon him in the shape of another inventor of a steam-engine in which all the distinctive principles of his own invention were embodied. "If he be engine mad," said Watt, "and if it be agreeable to you, he shall have my share of them, provided he will come to my price. I wish to retire, and eat my cake in peace, but will not go without the cake. All mankind seem to have resolved to rob us. Right or wrong, they *will* pluck the meal from our mouths."[25] Boulton, on his next journey to London, called upon the alleged inventor, a Mr. Ewer, and declared to Watt that the invention, so far as it was new, was not worth a farthing, and that all that was good in it was borrowed from their engine. "Though the white marks on your cow or your horse," said be, "may be changed to black, the cow and horse are not the less your property." He therefore counselled Watt to relieve himself of all anxiety on this account. Watt replied, "Ewer seems to have a genius more capable of inventing than of prudently examining the merits of his invention. Poets lose half the praise they would otherwise get did they but tell us what they discreetly blot. We must publish a book of blots."

Meanwhile Watt went on inventing; even while he was complaining of his inability to invent, and of the uselessness of inventing. Invention had grown into a habit with him, which he could not restrain. In the very letter in which he wrote "It is of no use inventing – everybody is seizing upon our schemes," he communicated to Boulton that he had contrived a machine, then erecting at Dalcoath, for the purpose of stopping the engine when at full speed, when any accident happened to the rods or outside chains, – first taking away the power, and then holding the bob fast whenever it might be at the turn.[26] A few days later he communicated that he had contrived a new way of opening the regulators. He was also finishing his plan of the new equalising beam, and the double expansion engine, which he requested might be proceeded with at once. "I have shown the equalising beam," said he, "to no person whatever. Please push it on. It is our *dernier ressort*, and may perhaps be all that villany will leave us, and that not long."[27] Boulton wrote back, bidding his partner

Old engine-house at Dalcoath (by R. P. Leitch)

to be of good heart. "If our spirits don't fail us," said he, "I think our engine won't."

At the same time Watt was inventing his new jointed top-working gear, which he reported answered exceedingly well with the Dalcoath engine; and, in pursuance of an idea thrown out by Boulton, he perfected the model of a horizontal-axled elliptical with one pulley, which he described as performing *à merveille*, being free from all untoward frictions. He was also busy inventing a new method of an equalising beam, by causing the gudgeon to change its place; and another by means of a roller acting upon a curve in the nature of the working gear. Besides his experiments in mechanics, he was prosecuting investigations as to the properties of nutgalls in combination with various chemical substances, for the purpose of obtaining the best kind of ink for use with his copying machines; and at another time we find him contriving various iron cements for joints, confessing that he had "lost all faith in putty;" the result of which was his discovery of the well-known metallic cement.

In the correspondence between the partners on these various topics, we seem to see the ideas out of which so many inventions grew, in their various stages of birth, growth and development. They concealed nothing from each other, but wrote with the most perfect unreserved. Each improved on the other's ideas, – Watt upon Boulton's, and Boulton upon Watt's; both experimenting on the same subject at the same time, and communicating the results in the most elaborate detail. The phrase often occurs in their letters: "I write thus fully *that you may see exactly what is passing in my mind.*" The letters were sometimes of extraordinary length, one of Boulton's (dated 25th September, 1781) extending to eight pages folio, closely written, containing upwards of 4000 words. Scarcely a day passed without their spending several hours in writing to each other. Boulton also kept up a correspondence with Mrs. Watt, in addition to his elaborate letters to her husband. The lady entered into various matters of personal interest, describing her occupations and domestic pursuits, and communicating the state of her husband's health, which was a matter of no less interest to Boulton than to herself.

As the autumn set in with its fogs and rains, Watt's headaches returned with increased severity, and he repeatedly complained to Boulton of being "stupid and ill, and scarcely able to think." "I tremble," said he, "at the thought of making a complete set of drawings. I wish you could find me out a draughts-man of abilities; as I cannot stand it much longer."[28] Watt's temper was also affected by the state of his health; and he confessed that he felt himself not at all cut out for the work he had to do, so far as related to business: "I am not philosopher enough," he said, "to despise the ills of life; and when I suffer myself to get into a passion, I observe it hurts me more than it does anybody else. I never was cut out for business, and wish nothing so much as not to be obliged to do any; which perhaps will never fall to my lot; therefore I must drag on a miserable existence the best way I can."[29]

Watt was very busy at this time in preparing the specification and drawings of the circular motion, which he said he found an extremely difficult job owing to the distracted state of his head. The letters patent for the invention had been secured on the 25th October, 1781, and he had four months allowed him in which to prepare and lodge the full description. He laboured at his work late and early, his mind being for months in the throes of invention. In the begin-ning of November we find him writing to Boulton, sending him the "first three yards of the specification," written out on folio sheets joined together. Watt's letters to his partner at this time contain numerous rough sketches of his proposed methods for securing circular motion without using the crank, from which he conceived himself to be in a measure precluded by Pickard's patent. He devised no fewer than five distinct methods by which this object might be accomplished, by means of wheels of various sorts rotating round an axis. The method eventually preferred was the one invented by Wm. Murdock,

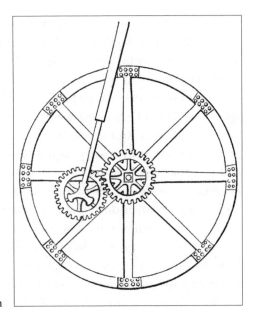

Sun and planet motion

and commonly known as the sun and planet motion.[30] "It has the singular property," said Watt, "of going twice round for each stroke of the engine, and may be made to go oftener round if required without additional machinery."

Rough sketches of these various methods were forwarded to Soho in order that the requisite careful drawings of might be prepared in time to be lodged with the specification; but when they reached Watt in Cornwall, he declared them to be so clumsily executed that he could not for very shame send them in; and though greatly pressed by mining business, and suffering from "backache, headache, and lowness of spirits," he set to work to copy them with his own hands. He worked up his spare time so diligently, that in ten days he had the plans finished and returned to Boulton, whom he wrote saying that he had improved the construction of several of the machines, and "got one copy of the specification drawing finished in an elegant manner upon vellum, being the neatest drawing he had ever made."[31] The necessary measures being then taken to perfect the patent, it was duly enrolled on the 23rd February, 1782.

During the time that Watt was busy completing the above specification and drawings, his mind was full of other projects, one of which was the perfecting of his new expansive engine.[32] It is curious to find him, in his letters to Boulton, anticipating the plan of super-heating the steam before entering the cylinders, which has since been carried into effect with so much success.

By the middle of March he had sufficiently matured his ideas of a reciprocating expansive engine to enable him to take out letters patent, and the
invention was enrolled on the 4th of July in the same year. It included the
double engine and double-acting engine (steam pressing the piston upwards
as well as downwards), the employment of steam on the expansive principle,
various methods of equalising the power of the engine, the toothed rack and
sector for guiding the piston-rod and a rotative engine or steam-wheel. While
perfecting these beautiful adaptations, Watt was often plunged in the depths
of distress through many causes, – by sickness, headaches, and low spirits; by
the pecuniary difficulties of the firm; by the repeated attempts of the Cornish
miners to lower their dues; and by threatened invasions of his patent from
all quarters. Another of his worries was the unsteadiness of his workmen.
His letters to Boulton were full of complaints on this score. Excepting Wm.
Murdock, who was in constant demand, there was scarcely one of them on
whom he could place reliance. "We have very little credit, indeed," said he, "in
our Soho workmen. James Taylor has taken to dram-drinking at a most violent rate, – is obstinate, self-willed, and dissatisfied." And again, "Cartwright's
engine has been a continued scene of botching and blunders. J. Smith and
the rest are ignorant, and all of them must be looked at daily, or worse follows. Had I had any one man of common prudence and experience, who
would have attended from morning till night, these things might have been
avoided, and my life would have been more comfortable. As things are, it is
much otherwise."[33] Three months later, matters had not mended. J. Smith
is pronounced "a very slow hand," and "J. Taylor is sometimes three days
together at the alehouse, except when he judged I should be going my rounds
… Dick Cartwright also continues too much devoted to beer … I have read
all our men lectures upon industry and good hours, though I fear it will not
be to much purpose; idleness is ingrained in their constitution."[34] Boulton
wrote to him to "send home the most rascally of the Sohoites;" but this was
impracticable, as better men to replace them were not at that time to be had.
Things were quite as bad at Soho itself; for early in 1782 we find Boulton
writing thus: "The forging-shop wants a total reformation; Peploe and others
constantly drunk; spoke mildly to them at first, then threatened, and am now
looking out for good hands, which are very scarce."[35]

William Murdock was by far the ablest and most efficient of the Soho men,
and. won golden opinions in all quarters; so much so, that he was in constant
request. We find him described as "flying from mine to mine," putting the
engines to rights. If anything went wrong, Murdock was immediately sent
for. He was active, quick-sighted, shrewd, indefatigable, and an excellent

workman. His wages, down to 1780, were only 20s. a week, and, thinking himself worth more, he asked for an advance to two guineas. Boulton, instead of refusing, adroitly managed to obtain a present of ten guineas from the owners of the United Mines, to which he added other ten, in acknowledgment of the admirable manner in which he had erected their new engine; Mr. Beauchamp, the Chairman of the Company, having publicly declared that "he regarded William as the most obliging and industrious workman he had ever known." Though Murdock's wages were not then raised, and though Bonze, the Cornish engineer – a man of means as well as of skill and experience – invited him to join in an engineering partnership, William remained loyal to the Boulton and Watt firm, and in due time he had his reward.

Murdook's popularity with the Cornishmen increased so much that Watt seems to have grown somewhat jealous of him, for when William was to be had, they preferred him to Watt himself.[36] At Wheal Virgin, the adventurers insisted upon having him all to themselves; but this was not practicable, as there were other engines in progress requiring constant attention, – Wheal Crenver, which Watt described as "in the enemy's country, Pool hardly completed yet, and Palcoath in its childhood."

"I cannot now leave Wheal Virgin a single day," wrote Watt, "without running the risk of some vile blunder, particularly as the boilers are now setting. Wm. Murdock was at Wheal Virgin one day this week, and that day was taken up with Mr. Wedgwood,[37] so that it was partly lost. Yesterday he was taken away by Crenver people and is not returned. I fear I cannot get much of his help, and I assure you I need it much, for there cannot be a greater plague than to have five engines making by ignorant men and no helpmate to look after them. I have been tolerably well these few days, but cannot get up my spirits, from having too much to think upon."

Combined with the troubles arising out of the perversities, blunderings, and bad conduct of his workmen, Watt had also to struggle against torment of mind and body, aggravated by bad news from home. Boulton was in the crisis of his troubles with his partner Fothergill, from which he was desperately struggling to shake himself free.[38]

Watt was made additionally miserable by the state of the bankers' account, which was still overdrawn to a very large amount. The bankers were urgent for repayment, but neither of the partners saw where the money was to come from. Watt again thought of giving up altogether, and selling his share of the business as the only means of relief which presented itself.

"I am almost moved," he wrote, "if Lowe, Vere, and Williams will free me from any demands on my future industry, to give up my present property altogether, and trust to Providence for my support. I cannot live as I am with any degree of comfort. The want of the superfluities of life is a trifle compared with continual anxiety. I do not see how you can pay L. V. & W. 1000*l.* per quarter; I am sure it cannot be from the engine business, unless we can reduce the amount of our general expenses to 0 and live upon air ourselves … Though you and I should entirely lose this business and all its profits, you will get quit of a burdonsome debt; and as both of us lived before it had a being, so we may do afterwards. Therefore consider what can be done, and do it without reluctance, or with as little as you can; and depend upon it that I am sincerely your friend, and shall push you to nothing that I do not think to be for your advantage."[39]

Two days later, while still in a heavily desponding humour, he wrote thus

If matters were to come to the worst, many methods may be fallen upon whereby we may preserve some consequence in the world. A hundred hours of melancholy will not pay one farthing of debt. Summon up your fortitude and try to turn your attention to business, and to correct the abuses at Soho … All the idlers should be told that in case they persevere in want of attention, then dismission must ensue … The Soho part of the business has been somehow a perpetual drain to us, and if it cannot be put on a better footing, must be cut off altogether by giving out the work to be done by others.[40]

To add to their troubles, a fire broke out in the house of Boulton and Watt's London agent for the sale of their copying machines, and the building, with its contents, was burnt to the ground, thereby causing a loss to the firm of above a thousand pounds. The mining trade was also wretchedly bad in Cornwall, several of the more important mines being unproductive, while ore was selling at low prices. The adventurers were accordingly urging Watt to abate the agreed dues for the use of their engines, and in several cases threatened to close the mines unless he did so. The United Mines asked to be reduced 50*l.* a month. Watt having refused to make the abatement, the mine was ordered to be stopped, on which he consented to give up the dues altogether for a period of six months. "There seemed," he wrote to Boulton, "to be no other course, if we would maintain our right, and at the same time do justice to the poor people, who must otherwise absolutely starve, and are already riotously disposed through the stopping of Wheal Virgin."[41] "In short," said he, "almost the whole county is against us, and look upon us as oppressors and tyrants, from whose power they believe the horned imps of Satan are to relieve them." Watt was indeed thoroughly sick of Cornwall, and longed to get back to Birmingham. He confessed he did not see how, under the present state of things, he could be of any more use there. The weather was very tempestuous, and he felt the fatigue of travelling from mine to mine too much for him to endure. On the 4th of April he wrote, – "I returned from the coast to Cosgarne last night with an aching head, after a peregrination of two days in very stormy weather." "Upon the whole," he wrote to Boulton, "I look upon our present Cornish prospects as very bad, and would not have you build too much upon them nor upon the engine business, without some material change. I shall think it prudent to look out for some other way of livelihood, as I expect that this will be swallowed up in merely paying its burdens."[42] Watt, accordingly, finding that he could do no more good in Cornwall, left it about the middle of April, and returned with an aching head and heavy heart to Birmingham.

NOTES

1   In June, 1780, we find Boulton describing to Colonel Watson the progress of the Soho business, as follows: – "Since I had the honour of seeing you in England we have erected upwards of 40 of our new steam-engines, and have (from so much experience) obviated every difficulty, and made it a most practicable and perfect machine. The steam wheel we have not meddled with since you were at Soho, as we have been fully employed upon large beam-engines; besides, we have applied the beam engine to rotative motions so successfully that the wheel engine seems almost unnecessary."

2   Watt had made use of the crank at a very early period. Thus we find him writing to Dr. Small on the 20th September, 1769, – "As to the condenser, I laid aside the spiral wheels because of the noise and thumping, and substituted a crank: in other respects it performed well enough."

3   The invention was patented by James Pickard, a Birmingham button-maker, on 23rd August, 1780 (No. 1263). Matthew Washborough of Bristol arranged with Pickard for employing it in the engine invented by him for securing circular motion. Washborough's own patent has no reference to the crank, though he is usually named the inventor of it.

4   At a later date we find him writing to his partner thus: – "I cannot agree with Mr. Palmer's notion about the crank engine, as, though a crank is not new, yet that application of it is new and never was practiced by us. It is by

no means our interest to demolish the crank patent, because then all our own machines of that kind will be of no use, and I am convinced that the crank can be made their superior." – Watt to Boulton, 15th October, 1781.

5   Watt to Boulton, 19th November, 1780

6   Boulton and Watt were by this time employing their engine for a like purpose, as appears from a letter of Boulton to S. Wyatt, dated 28th February, 1781, in which he says, – "We are now applying our engines to all kinds of mills, such as corn mills, rolling iron and copper, winding coals out of the pit, and every other purpose to which the wind or water mill is applicable. In such applications, one hunched weight of coals will produce as much mechanical power as is equal to the work of ten men for ten hours, and these mills may be made very much more powerful than any water-mills in England." To Mr. Henderson he wrote at the same date: – "I make no scruple to say but that I could readily build a more powerful and in every respect better copper-rolling mill by steam than any water-mill now in England. As soon as the Cornish engines are at work, I intend to turn millwright and make our steam–mills universally known."

7   Watt to Boulton, 21st April, 1781. On the following day (the 22nd April) Watt wrote another long letter to Boulton on the same subject. His mind could not be at rest, and he thus unburdened himself of his indignation: – "If you find yourself so circumstanced, as you say you are, that you *dare* not refuse [to erect the proposed engine for the Navy Board], then let them pay M. Washborough and have done with him, and let the engine be erected under our direction or Mr. Smeaton's. With the latter I will go hand in hand; nay I will do more – I will submit to him in all mechanical matters; but I will by no means submit to go on with thieves and puppies, whose knowledge and integrity I contemn. Though I am not so saucy as many of my countrymen, I have enough of innate pride to prevent me from doing a mean action because a servile prudence may dictate it. If a king were to think Matt Washborough a better engineer than me, I should scorn to undeceive him. I should leave that to Matthew. The connexion would be stronger as the evidence would be undeniable. So much for heroics! ... I will never meanly sue a thief to give me my own again, unless I have nothing left behind. As it now stands, I have enough left to make their patent tremble, and shall leave no mechanical stone unturned to aggrieve them. I will do more. I will publish my inventions, by which means they will be entirely precluded, because they must be fools indeed that will pay *them* for what they can have for nothing. I am very ill with a headache, therefore can write no more than passion dictates."

8   Washborough was much mortified by the decision of the Navy Board, and
    alleged that he had been badly used by them. The anxieties occasioned by
    his failure, and the pecuniary losses he had sustained, preyed heavily upon
    his mind, and he was seized by a fever which carried him off in October,
    1781, when only in his 28th year. He was unquestionably a young man of
    much ingenuity and merit, and had he lived would have achieved high
    eminence and distinction as an engineer.

9   Boulton to Watt, 21st June, 1781.

10 Watt to Boulton, 21st June, 1781.

11 While Boulton spoke good humouredly to his partner in Cornwall with
    the object of cheering him up, he privately unbosomed himself to his
    friend Matthews in London. When requesting him to call at once on
    the bankers and get the account reduced to an advance of 12,000*l.*, and
    thus obtain Mr. Watt's release, he complained of the distress which the
    communications of the latter had caused him. He thought his conduct
    ungenerous, taking all the circumstances into account, and considering
    that the firm were within a year of being tolerably easy in money matters.
    "When I reflect," he wrote, "on his situation in 1772 and my own at that
    time, I think I owe him little ... I some time ago gave him a security of
    all my two-thirds, after paying off L. V. and W. (the bankers), from which
    you may judge how little reason he has to complain. He talks of his duty
    to his wife and children; by the same rule I ought not to neglect mine.
    His wife's fortune joined to his own did not amount to sixpence: my wife
    brought me in money and land 28,000*l.* I advance him all he wanted
    without security, but in return he is not content with an ample security
    for advancing nothing at all but what he derived from his connexion with
    me." – Boulton to Matthews, 28th June, 1781. Boulton MSS.

12 Watt to Boulton, 24th June, 1781.

13 Watt befriended Jabez like the other members of his family, as appears
    from the following passage in a letter to Boulton (6th September, 1778):
    – "Capt. Paul has turned Jabez adrift, having for some time taken umbrage
    at him because he would do his work well and therefore expensively. Jabez
    had a bad wife, is poor and unhappy. He is very clever, a good engineer,
    and industrious, though he seems not to have the faculty of conciliating
    people's affections. I fear he will go to Holland, and as he can hurt us
    [there being no patent for the engine secured there] I must try to get him
    bread here." Later, Boulton wrote to Watt from Redruth (18th November,
    1780), – "Old Hornblower has disobliged Mr. Daniel. I have my fears they
    will not employ him; but when our own business is sealed to-morrow, I

will make a push in his favour. That family hath not been successful in conciliating the affections of the people in this neighbourhood."

14   Watt to Boulton, 16th July, 1781.

15   Watt to Boulton, 19th July, 1781. Boulton MSS.

16   Boulton to Watt, 28th June, 1781. On 3rd July following he writes, – "The great rotative engine is finished, and I expected the union between it and the little engine would have been performed this evening, but it can't be till to-morrow. Robert set the elliptic out so true that it had no shake and required no alteration. It goes so much better than the little model made by Joseph that I am now ashamed to send the little one. The great model makes a delightful horizontal foot-lathe. I gave it a few strokes with my foot, and it made 30 revolutions after I withdrew it, and that in a quiet and peaceable manner, which shows how steady and frictionless it is."

17   Watt to Boulton, 5th July, 1781.

18   "Yesterday I went to Penryn and swore that I had invented 'certain new methods of applying the vibrating or reciprocating motion of steam or fire engines to produce a continued rotation or circular motion round an axis or centre, and thereby to give motion to the wheels of mills or other machines, which affidavit and petition I transmit to Mr. Hadley by this post with directions to get it passed with all due expectation." – Watt to Boulton, 26th July, 1781.

19   Watt suggested caution as to making use of the cranks. "In relation to Wilkinson's forges, I wish you would execute them without the double crank. We shall soon have a bad enough lawsuit on our hands without it." – Watt to Boulton, 19th July, 1781.

20   Watt to Boulton, 28th July, 1781. A few days later Boulton wrote Watt that Dr. Priestley had proceeded with the experiments, and that he had come to the conclusion that "there is nothing to be feared from any of the tribe of gases, which cannot be produced nearly so cheap as steam; and as to steam *you* know its limits better than any man."

21   Watt to Boulton, 30 th July, 1781. Later he wrote, – "I am tired of making improvements which by some quirk or wresting of the law may be taken from us, as I think has been done in the case of Arkwright, who has been condemned merely because he did not specify quite clearly. This was injustice, because it is plain that he has given this trade a being – has brought his invention into use and made it of great public utility. Wherefore he deserved all the money he has got. In my opinion his patent should not have been invalidated without it had clearly appeared that he did not invent the things in question. I fear we shall be served with the

same sauce *for the good of the public!* And in that case I shall certainly do what he threatens. This you may be assured of, that we are as much envied here as he is at Manchester, and all the bells in Cornwall would be rung at our overthrow." – Watt to Boulton, 13th August, 1781.

22 Watt to Boulton, 13th November, 1781.

23 Watt to Boulton, 19th November, 1791.

24 Watt to Samuel Ewer, jun., 9th July, 1781. Boulton MSS.

25 Watt to Boulton, 30th August, 1781.

26 Watt to Boulton, 30th August, 1781. In a subsequent letter he explained the invention as follows: – "The method I propose to stop an engine when the pump rods break is by means of an air bellows or forcing pump of a good large diameter fixed in the shaft and having a solid piston in it which is wrought constantly by the engine and quite easily while it goes at its ordinary speed, because there is a large valve open in its bottom or rather top, which suffers the air to pace and repass easily; but whenever the engine attempts to move quick, that valve shuts and all exit from the air is cut off, and it becomes a feather-bed to save the blow of the engine. This is exemplified by turning the valve-hole of a common bellows upwards and stopping the nozzle, then working the bellows first slowly and then quickly. I think this contrivance will be of great use and may prevent damage, especially those bangs which occur in setting on an engine." – Watt to Boulton, 27th September, 1781.

27 Boulton to Watt, 10th September, 1781. Boulton immediately proceeded with the erection of the new engine as secretly as possible. "The principles of the expansion engine," said he to Watt, "you had invented before Dr. Small died, as Mr. Keir can testify as well as others. However, it is highly proper to execute every kind of beam that can be devised for the purpose of equalising the power. I have removed the little portions into the wooden house next the smith's shop, and have blinded the window and barred the door. There is a convenient well that can be filled from the back brook, and the engine may be applied to the raising of water, which is the best sort of load to calculate from."

28 Watt to Boulton, 20th September 1781.

29 Watt to Boulton, 18th October, 1781.

30 Watt, in a letter to Boulton, dated the 3rd July, 1782, speaks of it as an old plan of his own "revived and executed by William Murdock but we were informed by the late Mr. Josiah Parkes, that at an interview which he had with Mr. Watt at Heathfield, at which Murdock was present, Murdock spoke of the Sun and Planet motion as his invention, which Watt did not

contradict. Boulton also attributed the invention to Murdock, as appears
from his letter to Henderson, dated 22nd January, 1782; in which be says,
– "Mr. Watt's packet is not ready. I am to wait till his drawings [of the
rotatory motion] are completed, which he is executing himself. There was
some informality in those sent from Soho. Besides, he has another rotative
scheme to add, which I could have told him of long ago, when first
invented by William Murdock, but I did not think it a matter of much
consequence."

31   Watt to Boulton, 26th Jan., 1782.

32   "I have some time ago thought," wrote Watt, "of a new expansive engine
– a reciprocating engine with a heavy circular fly moved by a pinion from
the end of the beam, so as to make three turns per down-stroke and as
many contrariwise per return; so that in the first half of the stroke it may
acquire a momentum which will carry it through the last half; and if a
weight equal to half the load be put upon the inner end of the beam, and
the engine be made to lift it during the return, by making a vacuum above
the piston and using a rack instead of a chain, a cylinder of the present size
may work to the same depth by half the steam; and I believe the engine
will work very sweetly." – Watt to Boulton, 16th January, 1782.

33   Watt to Boulton, 20th September, 1781.

34   Watt to Boulton, 20th December, 1781.

35   Boulton to Watt, 26th March, 1782. The following was Boulton's method
of dealing with a refractory and drunken workman: – "I told you in my
former letters how Jim Taylor had gone on, – that I had talked to him in
a friendly way but all to no purpose. He came last Monday evening to
the smith's shop, drank more ale, was sent for, and he became abusive to
the men, saying we had nobody could work well but himself, and that
we could not do without him. The next morning I went into the shop
pre-determined to part with him. I stopped the noise of the bellows and
hammers, and appealed to the jury of the shop for the justice of my
determination, and made the best use I could of the example. I sent Taylor
off with deserved contempt, and to convince him that we really could do
without him. However we are very much behind in nozzles," – Boulton to
Watt, 19th April, 1782.

36   "To-day was account day at Wheal Virgin, when there was nothing
remarkable, only that Mr. Phillips insisted upon William Mordock being
wholly at Wheal Virgin, which I told him could not possibly be complied
with, unless I went to Crenver in his place, as I had nobody else to send

thither; nevertheless, that William should be here as much as possible. This did not satisfy him, and I know not what to do, as Crenver will be ready to work in three weeks and must not be delayed ... I think my personal attendance should satisfy Wheal Virgin adventurers, but as they seem to have more confidence in William, I will for peace's sake yield to their will, being satisfied that William will do the business well." – Watt to Boulton, 15th November, 1781.

37   One of the pleasantest events that occurred to Watt in the course of his stay in Cornwall was the visit of Wedgwood, who had come to inspect some of the mines in which, on Boulton's recommendation, he had taken an interest, and at the same time to seach for clays for use in his earthenware and porcelain manufacture at Etruria. "Mr. Wedgwood," he wrote Boulton, "has been in this country some days hunting clays and soap rooks, cobalts, &c.. I have had two visits of him at the expense of a day and a half. Nevertheless I don't grudge that, as I am glad to see a Christian. He has just left me." – Watt to Boulton, 18th October, 1781.

38   Fothergill died insolvent in 1782. Notwithstanding what he had suffered by the connexion, Boulton acted with great generosity towards Fothergill's family, providing for his widow and orphan children. "Whatever the conduct of any part of that family towards me may have been," said he, "their present distresses turn every passion into tender pity. I waited upon Mrs. Fothergill this morning, and administered all the consolation that words could give, but I must do more, or their distresses will be great indeed. I never wished for life and health so fervently as at present; for I consider it my duty to act as a father to that family to the best of my power, and the addition of a widow and seven children is no small one." Boulton was as good as his promises; and he not only helped the Fothergill family through their difficulties, but he undertook to pay an annual sum (though under no obligation to do so) to a Mrs. Swellingrebel – a widowed lady from whom Fothergill had obtained money which he lost; and who, but for Boulton's generous help, most have been left destitute.

39   Watt to Boulton, 16th March, 1782.

40   Watt to Boulton, 18th March, 1782.

41   Watt to Boulton, 27th March, 1782.

42   Watt to Boulton, 30th March, 1782.

XVI

More Difficulties and more Inventions – Boulton again in Cornwall

The battle of the firm had hitherto been all up-hill. Nearly twenty years had passed since Watt had made his invention. His life since then had been a constant struggle, and it was a struggle still. Thirteen years had passed since the original patent had been taken out, and seven since the Act had been passed for its extension. But the engine had as yet yielded no profit, and the outlay of capital continued. Notwithstanding Boulton's energy and resources, the partners were often in the greatest straits for money, and sometimes, as Saturday nights came round, they had to beat about among their friends for the means of paying the workmen's wages.

Though Watt continued to imagine himself on the brink of ruin, things were not really so gloomy as he supposed. We find Boulton stating in a confidential letter to Matthews, that the dues payable on the pumping-engines actually erected in 1782 amounted to 4320*l*. a year; and that when all the engines in progress had been finished, they would probably amount to about 9000*l*. It is true, the dues were paid with difficulty by the mining interest, still in a state of great depression, but Boulton looked forward with confidence to better days coming round. Indeed, he already saw his way through the difficulties of the firm, and encouraged his doleful partner to hope that in the course of a very few years more, they would be rid of their burdens.

As Cornwall was, however, now becoming well supplied with pumping-engines, it became necessary to open up new branches of business to keep the Soho manufactory in full work. With this object, Boulton became more and more desirous of applying the engine to the various purposes of rotary motion. In one of his visits to Wales, in 1781, he had seen a powerful copper-rolling mill driven by water, and when told that its defect was that it

was liable to be stopped in summer during drought, he immediately asked
– "Why not use our engine? It goes night and day, summer and winter, and
is altogether unaffected by drought." Immediately on his return home, he
made a model of a steam rolling-mill, with two cylinders and two beams,
connecting the power by a horizontal axis; and by the end of the year he
had a steam forge erected at Soho on this plan. "It answers very well," he
wrote to Matthews, "and astonishes all the ironmasters; for, although it is a
small engine, it draws even more steel per day than a large rolling-mill in this
neighbourhood draws by water." Mr. Wilkinson was so much pleased with
it that he ordered one to be made on a large scale for the Bradley ironworks;
and another was shortly after ordered for Rotherham. But the number of
iron mills was exceedingly limited, and Boulton did not anticipate any large
extension of business in that quarter. If, however, he could once get the rotary
engine introduced as the motive power for corn and flour mills, he perceived
that the demand would be considerable. Writing to Watt on the subject, he
said, "When Wheal Virgin is at work, and all the Cornish business is in good
train, we must look out for orders, as all our treaties are seemingly at an end,
having none now upon the tapis. There is no other Cornwall to be found,
and the most likely line for increasing the consumption of our engines is the
application of them to mills, which is certainly an extensive field."

Watt, on his return to Birmingham from Cornwall, proceeded to embody
his plan for securing rotary motion in a working engine, so that he might be
enabled to exhibit the thing in actual work. He was stimulated to action by
the report which reached his ears that a person in Birmingham had set ago-
ing a self-moving steam rotator, in imitation of his, on which he exclaimed,
"Surely the Devil of Rotations is afoot! I hope he will whirl them into Bedlam
or Newgate."[1] Boulton, who had by this time gone to Cornwall for the winter, wrote to him from Cosgarne, "It is certainly expensive; but nevertheless
I think, as we have so much at stake, that we should proceed to execute such
rotatives as you have specified … You should get a good workman or two to
execute your ideas with despatch, lest they perish. The value of their wages for
a year might be 100l., but it would be the means of our keeping the start that
we now have of all others. But above all, there is nothing of more importance
than the perfect completion of the double expansive reciprocating engine as
soon as may be."[2] Watt replied that he was busily occupied in getting the
rotative motion applied to one of the Soho engines. "These rotatives," said he,
"have taken up all my time and attention for months, so that I can scarcely
say that I have done anything which can be called business. Our accounts lie
miserably confused. We are going on in very considerable weekly expense at

Soho, and I can see nothing likely to be produced from it which will be an equivalent." Speaking of the prospect of further improvements, be added, "It is very possible that, excepting what can he done in improving the mechanics of the engine, nothing much better than we have already done will be allowed by Nature, who has fixed a *ne plus ultra* in most things."[3]

While thus hopelessly proceeding with the rotative engine, Watt was disquieted by the intelligence which reached him from Boulton, as to the untoward state of affairs in Cornwall. At some of the most important mines, in which Boulton and Watt held shares, the yield had greatly fallen off, and the price of the ores being still very low, they had in a great measure ceased to be remunerative. Hence appeals were made to Boulton on all sides for an abatement of the engine dues. Unwilling to concede this, the adventurers proceeded to threaten him with the Hornblowers, whose engine they declared their intention of adopting. As, however, Boulton and Watt's engines were all going exceedingly well, and as the Hornblowers had not yet been able to get one of their boasted engines to work satisfactorily,[4] the adventurers hesitated for the present to take any overt steps in the matter.

Boulton had a long and disagreeable battle to fight with the adventurers on this point, which lasted for many months, during which the Hornblowers continued to stimulate them with the agreeable prospect of getting rid of the dues payable in respect of the savings of fuel by the condensing engines. Boulton resisted them at every point single-handed; the battle being, as he said, "Boulton and Watt against all Cornwall."[5] He kept Watt fully informed from day to day of all that passed, and longed for more rapid means of communication, – the postal service being then so defective that no less than thirteen days elapsed before Boulton, at Truro, could receive an answer from Watt at Birmingham. On one occasion we find Watt's letter eleven days on the road between the two places. The partners even had fears that their letters were tampered with in transit; and, in order to carry on their correspondence confidentially, Watt proposed to employ a shorthand alphabet, which he had learnt from Dr. Priestley, in which to write at least the names of persons, "as our correspondence," he observed, "ought to be managed with all possible secrecy, especially as to names."

Boulton, as usual, led a very active life in Cornwall. Much of his time was occupied in riding from mine to mine, inspecting the engines at work, and superintending the erection of others. The season being far advanced, the weather was bad, and the roads miry; but, wet or dry, he went his rounds. In one of his letters he gives an account of a miserable journey home on horseback, on a certain rainy, windy, dark night in November, when he was "caught in water up to 12 hands." "It is very disagreeable," he adds, "that one cannot stay out till dark upon the most emergent business without risking one's life." But once at home he was happy. "The greatest comfort I find here," he says, "is in being shut out from the world, and the world from me. At the same time I have quite as much visiting as I wish for." One of his favourite amusements was collecting and arranging fossils, some for his friend Wedgwood, and others for his own "fossilry" at Soho. Boulton was well supported out of doors by William Murdock, now regarded as "the right hand" of the concern in Cornwall.

> "Murdock bath been indefatigable," he wrote Watt, "ever since they began [at Wheal Virgin new Engine]. He has scarcely been in bed or taken necessary food … After slaving day and night on Thursday and Friday, a letter came from Wheal Virgin that he must go instantly to set their engine to work or they would let out the fire. He went and set the engine to work: it worked well for the five or six hours he remained. He left it and returned to the Consolidated Mines about eleven at night, and was employed about the engines till four this morning, and then went to bed. I found him at ten this morning in Poldice Cistern, seeking for pins and casters that had jumped out, when I insisted on his going home to bed."[6]

On one occasion, when an engine superintended by Murdock stopped through some accident occurring to it, the water rose in the mine, and the miners were drowned out. Upon this occurring, they came "roaring at him" for having thrown them out of work, and threatened to tear him to pieces. Nothing daunted, he went through the midst of the men, and proceeded to the invalided engine, which he succeeded in very shortly repairing and setting to work again. The miners were so rejoiced that they were carried by their feelings into the opposite extreme; and when he came out of the engine-house they cheered him vociferously, and insisted upon carrying him home on their shoulders in triumph!

About this time, Boulton became increasingly anxious to ascertain what the Hornblowers were doing. They continued to brag of the extraordinary powers of the engine erected by them at Radstoke, near Bristol, whither he proposed to go, to ascertain its construction and qualities; as well as to warn the persons who were employing them as to the consequences of their infring-ing the existing patent. But he was tied to Cornwall by urgent business, and could not leave his post for a day. "During the forking of these two great mines," said he, "I dare not stir two miles from the spot, and it will yet be six weeks before I regain my liberty."[7] He determined, therefore, to send over James Law, a Soho man on whom he could rely, to ascertain, if possible, the character of the new engine and he also, asked his partner Watt to wait upon the proprietors of Radstoke so soon as he could make it convenient to do so. Law accordingly proceeded to Radstoke, and soon found out where the engine was; but as the Horners were all in the neighbourhood, keeping watch and ward over it turn and turn about, he was unable to see it except through the engine-house window, when it was not working. He learnt, however, that there was something seriously wrong with it, and that the engineers were considerably crestfallen about its performances.

Watt proceeded to Bristol, as recommended by his partner, for the purpose of having a personal interview with Hornblower's employers. On his arrival, he found that Major Tucker, the principal partner, was absent; and though he succeeded in seeing Mr. Hill, another of the partners, he could get no satisfactory reply from him as to the intentions of the firm with respect to the new engine. Having travelled a hundred miles on his special errand, Watt determined not to return to Birmingham until he had seen the principal partner. On inquiry he found that Major Tucker had gone to Bath, and thither Watt followed him. At Bath he found that the Major had gone to Melcompton. Watt took a chaise and followed him. The Major was out hunting; and Watt waited impatiently at a little ale-house in the village till three o'clock, when the Major returned – "a potato-faced, chuckle-headed fellow, with a scar, on the pupil of one eye. In short," said Watt, "I did not like his physiog." After shortly informing the Major of the object of his visit, who promised to bring the subject under the notice of his partners at a meeting to be held in about three weeks' time, Watt, finding that he could do no more, took his leave; but, before he left Bristol, he inserted in the local papers an advertisement, prepared by Boulton, cautioning the public against using the Hornblowers' engine, as being a direct infringement of their patent. For the present, indeed, there seemed but little reason to apprehend danger from the Hornblowers, whose engine was still undergoing alterations in detail, if not in principle; and it appeared doubtful, from the trials which had been made of it, whether it would ever prove an economical working engine.

Watt then returned to Birmingham, to proceed with the completion of his rotary motion. Boulton kept urging that the field for pumping-engines was limited, that their Cornish prospects were still gloomy, and that they must very soon look out for new fields. One of his schemes was the applying of the steam-engine to the winding of coals. "A hundred engines at 100*l.* a year each," he said, "would be a better thing than all Cornwall." But the best field of all, he still held, was mills. "Let us remember," said he, "the Birmingham motto, to 'strike while the iron is hot.'"

Watt, as usual, was not so sanguine as his partner, and rather doubtful of the profit to be derived from this source. From a correspondence between him and Mr. William Wyatt, of London, on the subject, we find him discouraging the scheme of applying steam-engines to drive corn-mills; on which Boulton wrote to Wyatt, –

You have had a correspondence with my friend Watt, but I know not the particulars ... You must make allowance in what Mr. Watt says ... he *under* values the merits of his own works ... I will take all risks in erecting an engine for a corn-mill ... I think I can safely say our engine will grind *four* times the quantity of corn per bushel of coal compared with any engine hitherto erected.[8]

About the same time we find Boulton writing to Watt, –

You seem to be fearful that mills will not answer, and that you cannot make Reynolds's amount to more than 20*l*. a year. For my part, I think that mills, though trifles in comparison with Cornish engines, present a field that is boundless, and that will be more permanent than these transient mines, and more satisfactory than these inveterate, ungenerous, and envious miners and mine lords. As to the trouble of small engines, I would curtail it by making a pattern card of them (which may be done in the course of next year), and confine ourselves to those sorts and sizes until our convenience admits of more.[9]

In the mean time Watt, notwithstanding his doubts, had been proceeding with the completion of his rotative machine, and by the end of the year applied it with success to a tilt-hammer, as well as to a corn-mill at Soho. Some difficulties presented themselves at first, but they were speedily surmounted. The number of strokes made by the hammer was increased from 18 per minute in the first experiment, to 25 in the second; and Watt contemplated increasing the speed to even 250 or 300 strokes a minute, by diminishing the height to which the hammer rose before making its descending blow. "There is now no doubt," said he, "that fire-engines will drive mills; but I entertain some doubts whether anything is to be got by them, as by any computation I have yet made of the mill for Reynolds [recently ordered] I cannot make it come to more than 20*l*. per annum, which will do little more than pay trouble. Perhaps some others may do better."[10]

The problem of producing rotary motion by steam-power was thus solved to the satisfaction even of Watt himself. But though a boundless field for the employment of the engine now presented itself, Watt was anything

"Old Bess"[II]

but elated at the prospect. For some time he doubted whether it would be worth the while of the Soho firm to accept orders for engines of this sort. When Boulton went to Dublin to endeavour to secure a patent for Ireland, Watt wrote to him thus: – "Some people at Burton are making application to us for an engine to work a cotton-mill; but from their letter and the man they have sent here, I have no great opinion of their abilities … If you come home by way of Manchester, please not to seek for orders for cotton-mill engines, because I hear that there are so many mills erecting on powerful streams in the north of England, that the trade must soon be overdone, and consequently our labour may be lost." Boulton, however, had no such misgivings. He foresaw that before long the superior power, regularity, speed, and economy, of the steam-engine, must recommend it for adoption in all branches of manufacture in which rotative motion was employed; and he had no hesitation in applying for orders notwithstanding the opposition of his partner. The first rotary engine was made for Mr. Reynolds, of Ketley, towards the end of 1782, and was used to drive a corn-mill. It was some time before another order was received, though various inquiries were made about engines for the purpose of polishing glass, grinding malt, rolling iron, and such like.[12] The first engine of the kind erected in London was at Goodwyn and Co.'s brewery; and the second, still working, though in an altered form, at the Messrs. Whitbread's. These were shortly followed by other engines of the same description, until there was scarcely a brewery in London that was not supplied with one.

In the mean time, the works at Soho continued to be fully employed in the manufacture of pumping-engines. But as the county of Cornwall was becoming well supplied, – no fewer than twenty-one having now been erected there, only one of the old Newcomen construction continuing in work, – it was probable that before long the demand from that quarter must slacken, if not come to an end. There were, however, other uses to which the pumping-engine might be applied; and one of the most promising was the drainage of the Fen lands. Some adventurers at Soham, near Cambridge, having made inquiries on the subject, Watt wrote to his partner, "I look upon these Fens as the only trump card we have left in our hand."[13] The adventurers proposed that Boulton and Watt should take an interest in their scheme by subscribing part of the necessary capital. But Watt decidedly objected to this, as he did not wish to repeat his Cornish difficulties in the Fens. He was willing to supply engines on reasonable terms, but as for shares he would have none of them. The conclusion he eventually arrived at with respect to his proposed customers was this, – "Consider Fen men as Cornish men, only more cunning."

In the midst of his great labours, Boulton was reminded that he was human. He had for years been working at too high pressure, and the tear and wear began to tell upon his health. Watt expostulated with him, telling him that he was trying to do half-a-dozen men's work; but in vain. He was committed to so many important enterprises – had so much at stake – the liabilities he had to meet from day to day were so heavy – that he was in a measure forced to be active. To his friend Matthews he lamented that he was under the necessity of "slaving from morning till night, working fourteen hours a day, in the drudgery of a Birmingham manufacturer and hardware merchant." But this could not last, and before long he was threatened with a break-down. His friends Drs. Withering and Darwin urged him at once to "knock off" and take a long holiday – to leave Soho and its business, its correspondence, and its visitors, and get as far away from it as possible.

Acting on their advice, he resolved on making a long-promised visit to Scotland, and he set out on his tour in the autumn of 1783. He went by Newcastle, where he visited the principal coal mines, and from thence to Edinburgh, where he had some pleasant intercourse with Dr. Black and Professor Robison. It is evident from his letters that he did not take much ease during his journey, for he carried about with him his steam engine – at least in his head. "I talked with Dr. Black and another chemical friend," he wrote, "respecting my plan for saving alkali at such bleach-grounds as our fire-engines are used at instead of water-wheels: the Doctor did not start any objections, but, on the contrary, much approved it." From Edinburgh he proceeded to the celebrated ironworks at Carron, a place in which he naturally felt a peculiar interest. There his friend Roebuck had started his great enterprise, and there Watt had erected his first engine. His visit there, however, was not so much for curiosity or pleasure, but for business and experiment. "During my residence in Scotland," said he, "one month of my time was closely employed at Carron Ironworks in settling accounts, but principally in making a great number of experiments on all their iron ores, and in putting them into the train of making good bar-iron, in which I succeeded to my wishes, although they had never made a single bar of tough iron at Carron before."[14] In the course of his journey be made a large collection of fossils for his museum, and the weight of his bags sensibly increased almost daily. On his way through Ayrshire he called on Lord Dundonald, a kindred spirit in chemical and mechanical scheming, and examined his mineral tar works. He wrote to Mr. Gilbert, the Duke of Bridgewater's manager at Worsley, that "the tar is better for the bottoms of vessels than the vegetable tar; and the coal-oil hath many uses. Query – if such a work might not be a useful appendage to your colliery and canal."

Boulton returned to Soho greatly improved in health, and was shortly immersed as before in the business of the factory. He found considerable arrears of correspondence requiring to be brought up. Several of the letters waiting for him were from schemers of new inventions connected with the steam-engine. Whenever an inventor thought he had discovered anything new, he at once rushed to Boulton with it. He was looked upon as the lord and leader of steam power. His reputation for enterprise and business aptitude, and the energetic manner in which he had pushed Watt's invention, were now so widely known, that every new schemer saw a fortune within his reach could he but enlist Boulton on his side. Hence much of his time was occupied in replying to letters from schemers, – from inventors of perpetual motion, of flying-machines, of locomotion by steam, and of various kinds of rotary motion. In one of his letters we find him complaining of so much of his time being "taken up in answering great numbers of letters he had lately been plagued with from eccentric persons of no business;" for it was his practice never to leave a letter unanswered, no matter how insignificant or unreasonable his correspondent might be.[15]

After a short visit to London, Boulton proceeded into Cornwall to look after the engines there, and watch the progress of the mining operations in which by this time he had become so largely interested. He found the adventurers in a state of general grumble at the badness of the times, the lowness of prices, the losses incurred in sinking for ore that could not be found, and the heaviness of the dues for engine-power payable to Boulton and Watt. At such times, the partners were usually beset with applications for abatement, to which they were under the necessity of submitting to prevent the mines being altogether closed. Thus the dues at Chacewater were reduced from 2500*l.* to 1000*l.* a year, and the adventurers were still pressing for further reductions.[16] What provoked Boulton most, however, was, not the loss of dues so much as the threats which were constantly held out to him that unless the demands of the adventurers were complied with, they would employ the Hornblowers.

> "It is a disagreeable thing," he wrote, "to live amongst one's enemies, and all the adventurers are so, except Phillips and the Foxes, who are fair men although they would rather have engines free. I have had many hints given me that the Trumpeters were reviving their mischief, and many causes for uneasiness, but I did not wish you to partake of them, and therefore have been silent; but they are now striking at the root of us, and therefore we must defend ourselves or fall … I think if we could but keep up our spirits and be active we might vanquish all the host. But I must own that I have been low-spirited ever since I have been here – have been indolent, and feel as if the springs of life were let down."

It does not, however, appear from the letter to Watt in which this complaint occurs, that Boulton had been at all indolent, as he speaks of being in almost daily attendance at the miners' meetings; one day at Poldice, the next at Consolidated Mines, and so on. Of the latter meeting he says, –

> There was a full attendance; Jethro looked impudent, but mortified to see the new little engine drawing kibbles from two pits exceedingly well and very manageable, and afterwards it worked six stamps each 2½=14 cwt., lifted twice at each revolution, or four times for every stroke of the engine. I suppose there were a thousand people present to see the engine work.

Watt was, on his part, rather opposed to making further concessions, which only seemed to have the effect of inviting demands for more.

"People," said he, "do not employ us out of personal regard, but to serve themselves; and why should not we look after ourselves in like manner ... John Taylor died the other day worth 200,000l. without ever doing one generous action. I do not mean that we should follow *his* example. I should not consent to oppression or to take any unfair advantage of my neighbour's necessity, but I think it blameable to exercise generosity towards men who display none towards us. It is playing an unfair game when the advantage is wholly on their side. If Wheal Virgin threatened to stop unless we abated one-half, they should stop for me; but if it appeared that, according to the mode settled in making the agreement, we had too high a premium, I should voluntarily reduce it to whatever was just."

While Boulton was fighting for dues in Cornwall, and labouring as before to improve the business management of the mines in which he was interested as a shareholder, Watt was busily occupied at Soho in turning out new engines for various purposes, as well as in perfecting several long-contemplated inventions. The manufactory, which had for a time been unusually slack, was again in full work. Several engines were in hand for the London brewers. Wedgwood had ordered an engine to grind flints;[17] and orders were coming in for rotative engines for various purposes, such as driving saw-mills in America and sugar-mills in the West Indies. Work was, indeed, so plentiful that Watt was opposed to further orders for rotatives being taken, as the drawings for them occupied so much time, and they brought in but small profit. "I see plainly," said he, "that every rotation engine will cost twice the trouble of one for raising water, and will in general pay only half the money. Therefore I beg you will not undertake any more rotatives until our hands are clear, which will not be before 1785. We have already more work in hand than we have people to execute it in the interval."[18]

One reason why Watt was more than usually economical of his time was, that he was then in the throes of the inventions patented by him in the course of this year. Though racked by headaches which, he complained, completely "dumfounded" him and perplexed his mind, he could not restrain his irrepressible instinct to invent; and the result was the series of inventions embodied in his patent of 1784, including, among other things, the application of the steam-engine to the working of a tilt-hammer for forging iron and steel, to driving wheel-carriages for carrying persons and goods, and for other purposes.

The specification also included the beautiful invention of the parallel motion, of which Watt himself said, "Though I am not over anxious after fame, yet I am more proud of the parallel motion than of any other mechanical invention I have ever made." Watt was led to meditate this contrivance by the practical inconvenience which he experienced in communicating the direct vertical motion of the piston-rod by means of racks and sectors, to the angular motion of the working beam. He was gradually led to entertain the opinion that some means might be contrived for accomplishing this object by motions turning upon centres; and, working upon this idea, he gradually elaborated his invention. So soon as he caught sight of the possible means of overcoming the difficulty, he wrote to Boulton in Cornwall, –

> I have started a new hare. I have got a glimpse of a method of causing a piston-rod to move up and down perpendicularly by only fixing it to a piece of iron upon the beam, without chains or perpendicular guides or untowardly friction, arch heads, or other pieces of clumsiness; by which contrivance it answers fully to expectation. About 5 feet in the height of her house may be saved in 8-feet strokes, which I look upon as a capital saving, and it will answer for double engines as well as for single ones. I have only tried it in a slight model yet, so cannot build upon it, though I think it a very probable thing to succeed. It is one of the most ingenious, simple pieces of mechanism I have ever contrived, but I beg nothing may be said on it till I specify."[19]

He immediately set to work to put his idea to the practical proof; and only eleven days later he wrote, –

> I have made a very large model of the new substitute for racks and sectors, which seems to bid fair to answer. The rod goes up and down quite in a perpendicular line without racks, chains, or guides. It is a perpendicular motion derived from a combination of motions about centres – very simple, has very little friction, has nothing standing higher than the back of the beam, and requires the centre of the beam to be only half the stroke of the engine higher than the top of the piston-rod when at lowest, and has no inclination to pull the piston-rod either one way or another, only straight up and down … However, don't pride yourself on it – it is not fairly tried yet, and may have unknown faults.[20]

Another of Watt's beautiful inventions of the same period was the Governor, contrived for the purpose of regulating the speed of the engine. This was a point of great importance in all cases where steam-power was employed in

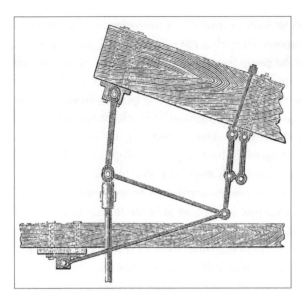

The Parallel Motion

processes of manufacture. To modify the speed of the piston in the single-acting pumping-engine, Watt had been accustomed to use what is called a throttle valve, which was regulated by hand as occasion required. But he saw that to ensure perfect uniformity of speed, the action of the engine must be made automatic if possible, and with this object he contrived the Governor, which has received no improvement since it left his hand. Two balls are fixed to the ends of arms connected with the engine by a moveable socket, which plays up and down a vertical rod revolving by a band placed upon the axis or spindle of the fly-wheel. According to the centrifugal force with which the balls revolve, they diverge more or less from the central fixed point, and push up or draw down the moveable collar; which, being connected by a crank with the throttle-valve, thereby regulates with the most perfect precision the passage of the steam between the boiler and the cylinder. When the pressure of steam is great, and the tendency of the engine is to go faster, the governor shuts off the steam; and when it is less, the governor opens the throttle-valve and increases the supply. By this simple and elegant contrivance the engine is made to regulate its own speed with the most beautiful precision.

Among the numerous proposed applications of the steam-engine about this time, was its employment as a locomotive in driving wheel-carriages. It will be remembered that Watt's friend Robison had, at a very early period, directed his attention to the subject; and the idea had since been revived by Mr. Edgeworth, who laboured with great zeal to indoctrinate Watt with his views. The latter, though he had but little faith in the project, nevertheless included a plan of a locomotive engine in his patent of 1784; but he took no steps to put it in execution, being too much engrossed with other business at the time. His plan contemplated the employment of steam either in the form of high-pressure or low-pressure, working the pistons by the force of steam only, and discharging it into the atmosphere after it had performed its office, or discharging it into an air-tight condenser made of thin plates or pipes, with their outsides exposed to the wind or to an artificial current of air, thereby economising the water which would otherwise be lost.

Watt did not carry his design into effect; and, so far as he was concerned, the question of steam locomotion would have gone no further. But the subject had already attracted the attention of William Murdock, who had for some time been occupied during his leisure hours in constructing an actual working model of a locomotive. When his model was finished, he proceeded to try it in the long avenue leading to the parsonage at Redruth, in the summer of 1784; and in so doing nearly frightened out of his wits the village pastor, who encountered the hissing, fiery little machine, while enjoying his evening walk.[21]

When Watt heard of this experiment, he wrote to Boulton, advising that Murdock should be gently counselled to give up his scheme, which might have the effect of withdrawing him from the work of the firm, in which he had become increasingly useful.

"As to my own part," wrote Watt, "I shall form no obstacle to the scheme. My only reasons against it were that I feared it would deprive us of a valuable man; that it would, if we were to be concerned in it, divert us from more valuable business, and perhaps prove a sinking fund; and lastly, that I did not like that a scheme which I had revolved in my mind for years and hoped to be able at some favourable time to bring to perfection, if capable of it, should be wrested from me, or that I should be compelled to go into it as a secondary person. But I have now made the latter objection give way. And as to the first, I think it will take place at any rate, so we must make the best of it."[22]

Boulton was accordingly recommended in the first place to endeavour to dissuade Murdock from pursuing the subject further, but if he could not succeed in that, rather than lose him, he was to let him have an advance to the extent of 100*l.*, to enable him to prosecute his experiments; and if within a year he succeeded in making an engine capable of drawing a postchaise carrying two ordinary persons and the driver, with 200 lbs. of luggage, fuel for four hours, and water for two hours, going at the rate of four miles an hour, then a partnership was to be entered into, in which Boulton and Watt were to find the capital, and Murdock was to conduct the business and take his share of the profits.

Murdock, however, had so many urgent matters to attend to, that, sanguine though he continued to be as to the success of his scheme, he could not find time to pursue it. He was a man after Boulton's own heart, unsparing of himself and indefatigable in whatsoever he undertook; nor was Boulton sparing of praises of him in his confidential letters to Watt.

"We want more Murdocks," he wrote on one occasion, "for of all our men he is the most active. He is the best engine erector I ever saw, and of his energy I had one of the best proofs this day. They stopped Poldice lower engine last Monday and took her all to pieces; took out the condenser, took up out of the shaft the greatest part of the pumps, took the nozzles to pieces, cut out the iron seatings and put in brass ones with new valves, mended the eduction-pipe, and did a

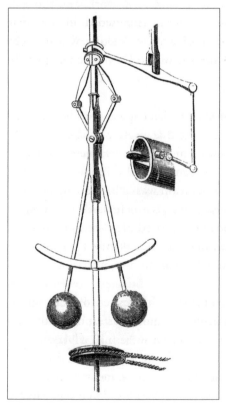

The Governor

great number of repairs about the beam and engine; put the pumps down into the new engine shaft, did much work at the new engine; and this done, about noon both the engines, new and old, were set to work again complete. When I look at the work done it astonishes me, and is entirely owing to the spirit and activity of Murdock, who hath not gone to bed for three nights, and I expect the mine will be in full fork again by Wednesday night. I have got him into good humour again without any coaxing, have prevailed on him not to give up Wheal Virgin engine, which he had been resolved to do from the ungenerous treatment he received from the captains. I have also prevailed on him to put off his determined journey to Scotland until North Downs engines are got to work, and have quieted his mind about wheel carriages till then."[23]

Notwithstanding Watt's fears of a falling off, the engine business still continued to prosper in Cornwall. Although the mining interests were suffering from continued depression, new mines were being opened out, for which pumping-engines were wanted; and Boulton and Watt's continued to maintain their superiority over all others. None of their threatened rivals had yet been able to exhibit an engine in successful work; and those of the old construction had been almost completely superseded. In 1784, new engines were in course of erection at Poldice, New Poldory, Wheal Maid, Polgooth, and other mines. Almost the last of the Newcomen engines in Cornwall had been discarded at Polgooth in favour of one of Boulton and Watt's 58-inch cylinder engines

The dues paid yearly in respect of these and other engines previously erected were very considerable; Boulton estimating that, if duly paid, they would amount to about 12,000*l.* a year. There seemed, therefore, every reasonable prospect of the financial difficulties of the firm at last coming to an end.

Boulton's visit to Cornwall on this occasion was enlivened by the companionship of his wife, and her friend Miss Mynd. Towards midsummer he looked forward with anticipations of increased pleasure to the visit of his two children – his son Matt and his daughter Nancy – during their school holidays. It was a source of much regret to him, affectionate as his nature was, that the engrossing character of his business prevented him enjoying the society of his family so much as he desired. But he endeavoured to make up for it by maintaining a regular correspondence with them when absent. His letters to his children were full of playfulness, affection, and good advice. To his son at school he wrote telling him of his life in Cornwall, describing to him the house at Cosgarne, the garden and the trees he had planted in it, the pleasant rides in the neighbourhood, and the visit he had just been paying to the top of Pendennis Castle, from which he had seen about a hundred sail of ships at sea, and a boundless prospect of land and water. He proceeded to tell him of the quantity of work he did connected with the engine business, how he had no clerk to assist him, but did all the writing and drawing of plans himself: "When I have time," said, he, "I pick up curiosities in ores for the purpose of assays, for I have a laboratory here. There is nothing would so much add to my pleasure as having your assistance in making solutions, precipitates, evaporations, and crystallisations." After giving his son some good advice as to the cultivation of his mind, as calculated to render him an intelligent and useful member of society, he proceeded to urge upon him the duty of cultivating polite manners, as a means of making himself agreeable to others, and at the same time of promoting his own comfort. "But remember," he added, "I do not wish you to be polite at the expense of honour, truth, sincerity, and honesty; for these are the props of a manly character, and without them politeness is mean and deceitful. Therefore, be always tenacious of your honour. Be honest, just, and benevolent, even when it appears difficult to be so. I say, cherish those principles, and guard them as sacred treasures."

At length his son and daughter joined him and took part in his domestic and out-door enjoyments. They accompanied him in his drives and rides, and Matt took part in his chemical experiments. One of their great delights was the fabrication of an immense paper balloon, and the making of the hydrogen gas to fill it with. After great preparations the balloon was made and filled, and sent up in the field behind the house, to the delight of all concerned. To Mrs. Watt he wrote expressing to her how much pleasanter his residence in Cornwall had become since his son and daughter's visit. "I shall be happier," he said, "during the remainder of my residence here than in the former part of it; for I am ill calculated to live alone in an enemy's country, and to contest lawsuits. Besides, the only source of happiness I look for in my future life is in my children. Matt behaves extremely well, is active and good humoured; and my daughter, too. has, I think, good dispositions and sentiments, which I shall cherish, and prevent as much as possible from being sullied by narrow and illiberal-minded companions." After a few months' pleasant social intercourse with his family at Cosgarne, varied by occasional bickerings with the adventurers out of doors about dues, Boulton returned to Birmingham, to enter upon new duties and undertake new enterprises.

Polgooth Engine-House (by R. P. Leitch)

NOTES

1 Watt to Boulton, 19th September, 1782.

2 Boulton to Watt, 28th September, 1782.

3 Watt to Boulton, 3rd October, 1782.

4 "On my road to this place (Cosgrane) I stayed two days at Bristol in order to learn the particulars of Hornblower's new engine erected in that neighbourhood, and I had the satisfaction to find that it is worse than a common engine, although made upon our principles; but from the various evasions introduced it is as bad as need be. Nevertheless I think we should stop it in order to stop the effects of the numerous lies they propagate in this county, and other mischiefs." – Boulton to Watt, 30th September, 1782.

5 "I don't know a man in Cornwall amongst the adventurers," he wrote "but what would think it patriotism to free the mines from the tribute they pay to us, and thereby divide our rights amongst their own dear selves. Nevertheless, let us keep our tempers, and keep the firm hold we have got; let us do justice, show mercy and walk humbly, and all, I hope, will be right at last." – Boulton and Watt, 2nd November, 1782.

6   Boulton to Watt, 30th September, 1782.
7   Boulton to Watson of Bristol, 7th November, 1782.
8   Boulton to Wyatt, 16th December, 1782.
9   Boulton to Watt, 7th December, 1782.
10   Watt to Boulton, 28th November, 1782.
11   The illustration represents the first engine employed at Soho, with the
     alterations subsequently introduced, for the purpose of producing rotary
     motion. The old Kinneil engine, "Beelzebub," as Watt called her, was
     entirely removed, and replaced by this engine, as explained by Watt in his
     MS. Memoir of Boulton now before us, wherein he states, – "The first
     engine of 18 inches cylinder, which was employed in returning the water
     to Soho mill, was replaced about 1778 or 1779 by a larger engine, the first
     on the expansive principle, which still remains there." The engine became
     known at Soho as Old Bess," and she continued in regular work until
     within the last eight years. The illustration shows the state in which the
     engine now stands in South Kensington Museum.
12   We have had a visit to-day from a Mr. Cort of Gosport, who says he has
     a forge there, and has found out some grand secret in the making of iron,
     by which he can make double the quantity at the same expense and in
     the same time as usual. He says he wants some kind of engine, but could
     not tell what; wants some of us to call on him, and says he had some
     correspondence with you on the subject. He seems a simple goodnatured
     man, but not very knowing. He says he has most of the smith-work for
     the king's yard, and has a forge, a rolling and slitting mill. I think him a
     brother projector." – Watt to Boulton, 14th December, 1782.
     A. steam cylinder; B. steam pipe; C. throttle valve; D. steam valve; 5.
     eduction valve; F. eduction pipe; G. valve gearing; H. condenser; I.
     air pump; K. air pump rod; L. foot valve; M. hand gear tappet rod; N.
     parallel motion; O. balance weight; P. rocking beam; Q. connecting
     rod ; R. feed pump rod; S. sun wheel; T. planet wheel; U. fly wheel; W.
     governor; X. feedwater cistern.
13   4th December, 1782.
14   Letter to Thomas Knox, M.P.
15   With an almost excess of politeness, Boulton wrote long letters to
     unknown correspondents to set them right about mechanical errors into
     which they seemed to him to have fallen. Thus a Mr. Knipe of Chelsea,
     supposing he had discovered a perpetual motion machine, wrote inviting
     Boulton to join him as a partner. Though the man was without means and
     evidently foolish, Boulton wrote him several long letters in the kindest

spirit, pointing out that his scheme was contrary to reason and science.
"It is impossible," said he, "for inanimate mechanism to *produce* the
least degree of power or to augment the sum total of the *primum mobile*.
Mechanism may communicate or concentrate or economise power, but
cannot create or augment it." Knipe replied at great length, vindicating his
invention. His enthusiasm pleased Boulton, who, in the generosity of his
nature, sent him a draft for ten guineas on his London bankers to enable
the poor inventor to secure his invention if there was really anything in it.
But nothing more was heard of Knipe's Perpetual Motion Machine.

16 No wonder the miners were so urgent for reductions in working expenses,
as we find from a communication from Watt to Boulton, of facts to be
laid before Parliament against the proposed tax on coal, that Chacewater
had sunk 50,000*l.* in setting the mine to work; Wheal Virgin 28,000*l.* in
ten months, and still unprosperous; Poldice a very large sum, and merely
paying expenses; Wheal Chance 35,000*l.*, and only moderately prosperous;
Pool 14,000*l.*, without much prospect of recovery; Roskere languishing,
and not paying expences; United Mines, which had been at death's door,
still in a tottering state; Wheal Union stopped, after losing about 8000*l.*;
Dalcoath 500*l.* spent on timber per month, and a new kibble-rope, of
above a ton weight, worn out in a fortnight. [To draw a kibble of ore then,
weighing about 3 cwt., took fully fifteen minutes, owing to the great depth
of that mine, and two-thirds of the stuff drawn was stones.] To which Watt
added, "if we had not furnished the miners with more effectual means of
draining the water, almost all the deep mines would have been abandoned
before now."

17 The engine was of 40-horse power. It was erected at the "Black Works,"
Etruria, where it continues working with the sun and planet motion, – one
of the very few engines of the old construction still remaining in existence.

18 Watt to Boulton, 22nd June, 1784.

19 Watt to Boulton, 30th June, 1784. Boulton MSS.

20 The parallel motion was first put in practice in the engine erected for Mr.
Whitbread; Watt informing Boulton (27th October, 1785) that "the parallel
motion of Whitbread's answers admirably."

21 'Lives of Engineers,' iii. 77.

22 In a letter dated 28th August, 1784, Watt communicated his views to his
partner on the subject of locomotive engines at great length. In the course
of the letter he says, –

"My original ideas on this subject were prior to my invention of the
improved engines, or before the crank or any other rotative motions were

thought of. My plan then was to have two inverted cylinders with toothed racks instead of piston rods, which were to be applied to the ratchet wheels on the axletree, and to act alternately; and I am partly of opinion that this method might be applied with advantage yet, because it needs no fly, and has other conveniences.

"From what I have said, and from much more which a little reflection will suggest to you, you will see that without several circumstances turn out more favourable than has been stated, the machine will be clumsy and defective, and that it will cost much time to bring it to any tolerable degree of perfection; and that for me to attempt to interrupt the career of my business to bestow any attention to it, would be imprudent. I even grudge the time I have taken to write these comments on it."

23 Boulton to Watt, 8th November, 1784. Though Murdock was thus occupied, he did not abandon his idea of making a working locomotive. Two years later we find Watt thus writing Boulton: –

"I am extremely sorry that W. Murdock still busies himself with the steam carriages. In one of my specifications I have secured it, as well as words could do, according to my idea of it, and if to that you add Symington's and Sadler's patents, it can scarcely be patentable, even if free of the general specification in the Act of Parliament; for even granting that what I have done cannot secure it, yet it can act as a prior invention against anybody else; and if it cannot be secured by patent, to what purpose should anybody labour at it? I have still the same opinions concerning it that I had, but to prevent as much as possible more fruitless argument about it, I have one of some size under hand, and am resolved to try if God will work a miracle in favour of these carriages. I shall in some future letter send you the words of my specification on that subject. In the mean time I wish William could be brought to do as we do, to mind the business in hand, and let such as Symington and Sadler throw away their time and money in hunting shadows." – Watt to Boulton, 12th Sept., 1786. In a subsequent letter, Watt expresses himself as much gratified to learn "that William applies to his business."

XVII

Commercial Politics – The Albion Mills – Riots in Cornwall – Prosperity of Boulton and Watt

When Boulton returned to Birmingham, he was urgently called upon to take part in a movement altogether foreign to his habits. He had heretofore been too much engrossed by business to admit of his taking any active part in political affairs. Being, however, of an active temperament, and mixing with men of all classes, he could not but feel an interest in the public movements of his time. Early in 1784, we find him taking the lead in getting up a loyal address to the King on the resignation of the Portland Administration and the appointment of Mr. Pitt as Prime Minister. It appears, however, that Pitt disappointed his expectations. One of his first projects was a scheme of taxation, which he introduced for the purpose of remedying the disordered state of the finances, but which, in Boulton's opinion, would, if carried, have the effect of seriously damaging the national industry. The Minister proposed to tax coal, iron, copper, and other raw materials of manufacture, to the amount of about a million a year. Boulton immediately bestirred himself to oppose the adoption of the scheme. He held that for a manufacturing nation to tax the raw materials of wealth was a suicidal measure, calculated, if persevered in, to involve the producers of wealth in ruin. "Let taxes," he said, "be laid upon luxuries, upon vices, and if you like upon property; tax riches when got, and the expenditure of them, but not the means of getting them; of all things, don't cut open the hen that lays the golden eggs."[1]

Petitions and memorials were forthwith got up in the midland counties, and presented against the measure; and Boulton being recognised as the leader of the movement in his district, was summoned by Mr. Pitt to London to an interview with him

on the subject. He then took the opportunity of pressing upon
the Minister the necessity of taking measures to secure reciprocity
of trade with foreign nations, as being of vital importance to the trade
of England. Writing to his partner Scale, he said, "Surely our Ministers
must be bad politicians, to suffer the gates of nearly every commercial city
in the world to be shut against us." "There is no doubt," he wrote to his
friend Garbett, "but the edicts, prohibitions, and high duties laid upon
our manufacturers by foreign powers will be severely felt, unless some
new commercial treaties are entered into with such powers. I fear our
young Minister is not sufficiently aware of the importance of the subject,
and I likewise fear he will pledge himself before Parliament meets to carry
other measures in the next session that will be as odious to the country as
his late attempts."

As Boulton had anticipated, the Ministry introduced several important
measures, calculated to have a highly injurious effect upon English industry,
and he immediately bestirred himself, in conjunction with Josiah Wedgwood
of Etruria, to organise a movement in opposition to them. Wedgwood and
Boulton met at Birmingham in February, 1785, and arranged to assemble a
meeting of delegates from the manufacturing districts, who were to meet
and sit in London "all the time the Irish commercial affairs were pend-
ing." A printed statement of the objects of the movement was circulated,
and Boulton and Wedgwood wrote to their friends in all quarters to meet
and appoint delegates to the central committee in London. Boulton was
unanimously appointed the delegate for Birmingham, and he proceeded to
London furnished with a bundle of petitions from his neighbourhood. The
delegates proceeded to form themselves into a Chamber of Manufacturers,
over the deliberations of which Wedgwood, Boulton, or John Wilkinson
usually presided.

The principal object of these meetings and petitionings was to prevent, if possible, the imposition of the proposed taxes on coal, iron, and
raw materials generally, as well as the proposed export duties on manufactured articles. At a time when foreign governments were seeking to
exclude English manufactures from their dominions by heavy import
duties, it was felt that this double burden was more than English industry
could bear. The Irish Parliament were at the same time legislating in a
hostile spirit towards English commerce; imposing taxes upon all manufactures imported into Ireland from England, while Irish manufactures
were not only sent into England duty free, but their own parliament
encouraged them by a bounty on exportation. The committee strongly

expostulated against the partial and unjust spirit of this legislation, and petitioned for free interchange on equal terms. So long as such a state of things continued, the petitioners urged that "every idea of reciprocity in the interchange of manufactures between Britain and Ireland was a mere mockery of words."

Although Watt was naturally averse to taking any public part in politics, his services were enlisted in the cause, and he drew up for circulation "An answer to the Treasury Paper on the Iron Trade of England and Ireland." The object of his statement was to show that the true way of encouraging manufactures in Ireland was, not by bounties, not by prohibitions, but by entire freedom of industry. It was asserted by the supporters of the propositions, that the natives of Ireland were ignorant, indolent, and poor. "If they be so," said Watt, "the best method of giving them vigour is to have recourse to British manufacturers, possessed of capital, industry, and knowledge of trade." The old covenanting spirit of his race fairly breaks out in the following passage:

It is contemptible nonsense to argue that because Ireland has never had iron manufactories she cannot soon have them ... One hundred years ago the Irish had no linen manufacture; they imported linen; and now they sell to us to the amount of a million annually. How came this about? The civil wars under Charles I, and the tyranny of the Scotch Privy Council under Charles II, chased the people out of Scotland, because they were Presbyterians. Ireland received and protected them; they peopled the northern provinces; many of them were weavers; they followed their business in Ireland, and taught others. Philip II chased the inhabitants out of Flanders, on account of religion; Queen Elizabeth received and protected them; and England learnt to manufacture woollen cloth. The persecutions of Lewis XIV occasioned the establishment of a colony in Spitalfields. And the Parliament of Britain, under the auspices of — and —, and others, imposed oppressive duties on glass; and —'s Act gave the Irish liberty to export it to our Colonies; the glass-makers fled from the tyranny of the Excise; Ireland has now nine glass-houses. Britain has lost the export trade of that article! More examples of the migrations of manufactures could be adduced, but it seems unnecessary; for it cannot be denied that men will fly from tyranny to liberty, whether Philip's Priests, Charles's Dragoons, or our Excisemen be the iustruinents of the tyranny. And it must also be allowed that even the Inquisition itself is not more formidable than our Excise Laws (as far as property is concerned) to those who unhappily are subjected to them.

Towards the end of the statement he asks, "Would it not be more manly and proper at once to invite the Irish to come into a perfect union with Britain, and to pay the same duties and excises that we do? Then every distinction of country might with justice be done away with, and they would have a fair claim to all the advantages which we enjoy." The result of the agitation was that most of the proposals to impose new taxes on the raw materials of manufacture were withdrawn by the Ministry, and the Irish resolutions were considerably modified. But the relations of British and Irish industry were by no means settled. The Irish Parliament might refuse to affirm the resolutions adopted by the British Parliament, in which case it might be necessary again to oppose the Ministerial measures; and to provide for this contingency, the delegates separated, with the resolution to maintain and extend their organisation in the manufacturing districts. Watt did not, however, like the idea of his partner becoming engrossed in political agitation, even in matters relating to commerce. He accordingly wrote to Boulton in London, "I find myself quite unequal to the various business now lying behind, and wish much you were at home, and that you would direct your attention solely to your own and to Boulton and Watt's business until affairs can be brought into reasonable compass."[2] Later he wrote, – "At Manchester they are busy making a collection for the Chamber of Manufacturers, which I fancy will be in vogue again next winter. But I hope that neither you nor I will be mad enough to be demagogues then. Let us leave that to those who can defy Ministers, and get our property secured, which may be done in the confusion."

Watt was at this time distressed by an adverse decision against the firm in one of the Scotch courts. "I have generally observed," be wrote, "that there is a tide in our affairs. We have had peace for some time, but now cross accidents have begun, and more are to be feared." His anxieties were increased by the rumour which reached his ears from several quarters of a grand combination of opulent manufacturers to make use of every beneficial patent that had been taken out, and cut them down by *scire facias*, as they had already cut down Arkwright's. It was said that subscriptions had been obtained by the association amounting to 50,000*l*. Watt was requested to join a counter combination of patentees to resist the threatened proceedings. To this, however, he objected, on the ground that the association of men to support one another in lawsuits was illegal, and would preclude the members from giving evidence in support of each other's rights. "Besides," said he, "the greater number of patentees are such as we could not associate with, and if we did it would do us more harm than good."[3]

Towards the end of 1785 the engines which had been in hand were nearly finished, and work was getting slacker than usual at Soho. Though new orders gave Watt trouble, and occasioned him anxiety, still he would rather not be without them. "It will be well," he wrote to his partner, "if we can get some orders now for engines worth while. What we have been doing lately has been very trifling, and if we don't get orders soon, our men will be idle. As it happens at present, we have at least three engineers too few here, there being eight engines to be done in two or three months, and only three engineers."[4] It was matter of gratification to Watt to be able to report that the engines last delivered had given great satisfaction. The mechanics were improving in skill, and their workmanship was becoming of a superior character. "Strood and Curtis's engine," said he, "has been at work some time, and does very well. Whitbread's has also been tried, and performs exceedingly well." The success of Whitbread's engine was such that it had the honour of a visit from the King, who was greatly pleased with its performances. Not to be outdone, "Felix Calvert," wrote Watt, "has bespoken one, which is to outdo Whitbread's in magnificence."

The slackness of work at Soho was not of long continuance. Orders for rotative engines came in gradually; one from Harris, of Nottingham; another from Macclesfield, to drive a silk-mill; a third from Edinburgh, for the purposes of a distillery; and others from different quarters. The influx of orders had the effect at the same time of filling Soho with work, and plunging Watt into his usual labyrinth of perplexity and distress. In September we find him writing to Boulton, –

"My health is so bad that I do not think I can hold .out much longer, at least as a man of business, and I wish to consolidate something before I give over." ... Again, "I cannot help being dispirited, because I find my head fail me much, business an excessive burden to me, and little prospect of my speedy release from it. Were we both young and healthy, I should see no reason to despair, but very much the contrary. However, we must do the best we can, and hope for quiet in heaven when our weary bones are laid to rest."[5]

A few months later, so many more orders had come in, that Watt described Soho as "fast for the next four months," but the additional work only had the effect of increasing his headaches. "In the anguish of my mind," he wrote, "amid the vexations occasioned by new and unsuccessful schemes, like

Lovelace I 'curse my inventions,' and almost wish, if we could gather our money together, that somebody else should succeed in getting our trade from us. However, all may yet be well. Nature can be conquered if we can but find out her weak side."

We return to the affairs of the Cornish copper-miners, which were now in a very disheartening condition. The mines were badly and wastefully worked; and the competition of many small companies of poor adventurers kept the copper trade in a state of permanent depression. In this crisis of their affairs it was determined that a Copper Company should be formed, backed by ample capital, with the view of regulating this important branch of industry, and rescuing the mines and miners from ruin. Boulton took an active part in its formation, and induced many of his intimate friends in the north to subscribe largely for shares. An arrangement was entered into by the Company with the adventurers in the principal mines, to buy of them the whole of the ore raised, at remunerative prices, for a period of eleven years. At the first meeting, held in September 1785, for the election of Governor, Deputy-Governor, and Directors, Boulton held in his hands the power of determining the appointments, representing, as he did by proxy, shares held by his northern friends to the amount of 86,000*l*. The meeting took place in the Town-hall at Truro, and the proceedings passed off satisfactorily; Boulton using his power with due discretion. "We met again on Friday," he wrote to Matthews, "and chose the assayers and other subordinate officers, after which we paid our subscriptions, and dined together, all in good humour; and thus this important revolution in the copper trade was finally settled for eleven years."

Matters were not yet, however, finally settled, as many arrangements had to be made for setting the Company to work, in which Boulton took the leading part; the Governor and Directors pressing him not to leave Cornwall until they were definitely settled. It happened to suit his convenience to remain until the Wheal Fortune engine was finished – one of the most formidable engines the firm had yet erected in Cornwall. In the mean time he entered into correspondence with various consumers of copper at home and abroad, with the object of finding a vend for the metal. He succeeded in obtaining a contract through Mr. Hope, of Amsterdam, for supplying the copper required for the new Dutch coinage; and he opened out new markets for the produce in other quarters. Being a large holder of mining shares, Boulton also tried to introduce new and economical methods of working the mines; but with comparatively little result. To Wilkinson he wrote, – "Poldice is in a desponding way, and must give up unless better managed. North Downs is managed as badly by incapable, ignorant, drunken captains, who hold their posts not by merit, but by their cousin-ship to some of the adventurers ... I should spend a great part of next year in Cornwall, and make myself master of the minutiæ. I think I could then accomplish many necessary regulations."[6]

Though actively bestirring himself for the good of the mining inter-est, Boulton had but small thanks for his pains. The prominence of his position had this disadvantage, that if the price of the ore went down, or profits declined, or the yield fell off, or the mines were closed, or any-thing went wrong, the miners were but too ready to identify him in some way with the evil; and the services which he had rendered to the mining interest[7] were in a moment forgotten. On one occasion the discontent of the miners broke out into open revolt, and Boulton was even threatened with personal violence. The United Mines having proved unprofitable in the working, notice was given by the manager of an intended reduc-tion of wages, this being the only condition on which the mines could be carried on. If this could not be arranged, the works must be closed, as the adventurers declined to go on at a loss. On the announcement of the intended lowering of wages being made, there was great excitement and discontent among the workpeople. Several hundreds of them hast-ily assembled at Redruth, and took the road for Truro, to pull down the offices of the Copper Mining Company, and burn the house of the manager. They were especially furious with Boulton, vowing vengeance on him, and declaring that they would pull down every pumping-engine he had set up in Cornwall. When the rioters reached Truro, they found a body of men, hastily armed with muskets taken from the arsenal, sta-tioned in front of the Copper Mining Company's premises, supported by six pieces of cannon. At sight of this formidable demonstration the miners drew back, and, muttering threats that they would repeat their visit, returned to Redruth as they had come. Two companies of soldiers and two of local militia were brought into the town immediately after; and the intended assault was not made. When Watt was informed of the violence with which his partner had been threatened, he wrote, – "In my opinion nothing can be more ungrateful than the behaviour of those people who endeavour to make you the object of the resentment of the mob, at a time when (setting aside former services) you are doing all that lies in your power to serve them ... If you still find the same spirit continue, for God's sake leave them immediately. The law can reach the adventurers, if it cannot the miners."

This was, however, but the wild and unreasoning clamour of misguided
and ignorant men. Boulton was personally much esteemed by all who
were able to appreciate his character, and to understand the position of
himself and his partner with reference to the engine patent. The larger
mining owners invited him to their houses, and regarded him as their
friend. The more intelligent of the managers were his strenuous supporters. First and foremost among these was Mr. Phillips, manager of the
Chacewater mines, of whom he always spoke with the highest respect,
as a man of the most scrupulous integrity and honour. Mr. Phillips was a
member of the Society of Friends, and his wife Catherine was one of the
most celebrated preachers of the body. Boulton and Watt occasionally
resided with them before the house at Cosgarne was taken, and conceived
for both the warmest friendship. If Watt was attracted by the Cornish
Anabaptists, Boulton was equally so by the Cornish Quakers. We find
him, in one of his letters to Mrs. Boulton, describing to her a great meeting of Friends at Truro whidh he had attended, "when," he said, "I heard
our friend Catherine Phillips preach with great energy and good sense for
an hour and a half, although so weak in body that she was obliged to lie
abed for several days before." Boulton afterwards dined with the whole
body of Friends at the principal inn, being the only person present who
was not of the Society; and he confessed to have spent in their company a
very pleasant evening.[8]

We return to the progress of the engine business at Soho. The most
important work in hand about this time was the double-acting engine
intended for the Albion Mill, in Southwark.[9] This was the first rotative
with a parallel motion erected in London; and as the more extended use
of the engine would in a great measure depend upon its success, the firm
naturally looked forward with very great interest to its performances. The
Albion Mill scheme was started by Boulton as early as 1783. Orders for
rotatives were then coming in very slowly, and it occurred to him that if
he had but the opportunity of exhibiting the powers of the new engine in
its best form, and in connexion with the best machinery, the results would
be so satisfactory and conclusive as to induce manufacturers generally
to follow the example. On applying to the London capitalists, Boulton
found them averse to the undertaking; and at length Boulton and Watt
became persuaded that if the concern was to be launched at all, they must
themselves find the principal part of the capital. A sufficient number of
shareholders was got together to make a start, and application was made
for a charter of incorporation in 1784; but it was so strongly opposed by

the millers and mealmen, on the ground that the application of steam-power to flour-grinding would throw wind and water mills out of work, take away employment from the labouring classes, and reduce the price of bread,[10] that the charter was refused; and the Albion Mill Company was accordingly constituted on the ordinary principles of partnership.

By the end of the year the Albion Mill engines, carefully designed by Watt, were put in hand at Soho; the building was in course of erection, after the designs of Mr. Wyatt, the architect; while John Rennie, the young Scotch engineer, was engaged to design and fit up the flour-grinding and dressing machinery. "I am glad," wrote Boulton to Watt, "you have agreed with Rennie. Mills are a great field. Think of the crank – of Wolf, Trumpeter, Wasp, and all the ghosts we are haunted by." The whole of the following year was occupied in the erection of the buildings and machinery; and it was not until the spring of 1786 that the mill was ready to start. Being the first enterprise of the kind, on an unprecedented scale, and comprising many novel combinations of machinery, there were many "hitches" before it could be got to work satisfactorily. After the first trial, at which Boulton was present, he wrote his partner expressing his dissatisfaction with the working of the double-acting engine, expressing the opinion that it would have been better if they had held by the single-acting one.[11] Watt was urged to run up to town himself and set matters to rights; but he was up to the ears in work at Soho, and could not leave for a day.

"I can by no means leave home at present," he wrote, "otherwise we shall suf-fer much greater losses than *can* come from the Albion Mill. The work for Cornwall which must be planned and put in train is immense, and there will more come from that quarter. Besides, I am pulled to pieces by demands for forwardness from every side. I have lost ten days by William Murdock, Wilson, Wilkinson, and headaches, and I have neither health nor spirits to make the necessary exertions. If I went to London I should be in torment all the while with the thoughts of what was lying behind here."

After pointing out what course should be taken to discover and remedy the faults of the engine, he proceeded: –

Above all, patience must be exercised and things coolly examined and put to rights, and care be taken not to blame innocent parts. Everything must, as much as possible, be tried separately. Remind those who begin to growl, that in new, complicated, and difficult things, human foresight falls short – that time and money must be given to perfect things and find out their defects, otherwise they cannot be remedied.[12]

Not being able to persuade Watt to come to his help, Boulton sent to Cornwall for Murdock, always ready to lend a hand in an emergency, and in the course of a few weeks he was in town at work upon the engines. The result is best told in Wyatt's letter to Boulton, who had by this time returned to Birmingham: –

> Mr. Murdock has just set the engine to work. All the rods are altered. I think he has done more good than all the doctors we have had before; and his manner of doing it has been very satisfactory – so different from what we have been used to. He has been through all the flues himself, and really takes uncommon pains. Pray write to him; thank him for his attention. He will not have left town before he gets your letter, and press him to stay as long as he can be essentially serviceable.

There was, however, so great a demand for Murdock's presence in Cornwall, that he could not be spared for another day, and he hurried back again to his multifarious duties at the mines.

The cost of erecting the mill proved to be considerably in excess of the original estimate, and Watt early feared that it would turn out a losing concern. He had no doubt about the engines or the machinery being able to do all that had been promised; but he feared that the absence of business capacity on the part of the managers would be fatal to its commercial success.[13] He was especially annoyed at finding the mill made a public show of, and that it was constantly crowded with curious and frivolous people, whose presence seriously interfered with the operations of the workmen. It reached his ears that the managers of the mill even intended to hold a masquerade in it, with the professed object of starting the concern with eclat! Watt denounced this as sheer humbug. "What have Dukes, Lords, and Ladies," said he, "to do with masquerading in a flour-mill? You must take steps to curb the vanity of — , else it will ruin him. As for ourselves, considering that we are much envied at any rate, everything which contributes to render us conspicuous ought to be avoided. Let us content ourselves with *doing*."[14] It was also found that the mill was becoming a nest for schemers and speculators occupied in devising all manner of new projects. Boulton bestirred himself to put matters in a more business-like train. Steps were taken to close the mill against the crowd of idle visitors; and Boulton shortly after reported that "the manufacturing of Bubbles and new schemes is removed from the Mill to a private Lodging."

When the mill was at length set to work, it performed to the entire satisfaction of its projectors. The engine, on one occasion, ground as much as 3000 bushels of wheat in twenty-four hours. The usual rate of work per week of six days was 16,000 bushels of wheat, cleaned, ground, and dressed into fine flour (some of it being ground two or three times over); or sufficient, according to Boulton's estimate, for the weekly consumption of 150,000 people. The important uses of the double rotative engine were thus exhibited in the most striking manner; and the fame of the Albion Mill extended far and wide. It so far answered the main purpose which Boulton and Watt had in view in originally embarking in the enterprise; but it must be added that the success was accomplished at a very serious sacrifice. The mill never succeeded commercially. It was too costly in its construction and its management, and though it did an immense business it was at a loss. The concern was, doubtless, capable of great improvement, and, had time been allowed, it would probably have come round. When its prospects seemed to be brightening,[15] it was set on fire in several places by incendiaries on the night of the 3rd of March, 1791. The villains had made their arrangements with deliberation and skill. They fastened the main cock of the water-cistern, and chose the hour of low tide for firing the building, so that water could not be got to play upon the flames, and the mill was burnt to the ground in a few hours. A reward was offered for the apprehension of the criminals, but they were never discovered. The loss sustained by the Company was about 10,000*l*. Boulton and Watt were the principal sufferers; the former holding 6000*l*., and the latter 3000*l*. interest in the undertaking.[16]

Meanwhile orders for rotative engines were coming in apace at Soho, – engines for paper-mills and cotton mills, for flour-mills and iron-mills, and for sugar-mills in America and the West Indies. At the same time pumping-engines were in hand for France, Spain, and Italy. The steam-engine was becoming an established power, and its advantages were every day more clearly recognised. It was alike docile, regular, economical, and effective, at all times and seasons, by night as by day, in summer and in winter. While the wind-mills were stopped by calms and the water-mills by frosts, the steam-mill worked on with untiring power. "There is not a single water-mill now at work in Staffordshire," wrote Boulton to Wyatt in December; "they are all frozen up, and were it not for Wilkinson's steam-mill, the poor nailers must have perished; but his mill goes on roll-

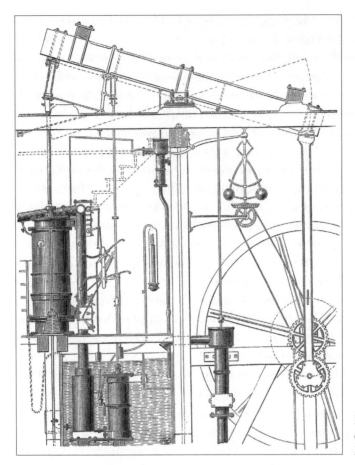

Double-acting
engine, Albion
Mill

ing and slitting ten tons of iron a day, which is carried away as fast as it can be bundled up; and thus the employment and subsistence of these poor people secured."

As the demand for rotative engines set in, Watt became more hopeful as to the prospects of this branch of manufacture. He even began to fear lest the firm should be unable to execute the orders, so fast did they follow each other. '"I have no doubt," he wrote Boulton, "that we shall soon so methodize the rotative engines as to get on with them at a great pace. Indeed, that is already in some degree the case. But have more men, and these we can only have by the slow process of breeding them."[17] A fortnight later he wrote, "Orders for rotative engines are coming in daily; but, if we part with any more men here, we must stop taking them in." Want of skilled workmen continued to be one of Watt's greatest difficulties. When the amount of work to be executed was comparatively small, and sufficient time was given to execute it, he was able to turn out very satisfactory workmanship;[18] but when the orders came pouring in, new hands were necessarily taken on, who proved a constant source of anxiety and trouble. Even the "old hands," when sent to a distance to fit up engines, being left, in a great measure, to themselves, were apt to become careless and ill-conditioned. With some, self-conceit was the stumbling-block, with others temper, but with the greater number, drink. "I am very sorry to bear," wrote Watt to Boulton, "that Malcolm Logan's disease increases. I think you should talk to him roundly upon it, and endeavour to procure him to make a solemn resolution or oath against drinking for some given term." Another foreman sent to erect an engine in Craven was afflicted with a distemper of a different sort. He was found to have put the engine very badly together, and, instead of attending to his work, had gone a-hunting in a pig-tail wig! "If the half of this be true," wrote Watt, "as I fear it is, he will not do to be sent to New River Head [an engine was about to be erected], and I have at present nobody else here ... I suppose I shall be obliged to send Joseph over, for we must not have a bad engine if it can be helped ... We seem to be getting into our old troubles again."[19]

William Murdock continued, as before, an admirable exception. He was as indefatigable as ever, always ready with an expedient to remedy a defect, and willing to work at all hours. A great clamour had been raised in Cornwall during his stay in London while setting the Albion Mill to rights, as there was no other person there capable of supplying his place, and fulfilling his numerous and responsible duties. Boulton deplored that more men such as Murdock were not to be had; – "He is now flying from mine to mine," he wrote, "and hath so many calls upon him that he is inclined to grow peevish; and if we take him from North Downs, Chacewater, and Towan (all of which engines he has the care of), they will run into disorder and ruin; they have not a man at North Downs that is better than a stoker."

Towards the end of 1786 the press of orders increased at Soho. A rotative engine of forty-horse power was ordered by the Plate Glass Company to grind glass. A powerful pumping-engine was in hand for the Oxford Canal Company. Two engines, one of twenty and the other of ten horse power, were ordered for Scotch distilleries, and another order was shortly expected from the same quarter. The engine supplied for the Hull paper-mill having been found to answer admirably, more orders for engines for the same purpose were promised. At the same time pumping-engines were in hand for the great French waterworks at Marli. "In short," said Watt, "I foresee I shall be driven almost mad in finding men for the engines ordered here and coming in." Watt was necessarily kept very full of work by these orders, and we gather from his letters that he was equally full of headaches. He continued to give his personal attention to the preparation of the drawings of the engines, even to the minutest detail. On an engine being ordered by Mr. Morris, of Bristol, for the purpose of driving a tilt-hammer, Boulton wrote to him, – "Mr. Watt can never be prevailed upon to begin any piece of machinery until the plan of the whole is settled, as it often happens that a change in one thing puts many others wrong. However, he has now settled the whole of yours, but waits answers to certain questions before the drawings for the founder can be issued."[20]

At an early period his friend Wedgwood had strongly urged upon Watt that he should work less with his own head and hands, and more through the heads and hands of others.[21] Watt's brain was too active for his body, and needed rest; but rest he would not take, and persisted in executing all the plans of the new engines himself. Thus in his fragile, nervous, dys- peptic state, every increase of business was to him increase of brain-work and increase of pain; until it seemed as if not only his health, but the very foundations of his reason must give way. At the very time when Soho was beginning to bask in the sunshine of prosperity, and the financial troubles of the firm seemed coming to an end, Watt wrote the following profoundly melancholy letter to a friend:

> I have been effete and listless, neither daring to face business, nor capable of it, my head and memory failing me much; my stable of hobby-horses pulled down, and the horses given to the dogs for carrion ... I have had seri- ous thoughts of laying down the burden I find myself unable to carry, and perhaps, if other sentiments had not been stronger, should have thought of throwing off the mortal coil; but, if matters do not grow worse, I may perhaps stagger on. Solomon said that in the increase of knowledge there is increase of sorrow; if he had substituted *business* for knowledge, it would have been perfectly true.[22]

As might be expected, from the large number of engines sold by the firm to this time, and the increasing amounts yearly payable as dues, their income from the business was becoming considerable, and prom- ised, before many years had passed, to be very large. Down to the year 1785, however, the outlay upon new foundries, workshops, and machinery had been so great, and the large increase of business had so completely absorbed the capital of the firm, that Watt continued to be paid his household expenses, at the rate of so much a year, out of the hardware business, and no division of profits upon the engines sold and at work had as yet been made, because none had accrued. After the lapse of two more years, matters had completely changed; and after long waiting, and indescribable distress of mind and body, Watt's invention at length began to be productive to him. During the early part of his career, though his income had been small, his wants were few, and easily satisfied. Though Boulton had liberally provided for these from the time of his settling at Birmingham, Watt continued to feel oppressed by the thought of the debt to the bankers for which he and his partrer were jointly liable. In his own little business he had been accustomed to deal with such small sums, that the idea of being responsible for the repayment of thousands of pounds appalled and unnerved him; and he had no peace of mind until the debt was discharged. Now at last he was free, and in the happy position of having a balance at his bankers. On the 7th of December, 1787, Boulton wrote to Matthews, the London agent, – "As Mr. Watt is now at Mr. Macgregor's, in Glasgow, I wish you would write him a line to say that you have transferred 4000*l.* to his own account, that you have paid for him another 1000*l.* to the Albion Mill, and that about Christmas you suppose you shall transfer 2007*l.* more to him, to balance."

But while Watt's argosies were coming into port richly laden, Boulton's were still at sea. Though the latter had risked, and often lost, capital in his various undertakings, he continued as venturesome, as enterprising as ever. When any project was started calculated to bring the steam-engine into notice, he was immediately ready with his subscription. Thus he embarked 6000*l.* in the Albion Mill, a luckless adventure in itself, though productive in other respects. But he sadly missed the money, and as late as 1789, feelingly said to Matthews, "Oh that I had my Albion Mill capital back again!" When any mining adventure was started in Cornwall for which a new engine was wanted, Boulton would write, "If you want a stop-gap, put me down as an adventurer;" and too often the adventure proved a failure. Then, to encourage the Cornish Copper Mining Company, he bought large quantities of copper, and had it sent down to Birmingham, where it lay long on his hands without a purchaser. At the same time we find him expending 5000*l.* in building and rebuilding two mills and a warehouse at Soho, and an equal amount in "preparing for the coinage." These large investments had the effect of crippling his resources for years to come; and when the commercial convulsion of 1788 occurred, he felt himself in a state of the most distressing embarrassment. The circumstances of the partners being thus in a measure reversed, Boulton fell back upon Watt for temporary help; but, more cautious than his partner, Watt had already invested his profits elsewhere, and could not help him.[23] He had got together his store of gains with too much difficulty to part with them easily; and he was unwilling to let them float away in what he regarded as an unknown sea of speculation.

To add to his distresses, Boulton's health began to fail him. To have seen the two men, no one would have thought that Boulton would have been the first to break down; but so it was. Though Watt's sufferings from headaches, and afterwards from asthma, seem to have been almost continuous, he struggled on, and even grew in strength and spirits. His fragile frame bent before disease, as the reed bends to the storm, and rose erect again; but it was different with Boulton. He had toiled too unsparingly, and was now feeling the effects. The strain upon him had throughout been greater than upon Watt, whose headache had acted as a sort of safety-valve by disabling him from pursuing further study until it had gone off. Boulton, on the other hand, was kept in a state of constant anxiety by business that could not possibly be postponed. He had to provide the means for carrying on his many businesses, to sustain his partner against despondency, and to keep the whole organisation of the firm in working order. While engaged in bearing his gigantic burden, disease came upon him. In 1784 we find him writing to his wine-merchant, with a cheque in payment of his account, – "We have had a visit from a new acquaintance – the gout." The visitor returned, and four years later we find him complaining of violent pain from gravel and stone, to which he continued a martyr to the close of his life. "I am very unwell indeed;" he wrote to Matthews in London; "I can get no sleep; and yet I have been obliged to wear a cheerful face, and attend all this week on M. l'Abbé de Callone and his friend Brunelle."[24] He felt as if life was drawing to an end with him: he asked his friend for a continuance of his sympathy, and promised to exert himself "otherwise," said he, "I will lay me down and die." He was distressed, above all things, at the prospect of leaving his family unprovided for, notwithstanding all the labours, anxieties, and risks he had undergone. "When I reflect," he said, "that I have given up my extra advantage of one-third on all the engines we are now making and are likely to make,[25] – when I think of my children, now upon the verge of that time of life when they are naturally entitled to expect a portion of their patrimony,

– when I feel the consciousness of being unable to restore to them the property which their mother intrusted to me, – when I see all whom I am connected with growing rich, whilst I am groaning under a load of debt and annuities that would sink me into the grave if my anxieties for my children did not sustain me, – I say, when I consider all these things, it behoves me to struggle through the small remaining fragment of my life (being now in my 60th year), and do my children all the justice in my power by wiping away as many of my incumbrances as possible."

It was seldom that Boulton wrote in so desponding a strain as this; but it was his "darkest hour," and happily it proved the one "nearest the dawn." Yet, we shortly after find him applying his energies, apparently unabated, in an entirely new direction – that of coining money – which, next to the introduction of the steam-engine, was the greatest enterprise of his life.

NOTES

1   Boulton to Wilson, 16th December, 1784. Boulton MSS.

2   Watt to Boulton, 31st March, 1785.

3   Watt to Boulton, 21st July, 1785. Writing to Boulton on a later occasion on the subject of these threatened attacks on all patents, he said, "A pursuance of such decisions as have been given lately in several cases must at length drive men of invention to take shelter in countries where their ingenuity will be protected; and the other states of Europe know their interest too well to neglect any opportunity of curbing the insolence and humbling the pride of Britain. If the minister should not think it right to amend and confirm the patent laws, the next best thing would be to make a law totally taking away the king's power of granting them. I mean, this would be the *honest* part." – Watt to Boulton, 19th March, 1786. Boulton himself had equally strong views on the subject of patents, believing that they tended to encourage industrious and ingenious men to labour for the common good. Referring to the decision against Argand's lamp patent, he wrote De Luc in 1787, – "It was hard, unjust, and impolitic, as it hath (to my knowledge) discouraged a very ingenious French chemist from coming over and establishing in this country an invention of the highest importance to one of our greatest manufactures. Moreover, it tends to destroy the greatest of all stimulants to invention, viz, the idea of

enjoying the fruits of one's own labour. Some late decisions against the
validity of certain patents have raised the spirits of the illiberal, sordid,
unjust, ungenerous, and inventionless misers, who prey upon the vitals
of the ingenious, and make haste to seize upon what their laborious
and often costly application has produced. The decisions to which I
refer have encouraged a combination in Cornwall to erect engines on
Boulton and Watt's principles, contrary to the Law of Patents and the
express provisions of an Act of Parliament; and this they are setting
about in order to drive us into a court of law, flattering themselves
that it is the present disposition of the judges to set their faces against
all patents. Should such a disposition (so contrary to Lord Mansfield's
decisions) continue to prevail, it will produce far greater evils to the
manufacturing industry of the kingdom than the gentlemen of the law
can have any idea of."

4   Watt to Boulton, 27th August, 1785.

5   Watt to Boulton, 24th September, 1785.

6   Boulton to Wilkinson, 21st November, 1785.

7   Writing to M. De Luc, the Queen's Librarian, of what he and his partner
had done for Cornwall, Boulton said, – "The copper and tin mines of
Cornwall are now sunk to so great a depth that had not Mr. Watt and
myself nearly expended our fortunes and hazarded our ruin by neglecting
our regular business, and by a long series of expensive experiments in
bringing our engine to its present degree of perfection, those mines
must inevitably have stopped working, and Cornwall at this time would
not have existed as a mining county. The very article of extra coals for
common engines would have amounted to more than the entire profits
of their working." – Boulton to De Luc, 31st March, 1787.

8   Two days after this event, when about to set out for Polgooth, a
messenger arrived at Boulton's lodgings, bringing him the sad news of
Mr. Philips's sudden death. He describes the scene at the funeral, at
which Catherine Philips, though strongly urged by him to stay away,
insisted on being present. "She was attended by a widow lady who lost
a good husband last year, and though she had not been accustomed
to speak in the congregation of the righteous, yet on this occasion
she stood with her hand upon her husband's coffin and spoke above
an hour, delivering one of the most pathetic discourses I ever heard."
A large concourse of people attended the internment, which took
place in a garden near Redruth. Boulton, in writing to Mrs. Boulton,
said, "I wish I had time to give you the history and character of my

departed friend, as you know but little of his excellences. I cannot say but that I feel gloomy pleasure in dwelling upon the life and death of a good man: it incites to piety and elevates the mind above terrestrial things. Now, let me ask you to hold a silent meeting in your heart for half an hour and then return to your work."

9 The Albion Mill engine was set to work in 1786. The first rotative with a parallel motion in Scotland, was erected for Mr. Stein, of Kennet Pans near Alloa, in the following year.

10 In a letter to Mr. Matthews (30th April, 1784) Boulton wrote, – "It seems the millers are determined to be masters of us and the public. Putting a stop to the fire-engine mills because they come into competition with water-mills, is as absurd as stopping navigable canals would be because they interfere with farmers and waggoners. The argument also applies to wind and tide mills or any other means whereby corn can be ground. So all machines should be stopped whereby men's labour is saved, because it might be argued that men were thereby deprived of a livelihood. Carry out the argument, and we must annihilate water-mills themselves, and thus go back again to the grinding of corn by hand labour!"

11 Watt, however, continued to adhere to his own views as to the superiority of the plan adopted: – "I am sorry to find," he observed in his reply to Boulton, "so many things are amiss at Albion Mill, and that you have lost your good opinion of double engines, while my opinion of them is mended. The smoothness of their going depends on the steam regulators being opened a little before the vacuum regulators, and not opened too suddenly, as indeed the others ought not to be. Otherwise the shock comes so violently in the opposite direction that no pins or brasses will stand it. Malcolm has no notion how to make gear work quietly, nor do I think he properly understands it. You must therefore attend to it yourself, and not leave it until it is more perfect." – Watt to Boulton, 3rd March, 1786.

12 Watt to Boulton, 10th March, 1756. – Boulton MSS

13 "The Albion Mill," wrote Watt to Boulton, "requires your close attention and exertions. I look upon it as a weight about our necks that will sink us to the bottom, unless people of real activity and knowledge of business are found to manage it. I would willingly forfeit a considerable sum to be clear of the concern. If anybody will take my share I will cheerfully give him 500*l.* and reckon myself well quit. My reasons are that none of the parties concerned are men of

business, that no attention has been hitherto paid to it by anybody except Mr. W. and ourselves, and that if we go on as expensively in carrying on the business as in the erection, it is impossible but that we should be immense losers, and thus probably our least loss will be to stop where we are. As to our reputation as engineers, I have no doubt but the mill will perform its business, but whether with the quantity of coals and labour is what I cannot say." – Watt to Boulton, 19th March, 1786.

14 Watt to Boulton, 17th April, 1786.

15 Watt wrote Boulton from London, 1st October, 1789, – "I called on Wyatt (the architect) last night. He says the mill sold above 4000*l*. worth of flour last week and is doing well."

16 For further particulars as to the Albion Mill, see Life of Rennie in 'Lives of the Engineers,' ii. 137

17 Watt to Boulton, 23rd September, 1786.

18 He spoke of Goodwyn's Brewery engine, finished in 1784, as the best that Soho had up to that time turned out – it "performed wonderful well – not the smallest leak and scarce any noise … The working gear and joints are the best I ever saw."

19 Watt to Boulton, 24th February, 1786.

20 Boulton to Morris, 2nd November, 1766.

21 "Your mind, my friend, is too active, too powerful for your body, and harasses it beyond its bearing. If this was the case with any other machine under your direction, except that in whose regulation your friends take so much interest, you would soon find out a remedy. For the present permit me to advise a more ample use of *the oil of delegation* through your whole machinery, and I am persuaded you will soon find some salutary effects from this application. Seriously, I shall conclude in saying to you what Dr. Fothergill desired me to say to Brindley – 'Spare your machine a little, or like others under your direction, it will wear out the sooner by hard and constant usage.'" – Josiah Wedgwood to Watt, December 10, 1782.

22 Watt to his brother-in-law, Gilbert Hamilton, Glasgow, June 18, 1786.

23 "Mr. Watt hath lately remitted all his money to Scotland, and I have lately purchased a considerable quantity of copper at the request of Mr. Williams … Besides which I have more than 45 tons of copper by me, 20 of which was bought of the Cornish Metal Company, and 20 of the Duke's at 70*l*., and not an ounce of either yet used. In short, I shall be in a very few weeks in great want of money, and it is now impossible

to borrow in London or this neighbourhood as all confidence is fled."
– Boulton to Wilson, 4th May, 1788.

24 Boulton to Matthews, 22nd December, 1788.

25 Boulton acted with his usual open-handed generosity in his partnership
arrangements with Watt. Although the original bargain between them
provided that Boulton was to take two-thirds, and Watt one-third
profits, Boulton providing the requisite capital and being at the risk and
expense of all experiments, he subsequently, at Watt's request, agreed to
the profits being equally divided between them.

XVIII

Friends of Boulton and Watt –
The Lunar Society

As men are known by the friends they make and the books they read, as well as by the recreations and pursuits of their leisure hours, it will help us to an appreciation of the characters of Boulton and Watt if we glance briefly at the social life of Soho during the period we have thus rapidly passed under review.

Boulton was of a thoroughly social disposition, and made friends wherever he went. He was a favourite alike with children and philosophers, with princely visitors at Soho, and with quiet Quakers in Cornwall. When at home, he took pleasure in gathering about him persons of kindred tastes and pursuits, in order at the same time to enjoy their friendship, and to cultivate his nature by intercourse with minds of the highest culture. Hence the friendships which he early formed for Benjamin Franklin, Dr. Small, Dr. Darwin, Josiah Wedgwood, Thomas Day, Lovell Edgeworth, and others equally eminent; out of which eventually grew the famous Lunar Society.

Towards the close of last century, there were many little clubs or coteries of scientific and literary men established in the provinces, the like of which do not now exist, – probably because the communication with the metropolis is so much easier, and because London more than ever absorbs the active intelligence of England, especially in the higher departments of science, art, and literature. The provincial coteries of which we speak, were usually centres of the best and most intelligent society of their neighbourhoods, and were for the most part distinguished by an active and liberal spirit of inquiry. Leading minds attracted others of like tastes and pursuits, and social circles were formed which proved in many instances the source of great intellectual activity as well as enjoyment. At Liverpool, Roscoe and Currie were the centres of one such group; at Warrington, Aikin, Enfield, and Priestley, of another; at Bristol, Dr. Beddoes and Humphry Davy of a third; and at Norwich, the Taylors and Martineaus of a fourth. But perhaps the most distinguished of these provincial societies was that at Birmingham, of which Boulton and Watt were among the most prominent members.

From an early period, the idea of a society, meeting by turns at each other's houses, seems to have been entertained by Boulton. It was probably suggested in the first by his friend Dr. Small. The object of the proposed Society was to be at the same time friendly and scientific. The members were to exchange views with each other on topics relating to literature, art, and science; each contributing his quota of entertainment and instruction. The meetings were appointed to be held monthly at the full of the moon, to enable distant members to drive home by moonlight; and this was the more necessary as some of them – such as Darwin and Wedgwood – lived at a considerable distance from Birmingham.

When Watt visited Soho in 1768, on his way home from London to Glasgow, some of the members of the Society – Dr. Small, Dr. Darwin, and Mr. Keir – were invited to meet him at *l'hôtel de l'amitié sur Handsworth Heath*, as Boulton styled his hospitable mansion. The Society must, however, have been in a somewhat undefined state at even a considerably later period, as we find Boulton writing to Watt in 1776, after the latter had settled in Birmingham, "Pray remember that the celebration of the third full moon will be on Saturday, March 3rd. Darwin and Keir will both be at Soho. I then propose to submit many motions to the members respecting new laws and regulations, such as will tend to prevent the decline of a Society which I hope will be lasting." The principal members, besides those above named, were Thomas Day, B. Lovell Edgeworth, Samuel Galton, Dr. Withering, Baskerville the printer, Dr. Priestley, and James Watt. Each member was at liberty to bring a friend with him, and thus many visitors of distinction were present at the meetings of the Society, amongst whom may be named Mr. Smeaton, Dr. Parr, Sir Joseph Banks, Sir William Herschel, Dr. Solander, De Luc, Dr. Camper, and occasional scientific foreigners.

Dr. Darwin was regarded as the patriarch of the Society. His fame as a doctor, philosopher, and poet, was great throughout the Midland Counties. He was extremely speculative in all directions, even in such matters as driving wheel-carriages by steam, – also a favourite subject of speculation with Mr. Edgeworth.[1] Dr. Darwin's time, however, was so much engrossed by his practice at Lichfield, that he was not very regular in his attendance at the meetings, but would excuse himself for his absence by such a letter as the following: –

Dear Boulton, – I am sorry the infernal divinities who visit mankind with diseases, and are therefore at perpetual war with Doctors, should have prevented
my seeing all your great men at Soho to-day. Lord! what inventions, what wit,
what rhetoric, metaphysical, mechanical, and pyrotechnical, will be on the
wing, bandied like a shuttlecock from one to another of your troop of philosophers! while poor I, I by myself I, imprison'd in a postchaise, am joggled, and
jostled, and bump'd, and bruised along the King's high road, to make war upon
a stomach-ache or a fever![2]

While Dr, Darwin and Mr. Edgeworth were amongst the oldest members
of the Society, Dr. Priestley, the discoverer of oxygen and other gases, was
one of the most recent. We find Boulton corresponding with him in 1775,[3]
principally on chemical subjects, and supplying him with parcels of fluor spar
for purposes of experiment. Five years later, in 1780, he was appointed minister of the Presbyterian Congregation assembling in the New Meeting-house,
Birmingham; and from that time forward he was one of the most active members of the Lunar Society, by whom he was regarded as a great acquisition.

Dr. Priestley was a man of extraordinaty gifts and accomplishments. He
had mastered many languages before he was twenty years old. He was well
versed in mechanical philosophy and metaphysics, a skilled dialectician, and
the most expert chemist of his time. Possessed of an irrepressible activity and
untiring perseverance, he became an enthusiast on whatever subject he undertook, whether it was an inquiry into history, theology, or science. He himself
likened experimental philosophy to hunting, and in his case it was the *pursuit*
of facts that mainly concerned him. He was cheerful, hopeful, and buoyant;
possessed of a most juvenile temperament; happiest when fullest of work;
ranging from subject to subject with extraordinary versatility; laying aside
metaphysics to pursue experiments in electricity, next taking up history and
politics, and resting from these to experiment on gases, – all the while carrying on some public controversy on a disputed point in religion or politics.
For it is a curious fact, that gentle, affectionate, and amiable though Priestley
was, – devout in temperament, and single-minded in the pursuit of truth,[4]
– he was almost constantly involved in paper wars. He described himself, and
truly, as "one of the happiest of men;" yet wherever he went, in England or
America, he stirred up controversy and exasperated opponents, seeming to be
the very Ishmael of polemics.

At the time when he settled at Birmingham, Priestley was actively engaged
in prosecuting inquiries into the constitution of bodies. He had been
occupied for several years before in making investigations as to the gases.

The discovery of carbonic acid gas by Dr. Black of Edinburgh, had attracted his attention; and, living conveniently near to a brewery at Leeds, where he then was, he proceeded to make experiments on the fixed air or carbonic acid gas evolved during fermentation. From these he went on to other experiments, making use of the rudest apparatus, – phials, tobacco-pipes, kitchen utensils, a few glass tubes, and an old gun-barrel. The pursuit was a source of constant pleasure to him. He had entered upon an almost unexplored field of science. Then was the childhood of chemistry, and he gazed with large-eyed wonder at the marvels which his investigations brought to light. He had no teacher to guide him – nothing but experiment; and he experimented constantly, carefully noting the results. Observation of facts was his great object; the interpretation of the facts he left to others. Such was Priestley, and such were his pursuits, when be settled at Birmingham in 1780.

There can be little doubt that his enthusiasm as an experimenter in chemistry exercised a powerful influence on the minds of both Boulton and Watt, who, though both full of work, anxiety, and financial troubles, were nevertheless found taking an active interest from this time forward in the progress of chemical science. Chemistry became the chief subject of discussion at the meetings of the Lunar Society, and chemical experiments the principal recreation of their leisure hours.

"I dined yesterday at the Lunar Society (Keir's house)," wrote Boulton to Watt; "there was Blair, Priestley, Withering, Galton, and an American 'rebel,' Mr. Collins. Nothing new except that some of my white Spathos Iron ore was found to contain more air than any ore Priestley had ever tried, and, what is singular, it contains no common air, but is part fixable and part inflammable."[5]

To Henderson, in Cornwall, Boulton wrote, two months later, –

Chemistry has for some time been my hobby-horse, but I am prevented from riding it by cursed business, except now and then of a Sunday. However, I have made great progress since I saw you, and am almost an adept in metallurgical moist chemistry. I have got all *that* part of Bergmann's last volume translated, and have learnt from it many new facts. I have annihilated Wm. Murdock's bedchamber, having taken away the floor, and made the chicken kitchen into one high room covered over with shelves, and these I have filled with chemical apparatus. I have likewise set up a Priestleyan water-tub, and likewise a mercurial tub for experiments on gases, vapours, &c., and next year I shall annex to these a laboratory with furnaces of all sorts, and all other utensils for dry chemistry.[6]

Dr. Priestley

The "Priestleyan water-tub" and "mercurial tub" here alluded to, were invented by Priestley in the course of his investigations, for the purpose of collecting and handling gases; and the pneumatic trough, with glass retorts and receivers, shortly became part of the furniture of every chemical laboratory.

Josiah Wedgwood was another member of the Lunar Society who was infected by Dr. Priestley's enthusiasm for chemistry; and, knowing that the Dootor's income from his congregation was small, he and Boulton took private counsel together as to the best means of providing him with funds so as to place him in a position of comparative ease, and enable him freely to pursue his investigations. The correspondence which took place on the subject is creditable to all parties concerned; and the more so to Boulton, as he was embarrassed at the time by financial difficulties of the most distressing kind, as has been already explained in a preceding chapter. Wedgwood had undertaken to sound Dr. Priestley, and he thus communicated the result to Boulton:

> The Doctor says he never did intend or think of making any pecuniary advantage from any of his experiments, but gave them to the public with their results,

just as they happened, and so he should continue to do, without ever attempting to make any private emolument from them to himself.

I mentioned this business to our good friend, Dr. Darwin, who agrees with us in sentiment, that it would be a pity that Dr. Priestley should have any cares or cramps to interrupt him in the fine vein of experiments he is in the midst of, and is willing to devote his time to the pursuit of, for the public good. The Doctor will subscribe, and has thought of some friends who, he is persuaded, will gladly do the same ...

You will see by the enclosed list that one cannot decently exceed ten guineas unless it be under the cover of a friend's name, which method I shall take if I think it necessary to write more than ten; but that is the subscription I shall begin with, and for three years certain.

Dr. Darwin will be very cautious who he mentions this affair to, for reasons of delicacy which will have equal weight with us all. I mentioned *your* generous intention to Dr. P., and that we thought of 20*l*. each; but that, you will perceive, cannot be, and the Doctor says much less will suffice, as he can go on very well with 100*l*. per annum.[7]

Boulton wrote Wedgwood in reply, requesting that the money subscribed should be collected and paid to Dr. Priestley in such a way as not to wound his sensitive feelings. He suggested that in order to avoid this, it might be better if, instead of an annual subscription, a dozen gentlemen were found willing to give a hundred pounds each for the purpose of buying an annuity, or investing the amount in stock for the Doctor's benefit.

"I have never yet spoken to him on the subject," he added; "I wish to avoid it, and so doth my neighbour Galton. Therefore I beg you will manage the affair so that we may contribute our mites to so laudable a plan, without the Doctor knowing anything of the matter, and favour us with a line on the subject at your leisure."[8]

In a subsequent part of the same letter he indicated the subject of Priestley's experiments at the time:

"We have long talked," said he, "of Phlogiston without knowing what we talked about; but now that Dr. Priestley hath brought the matter to light, we can pour that element out of one vessel into another, can take it out of one metal and put it into another, can tell how much of it, by accurate measurement, is necessary to reduce a calx to a metal, which is easily done, and without putting that calx into contact with any visible thing. In short, this goddess of levity can be measured and weighed like other matter. For the rest, I refer you to the Doctor himself."

The discussions at the Lunar Society were not, however, exclusively chemical, but were varied according to the visitors who from time to time honoured the members with their presence. Thus, in the autumn of 1782, the venerable Smeaton, having occasion to be in Birmingham upon canal business, was invited to attend a meeting of the Society held in Watt's house at Harper's Hill. Watt thus described the evening's proceedings in a letter to Boulton, then in London:

> He [Smeaton] grows old, and is rather more talkative than he was, but retains in perfection his perspicuity of expression and good sense. He came to the Philosophers' Meeting at my house on Monday, and we were receiving an account of his experiments on rotatives and some new ones he has made, when unluckily his facts did not agree with Dr. Moyes the blind philosopher's theories, which made Moyes contradict Smeaton, and brought on a dispute which lost us the information we hoped for, and took away all the pleasure of the meeting, as it lasted two hours without coming half an inch nearer to the point.[9]

A few days later, we find De Luc paying his first visit to Watt at Birmingham, accompanied by Baron Reden, who desired to inspect the Soho works. "M. De Luc," wrote Watt, "is a modest ingenious man. On Wednesday, Wilkinson, Reden, and he sent for me to 'The Castle' after dinner, and kept me to supper. On the following day De Luc came to breakfast and spent the whole forenoon, insensing[10] himself with steam and steam-engines. He is making a book, and will mention us in it. Dr. Priestley came also to dinner, and we were all good company till six o'clock, when Wilkinson set off for Broseley, and they for London."

Meanwhile Priestley continued to pursue his investigations with indefatigable zeal, discovering one gas after another,[11] and immediately proclaiming the facts which he brought to light, so that other minds might be employed on them besides his own. He kept nothing secret. Perhaps, indeed, he was too hasty in publishing the results of experiments still unfinished, as it occasionally led him into contradictions which a more cautious method of procedure would have enabled him to avoid. But he was thoroughly honest, ingenuous, and single-minded in all his proceedings, entertaining the conviction that in the end truth would vindicate itself, and that all that was necessary was to inquire ardently, to experiment incessantly, and to publish freely.

One of the most interesting speculations to which Priestley's experiments gave rise was the composition of water. The merit of discovering the true theory has been variously attributed to Watt, to Cavendish, and to Lavoisier; and perhaps no scientific question has been the subject of more protracted controversy. It had been known for some years that a certain mixture of inflammable and dephlogistioated air (hydrogen and oxygen), or common air and hydrogen, could be fired by the electric spark. The experiment had been made by Volta and Macquer in 1776–7; and in the spring of 1781 Priestley made what he called a "random experiment" of the same kind, to entertain some philosophical friends. He exploded a mixture of common air and hydrogen in a glass globe by sending an electric spark through it, and when the explosion had taken place it was observed that the sides of the glass were bedewed with moisture. Mr. Warltire, a lecturer on Natural Philosophy at Birmingham,[12] was present at the experiment, and afterwards repeated it in a copper flask for the purpose of trying "whether heat is heavy or not." In the mean time, Mr. Cavendish, who had for some years been occupied in the special study of pneumatic chemistry, and satisfactorily solved the question of the true composition of atmospheric air, having had his attention directed to Mr. Warltire's experiment, repeated it in London, in the summer of 1781, employing a glass vessel instead of a copper one; and again the deposit of dew was observed on the sides of the glass. This phenomenon, which Priestley had disregarded, appeared to him to be of considerable importance, and "likely to throw great light" upon the subject of the disappearance of oxygen during combustion, which he had been pursuing experimentally by means of his well-known eudiometer. "The liquid which resulted from the detonations was very carefully analysed, and proved in all the experiments with hydrogen and air, and in some of those with hydrogen and oxygen, to be pure water; but in certain of the latter it contained a sensible quantity of nitric acid. Till the source of this was ascertained, it would have been premature to conclude that hydrogen and oxygen could be turned into pure water."[13] These experiments, however, were not published, being still regarded as inconclusive. But with the communicativeness which distinguishes the true man of science, Cavendish made them known to Priestley and, through his friend Dr. Blagden, to Lavoisier. It was not until January, 1784, that he communicated the results of his long series of experiments on the subject to the Royal Society.

In the mean time Watt's attention had been directed to the same subject by the experiments of Priestley, and he was led to the same conclusions as Cavendish, though altogether independent of him, and by means of a differ-ent class of experiments. We find him writing to Boulton, then at Cosgarne, as follows, in 1782:

> You may remember that I have often said that if water could be heated red
> hot, or something more, it would probably be converted into some kind of
> air, because steam would in that case have lost all its latent heat, and that it
> would have been turned wholly into sensible heat, and probably a total change
> of the nature of the fluid would ensue. Dr. Priestley has proved this by experi-
> ment. He took lime and chased out all the fixed air, and made it exceedingly
> caustic by long-continued and violent heat. He then added to it two ounces of
> water, and as expeditiously as possible subjected it again to a strong heat, and
> he obtained two ounces' *weight* of air; and, what is most surprising, a balloon
> which he interposed between the retort and receiver was not sensibly moist-
> ened, nor at all heated that could be observed. The air produced was but very
> little more than common air, and contained scarce any fixed air. So here is a
> plain account of where the atmospheric air comes from. The Doctor does me
> justice as to the theory.[14]

The results of this experiment were by no means conclusive. That water was composed, at least in part, of air or gas of some kind was obvious; but what the gas was, and whether it existed in combination with other gases, was still a matter of conjecture. But Priestley, having proceeded to repeat Cavendish's experiment[15] of exploding a mixture of oxygen and hydrogen in a glass vessel, which was followed by the usual deposit of water, communicated the fact to Watt, and this at once put him on the track of the true theory. In a letter to Dr. Black, he communicated the result of Dr. Priestley's experiments, stating that "when quite dry pure inflammable air (hydrogen) and quite dry pure dephlogisticated air (oxygen) are fired by the electric spark in a close vessel, he finds, after the vessel is cold, a quantity of water adhering to the vessel equal, or very nearly equal, to the weight of the whole air … Are we not then authorised to conclude, that water is composed of dephlogisticated and inflammable air or phlogiston deprived of part of their latent heat; and that dephlogisticated or pure air is composed of water deprived of its phlogiston and united to heat and light; and if light be only a modification of heat, or a component part of phlogiston, then pure air consists of water deprived of its phlogiston or latent heat?"[16] At the same time Watt wrote to Priestley, – who did not himself see the force of the experiments as establishing the true com-position of water, – demonstrating the conclusions which they warranted, and which were identical with those already drawn by Cavendish.

Whether Priestley had communicated to Watt the theory of Cavendish does not appear; but it is probable that both arrived at the same conclusions inde-pendently of each other; Cavendish from the result of his own experiments, and Watt from those of Priestley. Each was quite competent to have made the discov-ery; nor is it necessary for the fame of either to strip a leaf of laurel from the brow of the other. Moreover, we are as unwilling to believe that Cavendish would have knowingly appropriated to himself the idea of Watt, as that Watt would have knowingly appropriated the idea of Cavendish. As it was, however, Cavendish and Watt both claimed priority in the discovery; the advocates of Watt's claim resting their case mainly on the fact of his having first stated his views on the subject in writing, in a letter which he wrote to Dr. Priestley for the purpose of being read to the Royal Society in April, 1783. Before that letter was read, Watt asked that it should be withheld until the results of some new erperiments of Dr. Priestley could be ascertained. These proving delusive, Watt sent a revised edition of the letter to his friend De Luc, in November, but the reading of it was delayed until the 29th April, 1784, before which time, on the 15th January, Cavendish's paper on the same subject had been communicated to the Society. Watt Was much annoyed at the circumstance, and alleged that Cavendish had been guilty of "plagiarism."[17] At a late period of his life, when all bitter feelings on the subject had subsided, Watt declared himself indifferent to the subject of controversy: "After all," said he, "it matters little whether Cavendish or I discov-ered the composition of water; the great thing is, that it *is* discovered."

Pneumatic chemistry continued to form the principal subject of discus-sion at the Lunar Society, as we find from numerous references in Boulton and Watt's letters. "The Lunar Society," wrote Watt to his partner, "was held yesterday at Mr. Galton's at Barr. It was rather dull, there having been no philo-sophical news lately except Mr. Kirwan's discovery of an air from phosphorus, which takes fire of itself on being mixed with common or dephlogisticated air."[18] Among Watt's numerous scientific correspondents was M. Berthollet, the eminent French chemist, who communicated to him the process he had discovered of bleaching by chlorine. Watt proceeded to test the value of the discovery by experiment, after which he recommended his father-in-law, Mr. Macgregor, of Glasgow, to make trial of it on a larger scale. This, however, was postponed until Watt himself could find time to superintend it in person. At the end of 1787, we find him on a visit to Glasgow for the purpose, and writ-ing Boulton that he is making ready for the trial. "I mean," he writes, "to try it to-morrow, though I am somewhat afraid to attack so fierce and strong a beast. There is almost no bearing the fumes of it. After all, it does not appear that it will prove a *cheap* way of bleaching, and it weakens the goods more than could be wished, whatever good it may do in the way of expedition."[19] The experiment succeeded, and we find Mr. Macgregor, in the following February, "engaged in whitening 1500 yards of linen by the process." The discovery, not being protected by a patent, was immediately made use of by other firms; but the offensive odour of the chlorine was found exceedingly objectionable, until it was discovered that chlorine could be absorbed by slaked lime, the solution of which possessed great bleaching power, and this process in course of time superseded all the old methods of bleaching by chlorine.

It has been recently surmised that the action of light upon nitrate of silver formed the subject of discussion at the Lunar Society, and of experiments by Boulton and Watt; but we find no indications of this in their correspondence. They were so unreserved with each other on all matters of business as well as science that, had any phenomena of so remarkable a character as those which have issued in the art of photography become known to either Boulton or Watt, we feel confident that they must have formed the subject of much personal discussion, and of many written communications. But both correspondents are alike entirely silent on the subject; and we infer that no such experiments were made by them, or, if made, that they led to no results![20]

Among the many foreigners who were attracted by this distinguished circle of scientific men, we find M. Faujas-Saint-Fond, who visited Birmingham in the course of his tour in England in 1785, while the circle was as yet unbroken, and Watt, Boulton, Priestley, and the rest, were in the full tide of business, invention, and inquiry. Saint-Fond had the pleasure of dining one day with Watt when Dr. Priestley was present, and describes in glowing terms the interest of their conversation. "Watt," he says, "joins to the frankness of a Scotchman the amiability and kindness of a man of the world. Surrounded by charming children, well educated and full of talent, he enjoys in their midst the happiness of regarding them as his friends, while he is almost worshipped by them as the best of fathers." A subsequent visit which he paid to Dr. Priestley in company with Dr. Withering, leads him to describe the philosopher's house at Fairhill, then about a mile and a half from Birmingham. "It is,' he says, "a charming residence, with a fine meadow on one side, and a beautiful garden on the other. There was an air of perfect neatness about the place within and without." He describes the Doctor's laboratory, in which he conducted his experiments, as "situated at the extremity of a court, and detached from the house to avoid the danger of fire."

It consists of several apartments on the ground floor. On entering it, I was struck with the sight of a simple and ingenious apparatus for making eperiments on inflammable gas extracted from iron and water reduced to vapour. It consisted of a tube, tolerably long and thick, made out of one piece of copper to avoid soldering. The part exposed to the fire was thicker than the rest. He introduced into the tube cuttings or filings of iron, and instead of letting the water fall into it drop by drop, he preferred introducing it as vapour. The furnace was fired by coke instead of coal, this being the best of combustibles for intensity and equality of heat … Dr. Priestley kindly allowed me to make a drawing of his apparatus for the purpose of communicating it to the French chemists who are engaged in the same investigations as himself … The Doctor has embellished his rural retreat with a philo ophical cabinet, containing all the instruments necessary for his scientific labours; as well as a library, containing a store of the most valuable books. He employs his time in a variety of studies. History, moral philosophy, and religion, occupy his attention by turns. An active, intelligent mind, and a natural avidity for knowledge, draw him towards the physical sciences; but a soft and impressible heart again leads him to religious and philanthropic inquiries … I had indeed the greatest pleasure in seeing this amiable savant in the midst of his books, his furnaces, and his philosophical instruments; at his side an educated wife, a lovely daughter, and in a charming residence, where everything bespoke industry, peace, and happiness.[21]

Only a few years after the date of this visit, while Priestley was still busied with his chemical investigations, his house at Fairhill, thus described by Saint-Fond, was invaded by a brutal mob, who ruthlessly destroyed his library, his apparatus, and his furniture, and forced him to fly from Birmingham, glad to escape with his life.

The Lunar Society continued to exist for some years longer. But one by one the members dropped off. Dr. Priestley emigrated to America; Dr. Withering, Josiah Wedgwood, and Dr. Darwin, died before the close of the century; and, without them, a meeting of the Lunar Society was no longer what it used to be. Instead of an assembly of active, inquiring men, it was more like a meeting of spectres with a Death's head in the chair. The associations connected with the meeting – reminding the few lingering survivors of the losses of friends – became of too painful a character to be kept alive; and the Lunar Society, like the members of which it was composed, gradually expired. Its spirit, however, did not die. The Society had stimulated inquiry, and quickened the zeal for knowledge of all who had come within the reach of its influence; and this spirit diffused and propagated itself in all directions. Leonard Horner, who visited Soho in 1809, thus referred to the continued moral influence of the association: – "The remnant of the Lunar Society," he says, "and the fresh remembrance in others of the remarkable men who composed it are very interesting. The impression which they made is not yet worn out, but shows itself, to the second and third generation, in a spirit of scientific curiosity and free inquiry, which even yet makes some stand against the combined forces of Methodism, Toryism, and the love of gain."[22]

NOTES

1   As early as August, 1768, we find Dr. Small in one of his letters describing Edgeworth to Watt as "a gentleman of fortune, young, mechanical, and indefatigable, who has taken a resolution to move land and water carriages by steam, and has made considerable progress in the short space of time that he has devoted to the study."

2   Dr. Darwin to Boulton, April 5, 1778. When the Doctor removed to Derby in 1782, he wrote, – "I am here cut off from the milk of science, which flows in such redundant streams from your learned Lunatics, and which, I can assure you, is a very great regret to me." In another letter he said, – "I hope philosophy and fire-engines continue to go on well. You heard we sent your Society an air-balloon, which was calculated to have fallen in your garden at Soho; but the wicked wind carried it to Sir Edward Littleton's. Pray give my compliments to your learned Society." In another letter he wrote, – "I hope Behemoth has strength in his loins. Belial and Astaroth are two other devils of consequence, and good names for engines of Fire." When he heard of the Albion Mill being burnt down, the Doctor wrote, – "The conflagration of the Albion Mill grieved me sincerely, both as it was a grand and successful effort of human art, but also because I fear you were a considerable sufferer by it. I well remember poor old Mr. Seward comparing the Immortality of the Soul (in a devout sermon) to a fire-engine. He might now have made it a type of the mortality of this world, and the conflagration of all things."

3   In a letter from Priestley to Boulton, dated London, 6th November, 1775, he wrote, – "I shall not quarrel with you on account of our different sentiments in politics. When I tell you what is fact, that the Americans have constructed a cannon on a new principle, by which they can hit a mark at a distance of a mile, you will say their ingenuity has come in aid

of their cowardice! I would tell you the principle of it, but that I am afraid it would set your superior ingenuity to improve upon it for the use of their enemies." From Boulton's memoranda-books we find that the subject of improved artillery had occupied his attention some ten years before.

4   Mrs. Schimmelpenninck, who had no sympathy for Dr. Priestley's religious views, nevertheless bears eloquent testimony to the beauty of his character. She speaks of him as "a man of admirable simplicity, gentleness, and kindness of heart, united with great acuteness of intellect. I can never forget," she says, "the impression produced on me by the serene expression of his countenance. He, indeed, seemed ever present with God by recollection, and with man by cheerfulness ... A sharp and acute intellectual perception, often a pointed, perhaps a, playful expression, was combined in him with a most loving heart ... Dr. Priestley always spent part of every day in devotional exercises and contemplation; and unless the railroad has spoilt it, there yet remains at Dawlish a deep and beautiful cavern, since known by the name of "Dr. Priestley's cavern," where he was wont to pass an hour every day in solitary retirement. – 'Life of Mary Ann Schimmelpenninck.'

5   Boulton to Watt, 3 rd July, 1781. Dr. Black denominated carbonic acid gas "fixed air" because of his having first discovered it in chalk, marble, &c. wherein it was fixed until the furnace or other means extracted it from its fixture.

6   Boulton to Henderson, 6th September, 1781.

7   Wedgwood to Boulton, Etruria, 10th March, 1781.

8   Boulton to Wedgwood, 30th March, 1781.

9   Watt to Boulton, 26th October, 1782.

10   A common word in the north, – meaning literally *putting sense into* one.

11   He discovered, in the course of his inquiries at different periods, no fewer than nine new gases, – oxygen, nitrogen (a discovery also claimed by Cavendish and Rutherford), nitric oxide, nitrous oxide, sulphurous acid, muriatic acid (chlorine), volatile ammonia, fluo-silicic acid, and carbonic oxide, – "a tribute to science," as is truly observed by Dr. Henry, "greatly exceeding in richness and extent that of any contemporary."

12   We find among the Boulton MSS., a letter from Priestley, dated Calne, 28th September 1776, introducing Warltire to Boulton as follows: – "As I know you will take pleasure in everything in which the advancement of science is concerned, I take the liberty to recommend to you Mr. Warltire, who has been some time in this part of the country, and who is going to read lectures on the subject of Air at Birmingham. I think him an excellent

philosopher, as well as a modest and agreeable man. He is perfectly acquainted with his subject, and has prepared a set of experiments which have given the greatest satisfaction wherever he has been. He has been so obliging as to spend some time with me, and has given me much assistance in my late experiments, of which he can give you some account."

13 Wilson's 'Life of Cavendish,' p. 60. In this work, the claims of Cavendish are strongly advocated. The case in favour of Watt is alike strongly and ably stated by Mr. Muirhead in his 'Correspondence of the late James Watt on his Discovery of the Theory of the Composition of Water.'

14 Watt to Boulton, 10th December, 1782.

15 De Luc, Watt's "ami zélé," as he described himself, confirms the fact of Cavendish having, in 1782, communicated to Priestley the nature of his experiments as well as his theory of the composition of water, in the following passage: – "Vers la fin de l'année 1782, j'allai à Birmingham, où le Dr. Priestley s'étoit établi depuis quelques années. Il me communiqua alors que M. Cavendish, d'après une rémarque de M. Warltire, qui avoit tonjours trouvé de l'eau dans les vases où il avoit brúlé un mélange de *l'air inflammable* et *d'air atmosphérique,* s'étoit appliqué a découvrir la source de cette eau, et qu'il avoit trouvé qu'un mélange *d'air inflammable* et *d'air déphlogistique* en proportion convenable, étant allumé par l'étincelle électrique, se convertissoit tout entier en eau. – Je fus frappé au plus haut degré de cette découverte." – 'Idées sur la Météorologie,' tome 2, 1787, pp. 206–7.

16 Watt to Black, 21st April, 1783.

17 That Watt felt keenly on the subject, is obvious from his letter to Mr. Fry of Bristol (15th March, 1784), wherein he says, – "I have had the honour, like other great men, to have had my ideas pirated. Soon after I wrote my first paper on the subject, Dr. Blagden explained my theory to M. Lavoisier at Paris; and soon after that, M. Lavoisier invented it himself, and read a paper on the subject to the Royal Academy of Sciences. Since that, Mr. Cavendish has read a paper to the Royal Society on the same idea, without making the least mention of me. The one is a French financier; and the other a member of the illustrious house of Cavendish, worth above 100,000*l.*, and does not spend 100*l.* a year. Rich men may do mean actions. May you and I always persevere in our integrity, and despise such doings."

18 Watt to Boulton, 20th September, 1785.

19 Watt to Boulton, 30th December, 1787. Boulton MSS.

20 Mr. W. P. Smith, of the Patent Museum, raised this question at a meeting

of the Photographic Society held on 3rd November, 1863. Certain photographic pictures on metal plates were found in Mr. Boulton's library at Soho, which, it was supposed, had not been opened for about fifty years; and it was accordingly inferred that these photographs had been the work of Mr. Boulton, or some member of the Lunar Society, about the year 1791. One of them was supposed to be a view of Soho House "before the alterations, which were made previous to 1791." But the evidence is very defective, as has been clearly shown by M. P. W. Boulton, Esq., the grandson of Mr. Boulton, in his 'Remarks concerning certain Photographs supposed to be of early Date' (Bradbury and Evans, 1864). Instead of having been closed for fifty years, the room in which the pictures were found, was in constant use, and the books were freely accessible. It is also very doubtful whether the house represented in one of the pictures is old Soho House; the strong probability being that it is not, but a house still standing at Winson Green. The explanation given by Mr. M. P. W. Boulton seems to be the true one – that the room in question having been used by a Miss Wilkinson, an experimenter in photography after its invention by Niepce, these photographs were merely the results of her first amateur experiments in the art. The late Mr. Murdock, son of William Murdock of Soho, who lived in the immediate neighbourhood, was also a very good photographist, and was accustomed to meet Miss Wilkinson to make experiments in the new art.

There can be no doubt that the Wedgwoods of Etruria, more particularly Josiah's son Thomas, as well as Humphry Davy, were early engaged in experimenting on the action of light upon nitrate of silver, but they wholly failed in fixing the pictures. A letter, dated "January, 1799," is quoted in the 'Photographic Journal' for Jan. 15, 1864, as from James Watt to Josiah Wedgwood (which must be an error, as Josiah died in 1795), in which the following words occur – "I thank you for your instructions respecting the silver pictures, about which, when at home, I will make some experiments." If such experiments were really made, we have been unable to find any record of them.

21   'Voyage en Angleterre, en Ecosse, et aux Iles Hébrides.' Par B. Faujas-Saint-Fond. 2 vols. Paris, 1797.

22   Horner's 'Memoirs and Correspondence,' ii. 2.

XIX

Boulton's Application of the Steam-engine to Coining

The manufacture of counterfeit money was very common at Birmingham about the middle of last century, – so common, indeed, that it had become an almost recognised branch of trade. The machinery which was capable of making a button with a device and letters stamped upon one side of a piece of metal, was capable, with a few modifications, of making a coin with a device and letters stamped upon both sides. It was as easy to counterfeit one kind of coin as another – gold and silver, as well as copper; the former only requiring a little extra skill in manipulation, to which the button-makers were found fully equal.

The profits of this illegal trade were of course very large; and so long as the coiners could find a vend for their productions, they went on producing. But at length the public, smarting from many losses, acquired sufficient experience to detect the spurious issues of the Birmingham mints; and when an unusually bright shilling or guinea was offered, they had little difficulty in pronouncing upon its "Brummagem"[1] origin. But though profitable, the prosecution of this branch of business was by no means unattended with risks. While some who pursued it on a large scale contrived to elevate themselves among the moneyed class, others, less fortunate, secured an elevation of a very different kind, – one of the grimmest sights of those days being the skeletons of convicted coiners dangling from gibbets on Handsworth Heath.[2]

The production of counterfeit gold and silver coins came to be avoided as too dangerous; but the production of counterfeit copper money continued active at Birmingham down to the middle of last century, when numerous illegal mints were found in active operation. A Royal proclamation was issued on the 12th July, 1751, warning the coiners against the consequences of their illegal proceedings; and shortly after, the Solicitor for the Mint went down to Birmingham, and had many of the more noted offenders tried, convicted, and sentenced to two years' imprisonment. The principal manufacturers and traders of the town met and passed strong resolutions, condemning the practice of illegal coining; but the evil still continued; and in 1753 it was estimated that not less than half the copper coin in circulation was counterfeit. This disgraceful state of the coinage suggested, and partly justified, companies, firms, and local bodies, in circulating copper coinages of their own. These were followed by provincial pence and halfpence, which were, in their turn, counterfeited by pieces of baser metal. Most of the new copper coins of all sorts, good and bad, were executed at Birmingham; and thus coining shortly became one of the leading branches of business there.

Boulton, as the owner of the largest and best-equipped nmanufactory in the neighbourhood, might have done any amount of coining that he desired; but the disreputable character of the business deterred him from entering upon it, and he refused all orders for counterfeit money, whether for home or abroad.[3] He took an active part in the measures adopted by the leading manufacturers to prevent illegal coining; and the interest which he felt in commercial questions generally continued to keep his attention directed to the subject. One of the greatest evils of debased coinage, in his opinion, consisted in the serious losses that it occasioned to the labouring people; many of the lower classes of traders and manufacturers buying counterfeit money from the coiners at half its current value, and paying it in wages at full value, thereby wronging and defrauding the workmen of their hire. He came to the conclusion that the public interest imperatively required that the whole of the so-called copper coinage in circulation should be swept away and superseded by the issue of new coins, the intrinsic value and superior workmanship of which should be so palpable as effectually to suppress counterfeiting and its numerous evils. He had many interviews with the ministers of state on the subject; and we find him alleging in one of his letters to a friend that "his principal reason for turning coiner was to gratify Mr. Pitt in his wishes to put an end to the counterfeiting of money."[4]

Other circumstances, doubtless, concurred in keeping his attention directed to the subject. Thus, he had become largely interested in the copper-trade of Cornwall through the shares he held in the mines as well as in the Copper Mining Company; and he was himself a large holder of copper, which he had purchased from that Company at a time when they could not dispose of it elsewhere. It was also one of his favourite ideas to apply the power of the steam-engine to the stamping of money, – an idea of which he has the exclusive merit. As early as 1774, Watt says Boulton had many conversations with him on the subject; but it was not until the year 1786 that he successfully applied the engine for the first time in executing his contract with the East India Company for above a hundred tons of copper coin. James Watt, in his MS. memoir of his friend Boulton, gives the following account of the origin of his connexion with the coining business: –

When the new coinage of gold took place in 178– , Mr. Boulton was employed to receive and exchange the old coin, which served to revive his ideas on the subject of coinage, which he had long considered to be capable of great improvement. Among other things, he conceived that the coin should all be struck in collars, to make it exactly round and of one size, which was by no means the case with the ordinary gold pieces; and that, if thus made, and of one thickness, the purity of the gold might be tested by passing it through a gauge or slit in a piece of steel made exactly to fit a properly made coin. He had accordingly a proof guinea made, with a raised border, and the letters *en creux*, somewhat similar to the penny pieces he afterwards coined for Government. This completely answered his intention, as any piece of baser metal which filled the gauge was found to be considerably lighter; or, if made to the proper weight, then it would not go through the gauge. Such money was also less liable to wear in the pocket than the common coin, where all the impression was prominent. The proposals on this head were not however approved by those who then had the management of His Majesty's Mint, and there the matter rested for the time.

In 1786 Mr. Boulton and I were in France, where we saw a very fine crown-piece executed by Mr. P. Droz in a new manner. It was coined in a collar split into six parts, which came together when the dies were brought in contact with the blank, and formed the edge and the inscription upon it. Mr. Droz had also made several improvements in the coining-press, and pretended to others in the art of multiplying the dies. As, to his mechanical abilities, Droz joined that of being a good die-sinker, Mr. Boulton contracted with him to come over to England at a high salary and work at Soho, Mr. B. having then the prospect of an extensive copper coinage for the East India Company as well as a probability of one from Government. In anticipation of this contract, a number of coining-presses were constructed, and a steam-engine was applied to work them.

Mr. Droz was found to be of a very troublesome disposition. Several of his contrivances, being found not to answer, were obliged to be better contrived or totally changed by Mr. Boulton and his assistants. The split collar was found to be difficult of execution, and being subject to wear very soon when in use, it was consequently unfit for an extensive coinage. Other methods were therefore invented and applied by Mr. Boulton, and the use of Droz's collar was entirely given up.[5]

Although the machinery of the "Hôtel de Monnaie," which Boulton erected at Soho, was found sufficient for the execution of his contract with the East India Company, its action was "violent and noisy," and did not work to his satisfaction. He accordingly, with his usual determination to reach the highest degree of mechanical perfection, proceeded to remodel the whole of his coining machinery, in the course of which he introduced many entirely new contrivances and adaptations. In this he was ably assisted by William Murdock, Peter Ewart, James Lawson, and John Southern; but he himself was throughout the leading spirit, and took the principal part of the work. He originated numerous essential improvements in the rolling, annealing, and cleaning of the metal, – in the forging, multiplying, and tempering of the dies, – and in the construction of the milling and cutting-out machines, – which were worked out in detail by his assistants, after various trials, examined and tested by himself; while the arrangement and methodising of the system of coining – in a word, the organisation of the mint – was entirely his own work. "To his indefatigable energy and perseverance," wrote Murdock many years later, "in pursuit of this, the favourite and nearly the sole object of the last twenty years of the active part of Mr. Boulton's life, is, in a great measure, to be attributed the perfection to which the art of coining has ultimately attained."[6]

While thus labouring at the improvement of his presses, dies, ad the application of the steam-engine to the process of coining, Boulton was actively engaged in stirring up public opinion on time subject of an improved copper coinage. Six presses were fitted and ready for work at Soho by the end of 1788;[7] but the only considerable orders which had as yet been executed were the copper coinage of the East India Company, another for the American Colonies, and a silver coinage for the Sierra Leone Company; so that the Soho mint, notwithstanding the capital, skill, and labour bestowed upon it, remained comparatively idle. Boulton continued to stir up the Government through his influential friends;[8] and he was at length called before the Privy Council and examined as to the best means of preventing the issue of counterfeit money. He stated his views to them at great length; and the members were so much impressed by his statements that they authorised him to prepare and submit to them a model penny, halfpenny, and farthing. This he at once proceeded to do, and forwarded them to the Privy Council, accompanied by an elaborate report, setting forth the superiority of the new coins over those then issued from the Mint; demonstrating that their adoption would effectually prevent counterfeiting of base copper money, and offering to guarantee the execution of a contract for a new coinage, at "not exceeding half the expense which the common copper coin hath always cost at his Majesty's Mint."[9]

Although the specimens submitted by Boulton to the Privy Council were approved and eventually adopted, the officials of the Mint were enabled, by mere passive resistance, to delay the adoption of the new copper coinage for more than ten years. With their lumbering machinery they could not execute one-third part of the copper coin required for the ordinary purposes of currency; but they could not brook the idea of inviting a private individual to do that which they were found unable to do with all the powers of the State at their back. Rather than thus publicly confess their incompetency, they were satisfied to execute only one-third of the copper coinage, leaving it to the forgers and private coiners to supply the rest.

Boulton began to fear that the coining presses which he had erected with so much labour, contrivance, and expenditure of money, in anticipation of the expected Government contract, would remain comparatively idle after all. But he did not readily give up the idea of executing the new coinage. "Of all the mechanical subjects I ever entered upon," he wrote Mr. Garbett, "there is none in which I ever engaged with so much ardour as that of bringing to perfection the art of coining in the reign of George III, as well as of checking the injurious and fatal crime of counterfeiting." It occurred to him that it might be possible to overcome the obstructiveness of officialism by means of public opinion; and he proceeded with his usual vigour to rouse the trading interests throughout the country on the subject. He had a statement printed and extensively circulated among the leading merchants and manufacturers, to whom he also sent specimens of his model penny and halfpenny, the superiority of which to the rubbishy government and counterfeit coin then in circulation, was made apparent at a glance. He also endeavoured to act upon the Ministry through the influence of the King, to whom he presented copies of his model gold, silver, and copper coins; but though his Majesty expressed himself highly pleased with them, the question of their adoption still remained as much in suspense as ever. The appeals to the public were followed by numerous petitions to Parliament and memorials to the Privy Council against counterfeit money, and in favour of the proposed Boulton coinage.[10]

In the mean time, to find employment for the coining presses he had set up, Boulton sought for orders from foreign and colonial governments. In 1790 and 1792 he executed a large quantity of beautiful copper coin[11] for the revolutionary government of France while we remained at peace with that country. The coin was afterwards suppressed when the government was overturned, to the great loss of the French contractors, who, nevertheless, honourably fulfilled their engagement with Mr. Boulton. In 1791 he executed for the colony of Bermuda a penny coinage; about the same time he turned out a large number of provincial halfpenny tokens;[12] and in 1794 he supplied the Madras Presidency with its four-faluce and two-faluce coinage. By way of exhibiting the artistic skill of Soho, and its ability to turn out first-class medal work, Boulton took advantage of the King's recovery in 1789, to execute a very fine medal commemorative of the event. He sent the first specimen to his friend M. De Luc, the Queen's Librarian at Windsor, for presentation to her Majesty, who expressed herself much pleased with the medal. In his letter to De Luc, Boulton stated that he had been the more desirous of turning out a creditable piece of workmanship, as the art of medalling was one of the most backward in England, and had made the least progress of any during the reign of his present Majesty. In preparing this medal, he had the co-operation of Benjamin West, President of the Royal Academy, who rendered him valuable assistance in supplying the best models and portraits of the King from which a satisfactory likeness could be made, and he also inspected and corrected the engraving of the dies.

The success of the medal commemorative of the King's preservation was such as to induce Boulton to prosecute this department of business, – not that it was attended with profit, for some of his most costly medals were produced for presentation to individuals, and not for sale, – but that it increased the reputation of Soho, and reflected new credit upon the art manufacture of England.

In preparing the dies for his various coins and medals, we find Boulton seeking and obtaining the assistance of Nollekens, Flaxman, Bacon, and Wilton (sculptors); Mayer (King's miniature painter); Gossett (modeller); but above all, he was mostly indebted for friendly help to Benjamin West, who cordially entered into his views of "establishing elegant records of the medallic arts in the reign of George III." Boulton also executed a series of medals commemorative of the great events of the French Revolution, for which there must have been a considerable demand, as we find him sending at one time not less than twenty tons of historical medals to Messrs. Monneron his Paris agents. Amongst these, we may mention his medals of the following subjects: – The Emperor of Russia; Assassination of the King of Sweden; Restoration of the King of Naples; Final Interview of the King of France; Execution of the King of France; Execution of the Queen of France; Serment du Roi; Lafayette; J. J. Rousseau; and Respublica Gallica.[13]

The Boulton MS. contains a brief description, in Mr. Boulton's handwriting, of the Soho Mint in 1792, from which we make the following extract:

This Mint consists of eight large coining-machines, which are sufficiently strong to coin the largest money in current use, or even medals; and each machine is capable of being adjusted in a few minutes, so as to strike any number of pieces of money from fifty to one hundred and twenty per minute, in proportion to their diameter and degree of relief; and each piece being struck in a steel collar, the whole number are perfectly round and of equal diameter. Each machine requires the attendance of one boy of only twelve years of age, and he has no labour to perform. He can stop his press one instant, and set it going again the next. The whole of the eight presses are capable of coining, at the same time, eight different sizes of money, such as English crowns, 6-livre pieces, 24-sous pieces, 12-sous, or the very smallest money that is used in France. The number of blows at each press is proportioned to the size of the pieces, say from fifty to one hundred and twenty blows per minute, and if greater speed is wanted, he has smaller machines that will strike 200 per minute.

As the blows given by Mr. B.'s machinery are much more uniform than what are given by the strength of men's arms when applied to the working of the common press, the dies are not so liable to break, nor the spirit of the engraving to be so soon injured; yet nevertheless, from the natural imperfections of steel, and other unavoidable causes, some time will be lost in changing the dies and other interruptions. However, it is decided by experience that Mr. Boulton's new machinery works with less friction, less wear, less noise, is less liable to be out of order, and can strike very much more than any apparatus ever before invented; for it is capable of striking at the rate of 26,000 écus or English crowns, or 50,000 of half their diameter, in one hour, and of working night and day without fatigue to the boys, provided two sets of them work alternately for ten hours each.

When Boulton's eight presses were in full work, the quantity of copper coin they turned out was very large. They could work off with ease twelve hundred tons of coin annually. The quantity of copper thus consumed was so great that a difficulty began to be experienced in keeping up the supply. Instead of being glutted with the metal, as Boulton had been before the Mint was started, he had now considerable difficulty in obtaining sufficient for his purposes. He seems to have been, in some measure, the victim of a combination to keep him out of a supply; for when the holders of copper found out that his contract with the East India Company required him to deliver the coin within a given time, and that he *must* have the metal, they raised the prices upon him, and copper went up about 6*l.* a ton. On this, the Birmingham white metal buttonmakers lowered the wages of their workmen, alleging as the cause the rise in the price of copper, "for which they must thank Mr. Boulton." The usual strikes followed, with meetings of trades delegates and street commotions. Though Boulton had confidence in the Birmingham workmen generally, among whom he had the reputation of being a good master, he feared that, in their excited state, malice might stir them to mischief; and he apprehended an attack upon his manufactory. For this he accordingly made due preparation, placing a strong armed guard of his own workmen upon Soho, having the fullest confidence in their fidelity. Writing to his friend Wilson in Cornwall, he said, –

… From the misrepresentations that have been made by the delegates, this town has been greatly misguided, and I expect every hour riots of a serious nature.

Workmen are parading the streets with cockades in their hats. They are assembled by beat of drum, and headed by Ignorance and Envy, with their eyes turned towards Soho.

Yet I am no competitor with the Birmingham trades. I follow no business but what I have been myself the father of, and I have done much more for the Birmingham manufactures than any other individual. I have declined the trade of White Metal Buttons, which is the article so much affected by the rise of metals, and that in which the rioters are employed.

I mix with no clubs, attend no public meetings, am of no party, nor am I a zealot in religion; I do not hold any conversation with any Birmingham persons; and therefore I know no grounds but what may be suggested by wicked and envious hearts for supposing me to be the cause of the late rise of copper.

However, I am well guarded by justice, by law, by men, and by arms.[14]

The danger, however, shortly passed, and the threatened attack was not made.

It was not until the year 1797 that Boulton was employed to execute a copper coinage for Britain. Ten years before, encouraged by the Lords of the Treasury, he had fitted up the Mint machinery at a heavy cost, in anticipation of this very order; and now, after executing coinages for many foreign governments, the order came at last. The new coins consisted of twopenny, penny, halfpenny, and farthing pieces. Altogether, about 4200 tons of these coins were issued from the Soho Mint between 1797 and 1806. So sensible were the authorities at the Royal Mint of the advantages of Mr. Boulton's improvements in coining machinery, that they employed him to erect the new Mint on Tower Hill, one of the most complete establishments of the kind until then in existence. The plans of the new Mint, as regarded the distribution of the buildings connected with the mechanical department, were arranged by him; and the coining machinery and steam-engines were executed at Soho under his immediate direction, though he was at the time labouring under the infirmities of age as well as suffering under the pressure of a painful disease. He had also the honour of supplying Royal Mints for the Russian, Spanish, and Danish governments; and at a later period for Mexico, Calcutta, and Bombay. "In short," said Mr. Watt, in the MS. memoir from which we have already quoted, "had Mr. Boulton done nothing more in the world than he has accomplished in improving the coinage, his name would deserve to be immortalised; and if it be considered that this was done in the midst of various other important avocations, and at enormous expense, – for which, at the time, he could have had no certainty of an adequate return, – we shall be at a loss whether most to admire his ingenuity, his perseverance, or his munificence. He has conducted the whole more like a sovereign than a private manufacturer; and the love of fame has always been to him a greater stimulus than the love of gain. Yet it is to be hoped that, even in the latter point of view, the enterprise answered its purpose."

Site of the Soho Mint, now removed

NOTES

1   The word "Brummagem" doubtless originated in the numerous issues of counterfeit money from the Birmingham mints.

2   The punishment for this crime was sometimes of a very brutal character. In March, 1789, a woman, convicted of coining in London, was first strangled by the stool being taken from under her, and then fixed to a stake and burnt before the debtor's door at Newgate!

3   "I lately received a letter from a Jew about making for him a large quantity of base money, but I should be sorry ever to become so base as to execute such orders. On the contrary I have taken steps to put a stop to the execution of them by others, and if Mr. Butcher hath any plan of that sort he would do well to guard against me; as I certainly shall endeavour all in my power to prevent the counterfeiting of British or other money – that being the principle on which I am acting." – Boulton to Matthews, December, 1787.

4   Boulton to Woodman, 13th November, 1789.

5   Watt says Droz "did not know so much on the subject as Boulton himself did," and being found incompetent, a pretender, and disposed to be

quarrelsome and litigious, he was shortly after dismissed with liberal payment.

6 In a letter written by James Lawson to Matthew Robinson Boulton shortly after his father's death, he observed, – "God only knows the anxiety and unremitting perseverance of your father to accomplish the end; and we all aided and assisted to the best of our powers, without ever considering by whose contrivance anything was brought to bear. Indeed the bringing of everything to bear was by your father's perseverance, and by his hints and personal attendancs; for often he attended and persevered in the experiments till we were all tired." – Lawson to M. B. Boulton, January 10, 1810. Boulton MSS.

7 We find numerous letters from Boulton to Joseph Harrison relative to the execution of the presses, and the manner in which the various details of the work were to be carried out. On the 16th of January, 1788, he wrote, – "Push forward with the utmost expedition six of the cutting-out presses and one of the coining presses. I have engaged to have six of each kind at work by this day four months … I shall be obliged to work after the rate of 1500 tons a year. I fear I must have eight presses [eight were eventually erected] in which case I most lengthen the building next the Gate road. Pray push forward, and be silent." Various details as to the working of the presses and the execution of the coin were given in succeeding letters.

8 To Lord Hawkesbury he wrote (14th April, 1789), – "In the course of my journeys I observe that I receive upon an average two-thirds counterfeit halfpence for change at toll-gates, &c.; and I believe the evil is daily increasing, as the spurious money is carried into circulation by the lowest class of manufacturers, who pay with it the principal part of the wages of the poor people they employ. They purchase from the subterraneous coiners 36 shillings'-worth of copper (in nominal value) for 20 shillings, so that the profit derived from the cheating is very large. The trade is carried on to so great an extent that at a public meeting at Stockport in Cheshire, in January last, the magistrates and inhabitants came to a resolution to take no other half-pence in future that those of the Anglesey Company [also an illegal coinage, though of full weight and value of copper], and this resolution they have published in their newspapers."

9 Boulton to the Lords of the Privy Council for Trade, 16th December, 1787.

10 In 1787, and again in 1789, we find the merchants, traders, and others in Southwark urgently memorialising the Lords of the Treasury on the

subject. The Memorial addressed to them in the latter year was signed
by 800 of the principal inhabitants of the Borough, and presented to
Mr. Pitt by a deputation, headed by Mr. Barclay, of Thrale's Brewery. It
set forth that the counterfeits of copper coin had become a very serious
burden and loss, more especially to poor manufacturers, labourers,
and others, many of whom were compelled to take counterfeit copper
coin in payment of their commodities and wages; and concluded by
stating that, having seen specimens of a new copper coinage made by
Mr. Boulton of Birmingham (under order of the Lords of the Privy
Council) the Memorialists take leave to represent, that such a coinage,
from its greater weight and superior execution, would in their opinion
afford to themselves and the public at large a certain remedy for
the present grievance, and they therefore strongly recommended its
adoption.

11   The coins were: in 1790, a five sous piece, "Pacte Fédératif;" in 1792,
a four sous "hercule;" and a two sous "Liberté." Boulton's reputation
as a coiner abroad, brought upon him while at Paris, a host of foreign
schemers, one of whom pretended that he had discovered an infallible
method of converting copper into gold! The schemer and his wife followed
Boulton to Soho, accompanied by a letter of introduction from his friend
Baumgarten. After taking measure of the schemer, Boulton replied to
Baumgarten as follows:

Dear Sir, –
    Who the devil have you sent me? Is he the angel or the demon
Gabriel? Is he a seraphim or a swindler? His propositions appear in such
questionable form, that I know not whether to pronounce him F. or R.
or S., which are favourite letters amongst English philosophers.
    Doth he mean to make gold by Alchemy, or after the family receipt by
which his mother and brother extracted two hundred guineas from my
simplicity when at Paris?
    I am content with the copper coinage, and shall leave the golden
one to you and Gabriel. The science of alchemy soars so much above
common sense that I never could obtain so much as a peep into
its lower regions. This said Gabriel and his angel have, however,
condescended to adopt common sense so far as to take up their
lodgings in my cottage!
    The worst of all is, I am at this juncture extremely busy and can't bear
interruption; but all that is a trifle when compared with the magnitude

of his project, viz. converting 1500*l.* into 60,000*l.*! But he says a small experiment may be made in three days and three nights in my laboratory. I must, however, own that I had rather be in Jonah's situation during that time.

I wish not to offend this angelic couple, but I should prefer that you had them back again, with all the favours and profits intended for me. However, I cannot help wishing you a better thing; for in spite of your last favour I sincerely desire for you and all that are dear to you, many many happy and prosperous years,

Ever your faithful and affectionate friend,

M. Boulton.

12   The following were the principal provincial halfpenny tokens executed at Soho: 1789, Cronebane and Dundee; 1791, Anglesey, Cornwall, Glasgow, Hornchurch, Southampton; 1793, Leeds, London, Penryn, John Wilkinson's; 1794, Inverness, Lancaster; 1795, Bishops Stortford; 1800, Enniscorthy.

13   The following medals were also struck by Mr. Boulton at Soho: – Prince and Princess of Wales on their marriage; Marquis Cornwallis on the peace with Tippo; Earl Howe on his victory of the First of June; Hudson's Bay Company; Slave Trade abolished; Chareville Forest; General Suwarrow on his successes in Italy; the Empress Catherine of Russia; in commemoration of British victories; Union with Ireland; on the peace of 1802; Battle of Trafalgar; Manchester and Salford Volunteers; Frogmore Medal; Prince Regent of Portugal; and the Emperor Alexander of Russia. The execution of the Trafalgar Medal furnishes a remarkable illustration of Boulton's princely munificence. It was struck on the occasion of Lord Nelson's last victory, and presented by him, with the sanction of government, to every officer and man engaged in the action. He gave an additional value to the present by confining the medal to this purpose only.

14   Boulton to Wilson, 26th February, 1792. Boulton MSS.

XX

Prosperity of Soho – Young Boulton and Watt – The Riots – William Murdock

The steam-engine had now become firmly established as a working power. Beginning as a water pumper for miners, it had gradually been applied to drive corn and cotton mills, to roll and hammer iron, to coin money, to work machinery, and to perform the various labour in which the power of men and horses, of wind and water, had before been employed. The numerous orders for new engines which came in at Soho kept the works increasingly busy. Many skilled workmen had by this time been trained into expertness and dexterity; and, being kept to their special departments of work, – fathers training their sons to work with them at the same benches, – a degree of accuracy and finish was reached which contributed to establish and maintain the prestige of the manufactory. The prosperity of the firm was also materially promoted by the able assistants who had been trained at Soho, and were in due time promoted to superintend special departments of the business. Among these were Murdock, Walker, Southern, Ewart, and Lawson, who enjoyed the fullest confidence of their chiefs, and repaid it with unswerving loyalty.

When the concern had become thoroughly organised under these able heads of departments, Boulton and Watt began to breathe more freely. Their financial difficulties had now disappeared, and instead of laying out capital, they had begun to accumulate it. They had laboured hard for their reward and richly earned it; and after their long up-hill struggle, they well deserved rest and peace at last. They now began to take occasional journeys of recreation, with which they varied their journeys of business. Thus, in the autumn of 1789, we find Boulton making a tour in Derbyshire, during which he was overtaken at Buxton by a letter from the Lords of the Privy Council on coining business, giving him "marching orders for London;" but a party having been formed to visit the Peak Cavern, he decided "to obey the Ladies rather than the Lords." Three days later, however, we find him in London, "writing in a full chattering coffee-house at Charing Cross," and desiring his friend Mr. Barrow to pay his respects to the ladies whom he had so hurriedly left. While in London, he received a letter inviting him to pay a visit to Holland and stand godfather to his friend Mr. Hoofletter's son; to which he replied, that he would be glad to stand godfather to the boy and have the name of Boulton associated with an honest race, but was sorry that he could not assist at the christening or at the dinner. "But pray act for me," he added; "do everything that's proper (as is the custom in the country); give the nurse five guineas from me, and I will repay you. My best respects to Mrs. Hoofletter, and my blessing on the young Christian."

Watt's troubles and anxieties also were in course of gradual abatement. Though still suffering from headaches, asthma, and low spirits, he seems on the whole to have become more satisfied with his lot. Prosperity agreed with him as it does with most people. It is a condition easy to bear, and Watt took to it kindly. As years passed over his head, he became placid, contented, and, even cheerful. His health improved, and he enjoyed life in his old age as he had never done in his youth. He ceased longing for the rest of the grave, and gave over "cursing his inventions." On the other hand, he took pleasure in looking back over the long and difficult road he had traversed, and in recounting the various steps by which he had perfected his great inventions. Nor did he cease to invent; for he went on inventing new things to the close of his life; but he followed the pursuit as a recreation and delight, and not as a business and a drudgery.

Watt too, like his partner, began to make tours of pleasure, for the purpose at the same time of gathering health and seeing the beauties of nature. In August, 1789, he wrote Boulton from Cheltenham, that he had been making a delightful journey through the Western Counties, by way of Worcester, Malvern, Hereford, and Chepstow, and that he felt in better health and spirits than he had been, for a very long time. Occasional letters reached him from Birmingham about orders received for engines, nothing being done without first consulting him. That the concern was thriving, may be inferred from the comparative indifference with which he now regarded such orders. An engine having been ordered by a doubtful person, Watt wrote – "I look upon such orders as of little value. They are so precarious in their duration, and in this case there is risk of bad payment or swindling. Whatever care we take, he is like a shaved pig with a soaped tail." On a demand being made upon him for abatement of dues, he wrote – "We have never made concessions to anybody but they have been attended with loss to us and half a dozen more; and it would appear that, if our patent lasted long enough, the power of a horse would grow to that of an elephant."[1]

In the course of the following summer, Watt visited the pleasantest spots in the neighbourhood of London, and amongst other places took Windsor in his way, where he had the honour of an interview with the King. He had already met his Majesty at Whitbread's brewery in the early part of 1787, for the purpose of explaining to him the action of the new rotary engine; and the King had expressed the desire to see him again when in the neighbourhood of Windsor. The following is Watt's brief account of the visit:

> At Windsor I had a short conversation with the King. He never mentioned you nor the coinage, nor anything that led to it; therefore I could not bring it on; nor do I believe it could have been of any service. He ached about engines, and how the Albion mill was going on? – *Answer*: Very well in respect to grinding, but not so well in regard to the trade. *Asked*: Who was the manager? – *Answer*: Mr. J. Wyatt, who made the wooden hospitals. He observed, that Wyatt was not bred to the milling business; how had he learnt it? – *Answer*: That he was a man of ability and observation. *Asked*: What sort of engines were we making? – *Answer*: For almost everything, but at present principally for brewers, distillers, cotton-spinners, iron-men, &c. – *Asked*: How we were paid for them? – *Answer*: By horses power, 5*l.* a year in the country, and that we made none under four-horses power. – *Asksd*: If these premiums afforded sufficient profit? – *Answer*: That they did in large engines, but not in small.[2]

As Boulton and Watt advanced in years they looked forward with pleasure to the prospect of their two eldest sons – Matthew Robinson Boulton and James Watt, junior – joining them in the business they had established, and relieving them of the greater part of their anxieties and labours in connexion with it. Both were young men of intelligence and character, carefully educated, good linguists, and well versed in practical science. We find many references to the education of the two young men in the letters of Boulton; few or none in those of Watt. The former alike attracted young people and was attracted by them, entering heartily into their pursuits; the latter was too much absorbed by study, by inventions, and by business, to spare time for the purpose. Besides, he was, like his countrymen generally, reserved and undemonstrative in all matters relating to the feelings and affections.

Both boys were trained and educated so as to follow in their fathers' steps. Every pains was taken to give them the best culture, and to imbue them with the soundest principles. The two boys usually spent their holidays together at Soho; and, growing up together, they learnt to think, and feel, and work together.

"Jim returns to school this evening," wrote Boulton, to Watt in Cornwall; "he has behaved exceedingly well, and not a single bill of indictment has been found against him. He had got it into his head that he would not be an engineer, which I did not contradict, but I gave him and Matt the small wooden water-wheel, which they proceeded to erect below my duck-pond, and there worked a forge; but not having water enough, necessity has put them upon erecting a Savery's engine, which is not yet finished, though they are both exceedingly keen upon it. We have killed many poor robins by pouring fixable air upon them, and had some amusement in our electrical and chemical hobby-horsery, which the young ones like much better than dry Latin. Jim desires me to ask you to give him leave to learn French."

At the same time Boulton's own son was making good progress under the Rev. Mr. Stretch, to whom Boulton wrote, –

Baron Reden has gone to the North. On his return, he will leave his son with you for a year or two, and then invites Matt to return with him to Germany. Youth is the time to learn languages, and the Baron's offer is certainly a great temptation ... let him [Matt] not neglect the present, but apply himself so as to become well grounded in Grammar and Latin ... he is capable, but not of close application, to which he must be inured, as no proficiency of any kind can be acquired without it.

The Baron's offer was not, however, accepted; but desirous that his son should acquire proficiency in French, Boulton took him over to Paris, towards the end of 1786, and placed him under a competent master. Many kindly let-ters passed between father and son during the latter's stay at Paris. The young man spent rather more money than his father thought could do him good. He therefore asked him to keep an account of his personal expenses, which "must balance exactly," and implored him above all things to "keep out of bad company."

"The future reputation and happiness of your life," wrote the anxious father, "depend upon your present conduct. I must therefore insist that you do not go strolling about Sodom and Gomorrah under any pretence whatever ... It will not be pleasant to you to read this, but I must do my duty to you or I shall not satisfy my own conscience. I therefore hope you will do your duty to yourself, or you cannot do it to me. There is nothing on earth I so much wish for as to make you a man, a good man, a useful man, and consequently a happy man."[3]

The father's anxieties abated with time; the son applied himself assiduously to French and German, and gave promise of becoming a man of ability and character. Writing to his friend Matthews, Boulton said "Matt is a tolerable good chemist ... He hath behaved very well, and I shall be glad when the time arrives for him to assist me in the business." In the summer of 1788, young Boulton paid his father a holiday visit at Soho, returning again to Paris to finish his studies. Writing of his departure, to Matthews in London, the father said – "I hope that my son is set off for Dover: my heart overflows with blessings and love to him."[4]

The education of young Watt was equally well cared for. After leaving school at Birmingham, his father sent him for a year to Mr. Wilkinson's ironworks at Bersham, to learn carpentry in the pattern shop.[5] He then returned to his father's, from whence he was sent to school at Geneva, where he remained for three years perfecting himself in the modern languages. On his return to England in 1788, we find Boulton writing to Mr. Barrow of Manchester, asking him to obtain a position for young Watt in some respectable count-ing-house, with a view to his acquiring a thorough commercial training. He was eventually placed in the house of Messrs. Taylor and Maxwell, where he remained for about two years, improving himself in his knowledge of busi-ness affairs. His father's reputation and standing, as well as his own education and accomplishinents, served to introduce the young gentleman to many friends in Manchester; and, although far from extravagant in his habits, he shortly found that the annual sum allowed him by his father was insufficient to pay for his board, clothing, and lodging, and at the same time enable him to keep clear of debt. Knowing Boulton's always open hand and heart, and his sympathy for young people, the embarrassed youth at once applied to him for help. Why he did not apply to his father will be best understood from his own letter: –

"I am at this moment," he explained, "on the best footing possible with my father, but were I to inform him of my necessities, I do not know what would be the consequence. Not that I suppose the money in itself would be an object to him, but because he would look upon it in the light of encouraging what he would call my extravagances. Never having been a young man himself, he is unacquainted with the inevitable expenses which attend my time of life, when one is obliged to keep good company, and does not wish to act totally different from other young men. My father's reputation, and his and my own station in life, require that I should live at least on a decent footing. I am not conscious of having committed any foolish extravagances, and I have avoided company as much as possible; but I have also constantly avoided the reputation of avarice, or of acting meanly on any occasion. My father, unfortunately for me, measures the present tunes and circumstances by those when he was of my age, without making the proper allowances for their immense disparity; consequently it is in vain for me to endeavour to convince him of the necessity of my conduct."[6]

He concluded by expressing his sense of Mr. Boulton's many friendly acts towards him, and confessing that there was no other person on whom he could so confidently rely for help in his emergency. The reply of Boulton was all that he could desire. With sound fatherly advice,[7] such as he would have given to his own son under similar circumstances, he sent him a draft for 50*l.*, the amount required by young Watt to clear him of his debts.

Among the friendships which he formed at Manchester, was one of an intimate character with Mr. Cooper, a gentleman engaged in an extensive business, fond of books, and a good practical chemist. We find young Watt requesting Boulton to recommend to Mr. Cooper "a person to keep his library in order and to make experiments for him, he not having time enough to attend to the details of them himself."[8] Cooper was besides a keen politician, and took an active interest in the discussion of the important questions then agitating the public mind. Watt was inflamed by the enthusiasm of his friend, and with the ardour of youth entered warmly into his views as to the regeneration of man and the reconstruction of society.

Mrs. Schimmelpenninck has, in her autobiography, given a vivid picture of the interest excited in the circle of friends amongst whom she moved, by the thrilling events then occurring in France, and which extended even to the comparatively passionless philosophers of the Lunar Society. At one of the meetings held at her father's house in the summer of 1788 "Mr. Boulton," she says, "presented to the company his son, just returned from a long sojourn at Paris. I well remember my astonishment at his full dress in the highest adornment of Parisian fashion; but I noticed, as a remarkable thing, that the company (which consisted of some of the first men in Europe) all with one accord gathered round him, and asked innumerable questions, the drift of which I did not fully understand. It was wonderful to me to see Dr. Priestley,

Dr. Withering, Mr. Watt, Mr. Boulton himself, and Mr. Keir, manifest the most intense interest, each according to his prevailing characteristics, as they almost hung upon his words; and it was impossible to mistake the indications of deep anxiety, hope, fear, curiosity, ardent zeal, or thoughtful gravity, which alternately marked their countenances, as well as those of my own parents. My ears caught the words 'Marie Antoinette,' 'The Cardinal de Rohan,' 'diamond necklace,' 'famine,' 'discontent among the people,' 'sullen silence instead of shouts of 'Vive le Roi!' All present seemed to give a fearful attention. Why, I did not then well know, and, in a day or two, these things were almost forgotten by me; but the rest of the party heard, no doubt in this young man's narrative, the distant, though as yet faint rising of the storm which, a year later, was to burst upon France and, in its course, to desolate Europe."[9] A few short months passed, and the reign of brotherhood began. "One evening, towards the end of July," continues Mrs. Schimmelpenninck, "we saw at a distance a vehicle (usually employed to carry servants to town or church) returning at more than its usual speed. After some minutes the door of the drawing-room opened, and in burst Harry Priestley, a youth of sixteen or seventeen, waving his hat, and crying out, 'Hurrah! Liberty, Reason, brotherly love for ever! Down with kingcraft and priestcraft. The majesty of the people for ever! France is free, the Bastille is taken!"[10] "I have seen," she adds, "the reception of the victory of Waterloo and of the carrying of the Reform Bill; but I never saw joy comparable in its intensity and universality to that occasioned by the early promise of the French Revolution."

The impressionable mind of Dr. Priestley was moved in an extraordinary degree by the pregnant events which followed each other in quick succession at Paris; and he entered with zeal into the advocacy of the doctrines of liberty, equality, and fraternity, so vehemently promulgated by the French "friends of man." His chemical pursuits were for a time forgotten, and he wrote and preached like one possessed, of human brotherhood, and of the downfall of tyranny and priestcraft. He hailed with delight the successive acts of the National Assembly abolishing monarchy, nobility, church, corporations, and other long established institutions. He had already been long and hotly engaged in polemical discussions with the local clergy on disputed points of faith; and now he addressed a larger audience in a work which he published in answer to Mr. Burke's famous attack on the 'French Revolution'. Burke, in consequence, attacked him in the House of Commons; while the French Revolutionists on the other hand hailed him as a brother, and admitted him to the rights of French citizenship.[11]

These proceedings concentrated on Dr. Priestley an amount of local exas-
peration that shortly after burst forth in open outrage. On the 14th of July,
1791, a public dinner was held at the principal hotel to celebrate the second
anniversary of the French Revolution. About eighty gentlemen were present,
but Priestley was not of the number. A mob collected outside, and after shout-
ing "Church and King," they proceeded to demolish the inn windows. The
magistrates shut their eyes to the riotous proceedings, if they did not actually
connive at them. A cry was raised, "To the New Meeting-house," the chapel
in which Priestley ministered; and thither the mob surged. The door was at
once burst open, and the place set on fire. They next gutted the old Meeting-
house, and made a bonfire of the pews and bibles in the burying-ground.
It was growing dusk, but the fury of the mob had not abated. They made
at once for Dr. Priestley's house at Fairhill, about a mile and a half distant.
The Doctor and his family had escaped about half an hour before their arrival;
and the house was at their mercy. They broke in at once, emptied the cellars, smashed the furniture, tore up the books in the library, destroyed the
philosophical and chemical apparatus in the laboratory, and ended by setting
fire to the house. The roads for miles round were afterwards found strewed
with shreds of the valuable manuscripts in which were recorded the results of
twenty years labour and study, – a loss which Priestley continued bitterly to
lament until the close of his life.

Thus an utter wreck was made of the philosopher's dwelling at Fairhill. The
damage done was estimated at upwards of 4000*l.*, of which the victim recovered little more than one-half from the county. The next day, and the next,
and the next, the mob continued to run riot, burning and destroying. On the
second day, about noon, they marched to Easyhill and attacked and demol-
ished the mansion of Mr. Ryland, one of the most munificent benefactors of
the town. Bordesley Hall, the mansion of Mr. Taylor, the banker, was next
sacked and fired. The shop of the estimable William Hutton, the well-known
bookseller and author, was next broken open and stripped of everything that
could be carried away; and from his shop in the town they proceeded to his
dwelling at Bennett's Hill in the country, and burnt it to the ground.[13] On
the third day, six other houses were sacked and destroyed; three of them were
blazing at the same time. On the fourth day, which was a Sunday, the rioters
dispersed in bands over the neighbourhood levying contributions in money
and drink; one body of them burning on their way the Dissenting chapel-
house and minister's dwelling-house at Kingswood, seven miles off. Other
Dissenters, of various persuasions, farmers, shopkeepers, and others, had their
houses broken into and robbed in open day. It was not until the Sunday eve-

ning that three troops of the Fifteenth Light Dragoons entered Birmingham amidst the acclamations of the inhabitants, who welcomed them as deliverers. At the instant of their arrival, the mob had broken into Dr. Withering's house at Edgbaston Hall, and were rioting in his wine-cellars, but when they heard that "the soldiers" had come at last, they slunk away in various directions.

The members of the Lunar Society, or "the Lunatics," as they were popularly called, were especially marked for attack during the riots. A common cry among the mob was "No philosophers – Church and King for ever!" and some persons, to escape their fury, even painted "No philosophers" on the fronts of their houses! There could be no doubt as to the meaning of this handwriting on the wall. Priestley's house had been sacked, and Withering's plundered. Boulton and Watt were not without apprehensions that an attack would be made upon them, as the head and front of the "Philosophers" of Birmingham. They accordingly prepared for the worst; called their workmen together, pointed out to them the criminality of the rioters' proceedings, and placed arms in their hands on their promising to do their utmost to defend the premises if attacked. In the mean time everything portable was packed up and ready to be removed at a moment's notice. Thus four days of terror passed, but the mob came not; Watt attributing the safety of Soho to the fact that most of the Dissenters lived in another direction.[14]

Many of the rioters were subsequently apprehended, and several of them were hanged; but the damage inflicted on those whose houses had been sacked was irreparable, and could not be compensated. As for Dr. Priestley, he shook the dust of Birmingham from his feet, and fled to London; from thence emigrating to America, where he died in 1804.

While such was the blind fury of the populace of Birmingham, the principles of the French Revolution found adherents in all parts of England. Clubs were formed in London and the principal provincial towns, and a brisk correspondence was carried on between them and the Revolutionary leaders of France. Among those invested with the rights of French citizenship were Dr. Priestley, Mr. Wilberforce, Thomas Tooke, and Mr. (afterwards Sir) James Mackintosh. Thomas Paine and Dr. Priestley were chosen members of the National Convention; and though the former took his seat for Calais, the latter declined, on the ground of his inability to speak the language sufficiently. Among those carried away by the political epidemic of the time, were young James Watt and his friend Mr. Cooper of Manchester. In 1792 they were deputed, by the "Constitutional Society" of that town, to proceed to Paris and present an address of congratulation to the Jacobin Club, then known as the "Société des Amis de la Constitution."[15] While at Paris, young

Burning of Dr. Priestley's house at Fairhill [12]

Watt seems to have taken an active part in the fiery agitation of the time. He was on intimate terms with the Jacobin leaders. Southey says that he was even the means of preventing a duel between Danton and Robespierre, to the former of whom he acted as second.[16] Robespierre afterwards took occasion to denounce both Cooper and Watt as secret emissaries of Pitt, on which young Watt sprang into the tribune, pushing Robespierre aside, and defended himself in a strain of vehement eloquence, which completely carried the assembly with him. From that moment, however, he felt his life to be unsafe, and he fled from Paris without a passport, never resting until he had passed the frontier and found refuge in Italy.

The public part he had taken in French Revolutionary politics could not fail to direct attention to him on this side of the channel. His appearance at a public procession, in which he carried the British colours, to celebrate the delivery of some soldiers released from the galleys, was vehemently denounced by Mr. Burke in the House of Commons. The notoriety which he had thus achieved, gave his father great anxiety; and after young James's return to England in 1794, he was under considerable apprehensions for his safety. Several members of the London political societies had been apprehended and lodged in the Tower, and Watt feared lest his son might in some way be compromised by his correspondence with those societies. Boulton, then in London, informed him of the severe measures of the Government, and of the intended suspension of the Habeas Corpus Act; to which Watt replied, –

I thank you for your intelligence, which I have communicated with due caution to Mr. S. and my son. The former says he has had no correspondence whatever with any of these societies, nor has frequented any here, – that he may have uttered unguarded or foolish words in private companies, but that he knows nothing of, nor is he concerned in, any plot or political scheme whatsoever. The latter says he never corresponded with any of them at any time, though he once executed a commission for one of them, and sent his.answer to Mr. Tr., – that for these two years he has had no sort of connexion with any of them, and for more than a year all his correspondence has been recommending his friends not to intermeddle with public afihirs. As he proposes to see you to-morrow, he will explain himself, and I need not bid you council him for the best.[17]

A few days later, his apprehensions of danger to his son not being removed, he wrote Boulton again as follows:

I am made very uneasy on account of James by this Bastille Act[18] now (I fancy) passed, and which I cannot help thinking *un peu trop*. I submit whether it might not be best for you to endeavour to make his peace with M[inist]ry by a candid avowal of his errors, and of his subsequent change of sentiment and renunciation of all correspondence with these traitors. In the mean time he had better make the best of his way to here, Liverpool, or Scotland; from either of the latter he might find his way to America if necessary. In any case let him not go in company with any of the persons who have laid themselves open to suspicion. I would not, however, have him rashly run out of the country. M[inist]ry must know who have been the active abettors of the plot, and, if they act wisely, will not molest those who have seen their error or have had the good sense to resist all temptations of engaging in plots against the peace of the country, whatever their opinions about parliamentary representation might be ... Query, whether Denmark,

Hamburg, or Norway, might not be preferable to America, lest we go to war with the latter. If you find he is obnoxious, his letters to me should be directed by another hand, and not signed.[19]

Four days later, Watt's alarm was not abated by the appearance in Birmingham of king's messengers making seizures of persons concerned in seditious correspondence. "They have taken up," he wrote, "one Pare, who kept a reforming club at his house, and one or two others. The soldiers were ordered under arms to prevent tumult. I hear also that Wilkinson has been threatened with a mob at Bradley, and has prepared to defend himself with cannon, pikes, &c., but that matters are now quiet there. In respect to James, you must advise him, I cannot; but I think he would be better at home, follow-ing his business, than elsewhere."[20] James eventually returned to Birmingham, where we find him from this time forward taking an increasingly active part in the affairs of the concern. He took entire charge of the manufacture of the letter-copying machines, now become a considerable branch of the business; and he shortly after entered the engine firm as a partner, in conjunction with Mr. Boulton's eldest son, Matthew Robinson.

The infusion of young blood had the effect of imparting new vigour to all the branches of manufacture at Soho, and at the same time of relieving the senior partners from a considerable amount of labour and anxiety. The business was now in a very thriving state; there was abundance of orders for engines to execute them. Thus we find Watt junior writing to Boulton junior in January, 1795, – "We must have additional men, rather too many than too few, until we have got the start of our orders, for without that we shall always feel ourselves embarrassed and clogged. I shall therefore desire Rennie to renew his applications at Lancaster, which appear as yet to have been unsuc-cessful."

The junior members of the firm were also useful in protecting the engine patent right, the infringement of which had become general all over the coun-try. This was a disagreeable part of their business; but, if not attended to, the patent must be given up as worthless. The steam-engine was now regarded as an indispensable power in manufacturing operations. It had become employed in all important branches of industry; and it was, of course, the interest of the manufacturers to avoid the payment of dues wherever they could. An instance of this evasion was detected at the Bowling Ironworks near Bradford, and notice was given of proceedings against the Company for recovery of dues. On this the Bowling Company offered to treat, and young Watt went down to Leeds for the purpose of meeting the representatives of

the Bowling Company on the subject. On the 24th February, 1796, he wrote
his friend Matthew Robinson Boulton as follows:

> Inclosed you have a copy of the treaty of peace, not amity, concluded at Leeds,
> on Saturday last, between me, Minister Plenipotentiary to your Highnesses on
> the one part, and the Bowling Pirates in person on the other part. I hope you
> will ratify the terms, as you will see they are founded entirely upon the prin-
> ciple of indemnity for the past and security for the future. The diameter and
> length of stroke of their different engines, four in number, I have; the times of
> their commencing to work will be sent you by Mr. Paley; and the amounts of
> the premiums may be definitively calculated upon my arrival, which will be
> about the latter end of this week.

Another engine constructed after Watt's patent was discovered working at
a mill at Carke, in Cartmel, Lancashire. Mr. Stockdale, son of the proprietor, tells the following story of its detection. He states that the first engine
employed at the works was one on Newcomen's construction, which was used
to pump water into the reservoir which supplied the water-power by which
the mill was driven. It was then determined to apply the steam-power direct
to the machinery, and a new engine was ordered from Manchester, without
communicating with the patentees. The mill was in full work when a stranger
called, representing that he belonged to the concern of Boulton and Watt,
and requesting to inspect the engine. The request was complied with, and
Mr. Stockdale afterwards invited him to stay to dinner; but it was the dearest
dinner he ever gave, as only a few weeks later a claim for 1800*l.* was made by
Boulton and Watt for dues upon the engine, which was, however, eventually
compromised by the payment of 400*l.*

The most unscrupulous pirates, however, were the Cornishmen who,
emboldened by the long quiescence of Boulton and Watt, and knowing that
the patent had only five or six more years to run, believed that they might set
the patentees at open defiance, which they proceeded to do. Notwithstanding
the agreements entered into and ratified on both sides, they refused point
blank to pay further dues; and Boulton and Watt were thus at last driven to
have recourse to the powers of the law. Had they remained passive, it might
have been construed into a tacit admission that the patent right had from
the first been indefensible, and that the sums which they had up to that time
levied for the use of their engine had been wrongfully paid to them. But neither had ceased to have perfect faith in the validity of their patent, and both
determined, even at this late stage, to defend it. "The rascals," wrote Watt

to Boulton, "seem to have been going on as if the patent were their own ...
We have tried every lenient means with them in vain; and since the fear of
God has no effect upon them, we must try what the fear of the devil can
do."[21] Legal proceedings were begun accordingly. The two actions on which
the issues were tried were those of Boulton and Watt *v.* Bull, and Boulton and
Watt *v.* Hornblower and Maberley; and they were fought on both sides with
great determination. The proceedings extended over several years, being carried from court to court; but the result was decisive in both cases in favour of
Boulton and Watt. It was not until January, 1799, that the final decision of the
judges was given;[22] almost on the very eve of expiry of the patent, which had
not then a full year to run. It was not, however, with a view to the future that
these costly, anxious, and protracted legal proceedings had been carried on,
but mainly for the recovery of dues under existing agreements, and for dues
on engines erected in various quarters in infringement of the patent. Most of
the Cornish adventurers had paid nothing for years. Thus Poldice had paid
nothing since October, 1793, and was in arrear 2330*l.* Wheal Gons had paid
nothing since May, 1793, and was in arrear 4290*l.* The Wheal Treasure adventurers, and many others, had set Boulton and Watt at open defiance, and paid
nothing at all.

On the issue of the proceedings against Bull, Boulton and Watt called
upon the Mining Companies to "cash up," and arrears were shortly collected,
though with considerable difficulty, to the amount of about 30,000*l.* Young
Boulton went into Cornwall for the purpose of arranging the settlements,
and managed the business with great ability. "I am now to congratulate you,"
Watt wrote to his partner from Glasgow, whither he had gone on a visit, "on
the success of Mr. R. Boulton's very able transactions in Cornwall; and I hope
that at last we may be freed from the anxiety of the issue of law which has
so long attended us, and enjoy in peace the fruits of our labours. When you
write to Mr. B. I beg you will present my best wishes and best respects to him,
expressing my warmest approbation of his exertions." On another occasion,
while the cause was in progress before the courts of law, Watt wrote, – "In the
whole affair, nothing was so grateful to me as the zeal of our friends and the
activity of our young men, which was unremitting."

The senior members of the firm had for some time been gradually withdrawing from the active management of the concern. We find Watt writing to
Dr. Black in 1798, – "In regard to the engine business, I now take little part in
it, but it goes on successfully." Foufy years later he wrote, – "Our engine trade
thrives; the profits per cent, are, however, very, very moderate; it is by the great
capital and expensive establishment of engineers, &c., that we keep it up; with-

out our tools and men very little could be done, as we have many competitors, some of whom are men of abilities." But the business was now safe in the hands of the young and active partners, who continued to carry it on for many years, with even greater success than their fathers had done. They reaped the harvest of which the others had sown the seed. The patent right expired in 1800; but the business of the firm, nevertheless, became larger and more remunerative than it had ever been before. The superior plant which they had accumulated, their large and increasing capital, the skilled workmen whom they had trained, and the first-class character of the work which they turned out, gave the establishment of Boulton and Watt a prestige which they long continued to maintain.

The young partners had also the great advantage of the skilled heads of the different departments, who had been trained by long and valuable experience. For many years William Murdock was the Mentor of the firm. Though tempting offers of partnerships were made to him, he remained loyal to Boulton and Watt to the last. They treated him generously, and he was satisfied to spend his life in their service. He had gradually worked his way to the foremost place in their establishment, besides achieving reputation as an inventor and a man of practical science. His model locomotive of 1784 was the first machine of the kind made in this country; and it is to be regretted that he did not pursue the subject. But Murdock was a very modest, unambitious man, content to keep in the background, and not possessed by that "pushing" quality which helps so many on to fortune. We have already stated that he invented the sun and planet motion, which was eventually adopted by Watt in preference to his own method of securing rotary motion. His daily familiarity with pumping-engines in Cornwall also led him to suggest and introduce many improvements in their details, which Boulton and Watt were always ready to adopt. He was a great favourite in Cornwall, and not less esteemed for his estimable and manly qualities than for his mechanical skill. When the adventurers heard of his intention to return to Soho, in 1798, they offered him 1000*l.* a year to continue at the mines, but he could not be tempted to remain.

Returned to Soho, Murdock was invested with the general supervision and management of the mechanical department, in which he proved of essential value. He was regarded as "the right hand" of Boulton and Watt. He proceeded to introduce great improvements in the manufacture of the engines, contriving numerous machines for casting, boring, turning and fitting the various parts together with greater precision. His plan of boring cylinders by means of an endless screw (turned by the moving power) working into a toothed wheel, whose axis carried the cutter head, instead of by spur gear, was found very useful in practice, and produced a much more smooth and steady motion of the machine. As early as 1785; he invented the first oscillating engine,[23] which still continues in use in various improved forms. His invention of the double D slide valve, in place of the four poppet valves in Watt's double engine,[24] was also found of great value, saving steam, and ensuring greater simplicity in the construction and working of the engine. In his oscillating engine the motion is given to the slide valve by the oscillation of the cylinder, and engines of small power still continue to be worked in this manner. Another of his improvements in engine construction was his method of casting the steam cases for cylinders in one piece, instead of in separate segments bolted together, according to the previous practice. He also invented a rotary engine of an ingenious construction; but though he had one erected to drive the machines in his private workshop, where it continued employed for about thirty years, it never came into general use.[25] Murdock had a good deal of the temperament of Watt: he was always scheming improvements, and was most assiduous in carrying them out. In such cases he would not trust to subordinates, but executed his designs himself wherever practicable; and he sometimes carried his labours so far into the night that the rising sun found him at his anvil or his turning lathe.

Murdock is also entitled to the merit of inventing lighting by gas. The inflammable qualities of the air obtained by distillation of coal had long been known,[26] but Murdock was the first to apply the knowledge to practical uses. The subject engaged much of his attention in the year 1792, when he resided at Redruth. As his days were fully occupied in attending to his employers' engine business, it was only in the evenings, after the day's work was over, that he could pursue the subject. It is not improbable that he was led to undertake the investigation by Mr. Boulton's chemical enthusiasm, which communicated itself to all with whom he came in contact. It will be remembered that the latter occupied much of his leisure at Cosgarne in analysing earths, minerals, and vegetable substances, trying to find out the gases they contained; and Murdock was his zealous assistant on these cccasions. In the paper which he communicated to the Royal Society on the subject of lighting by coal-gas in 1808, for which they awarded him their large Rumford Gold Medal, he observed, –

It is now nearly sixteen years since (1792), in the course of experiments I was making at Redruth, in Cornwall, upon the quantities and qualities of the gas produced by distillation from different mineral and vegetable substances, that

I was induced by some observations I had previously made upon the burning of coal, to try the combustible property of the gases produced from it, as well as from peat, wood, and other inflammable substances; and being struck with the great quantities of gas which they afforded, as well as the brilliancy of the light, and the facility of its production, I instituted several experiments with a view of ascertaining the cost at which it might be obtained, compared with that of equal quantities of light yielded by oils and tallow. My apparatus consisted of an iron retort, with tinned iron and copper tubes, through which the gas was conducted to a considerable distance; and there, as well as at intermediate points, was burnt through apertures of various forms and dimensions. The experiments were made upon coal of different qualities, which I procured from different parts of the kingdom for the purpose of ascertaining which would give the most economical results. The gas was also washed with water, and other means were employed to purify it.[27]

Murdock put his discovery to the best practical test by lighting up his house and offices at Redruth with gas; and he had a gas lantern constructed, with a jet attached to the bottom of the lantern and a bladder of gas underneath, with which he lighted himself home at night across the moors when returning from his work to his house at Redruth.[28] On the occasion of a visit which he made to Soho in 1794, he took the opportunity of mentioning to Mr. Watt the experiments he had made, and their results; expressing his conviction of the superior economy, safety, and illuminating qualities of coal-gas, compared with oils and tallow. He then suggested that a patent should be taken out for the application, and at various subsequent periods he urged the subject upon the attention of his principals. But they were at the time so harassed by litigation in connexion with their own steam-engine patent, that they were unwilling to enter upon any new entetprise which might possibly lead them into fresh embroilments and nothing was done to protect the invention.

On Murdock's return to Soho in 1798, he proceeded with his investigations, and contrived an apparatus for making, purifying, and storing the gas on a large scale; and several of the offices in the building were regularly lighted by its means. On the general illumination which took place in celebration of the Peace of Amiens in 1802, the front of Soho Manufactory was brilliantly illuminated with gas, to the astonishment and admiration of the public. The manageableness, the safety, the economy, and the brilliancy of the new light being thus proved, Boulton and Watt in 1803 authorised Murdock to proceed with the general fitting up of the manufactory with pipes and burners, and, from that date, it continued to be regularly lit up with coal-gas. Several large

firms followed their example; amongst others Phillips and Lee, Burley, and
Kennedy, at Manchester, and Gott and Sons, at Leeds; and the manufacture
of gas-making apparatus became one of the regular branches of business at
Soho. Several years later, in 1805, when Watt went down to Glasgow, he found
gas in pretty general use.

"The new lights," he wrote to Boulton, "are much in vogue here; many have
attempted them, and some have succeeded tolerably in lighting their shops
with them. I also hear that a cotton-mill in this neighbourhood is lighted up
with gas. A long account of the new lights was published in the newspapers
some time ago, in which they had the candour to ascribe the invention to Mr.
Murdock. From what I have heard respecting these attempts, I think there is
full room for the Soho improvements,[29] though, when once they see one properly executed, it will have numerous imitations,"

William Murdock

Several years after the introduction of the new light, a German, named Wintzer or Winsor, brought out (in 1809) a scheme similar to one projected in Paris by Le Bon, for lighting the streets by gas. He proposed a Joint Stock Company, with a capital of 300,000*l.*, and held forth to subscribers the prospect of a profit of ten thousand per cent.![30] He applied to Parliament for a Bill, against which Murdock petitioned, and was examined before the Committee. Though they were staggered by the crudities of Winsor, they had some difficulty even in accepting the more modest averments of Murdock as to the uses of coal-gas for lighting purposes. "Do you mean to tell us," asked one member, "that it will be possible to have a light *without a wick*?" "Yes, I do, indeed," answered Murdock. "Ah, my friend," said the legislator, "you are trying to prove too much." It was as surprising and inconceivable to the honourable member as George Stephenson's subsequent evidence before a Parliamentary Committee to the effect that a carriage might be drawn upon a railway at the rate of twelve miles an hour *without a horse*.

No wonder that strange notions were entertained about gas in those early days. It seemed so incredible a contrivance, to make air that could be sent along pipes for miles from the place at which it was made to the place at which it issued as jets of fire, that it ran entirely counter to all preconceived notions on the subject of illumination. Even Sir Humphry Davy ridiculed the idea of lighting towns with gas, and asked one of the projectors if it were intended to take the dome of St. Paul's for a gasometer; and Sir Walter Scott made many clever jokes about the absurdity of lighting London with smoke, though he shortly after adopted the said "smoke" for lighting up his own house at Abbotsford. It was popularly supposed that the gas was carried along the pipes *on fire*, and that hence the pipes mut be intensely hot. Thus, when the House of Commons was first lighted up with gas, the architect insisted on the pipes being placed several inches from the wall for fear of fire, and members might be seen applying their gloved hands to them to ascertain their temperature, expressing the greatest surprise on their being found as cool as the adjoining walls.[31]

The advantages of the new light, however, soon became generally recognised; and gas companies were established in most of the large towns. Had Murdock patented the invention, it must have proved exceedingly remunerative to him; but he derived no advantage from the extended use of the new system of lighting except the honour of having initiated it, – though of this more than one attempt was made to deprive him. As he himself modestly said, in his paper read before the Royal Society, "I believe I may, without presuming too much, claim both the first idea of applying, and the first actual application of this gas to economical purposes."

Murdock's attention was, however, diverted from prosecuting his discovery of the uses of gas to a profitable issue by his daily business, which was of a very engrossing character. He continued, nevertheless, an almost incessant contriver, improver, and inventor; following, like his master Watt, the strong bent of his inclinations. One of his most cherished schemes was the employment of compressed air as a motive power. He contrived to work a little engine of 12-inch cylinder and 18-inch stroke, which drove the lathe in the pattern-shop, by means of the compressed air of the blast-engine employed in blowing the cupolas at the Soho Foundry; and this arrangement continued in use for a period of about thirty-five years. He also constructed a lift worked by compressed air, which raised and lowered the castings from the Boring-mill to the level of the Foundry and the Canal Bank.[32] He used the same kind of power to ring the bells in his house at Sycamore Hill; and the contrivance was afterwards adopted by Sir Walter Scott at Abbotsford.[33] He experimented on the power of high-pressure steam in impelling shot, and contrived a steam-engine in 1803, with which he made many trials at Soho, in anticipation of Perkins's apparatus. He was the inventor of the well-known cast-iron cement so extensively used in engine and machine work; and the manner in which he was led to it affords a striking illustration of his quickness of observation. Finding that some iron-borings and salammoniac had got accidentally mixed together in his tool-chest and rusted his saw-blade nearly through, he took note of the circucumstance, mixed the articles in various proportions, and at last arrived at the famous cement, which eventually became an article of extensive manufacture at the Soho works, completely superseding the cement invented by Watt. In 1810 he took out a patent for boring stone pipes for wafer, and cutting columns out of solid blocks by one operation. In 1815 he invented an apparatus for heating the water for the Baths at Leamington by the circulation of water through pipes from a boiler, – a method since extensively adopted for heating buildings and garden-houses. While occupied in erecting the apparatus at Leamington, a heavy cast-iron plate fell upon his leg and severely crushed it, laying him up for many months.

His ingenuity was constantly at work, even upon matters which lay entirely ontside his special calling. Mr. Fairbairn informs us that he contrived a variety of curious machines for consolidating peat moss, finely ground and pulverised, under immense pressure, and moulding it into beautiful medals, armlets, and necklaces, which took the most brilliant polish, and had the appearance of the finest jet. Observing that fish-skins might be used as an economical substitute for isinglass, he went up to London to explain to the brewers the best method of preparing and using them.[34] While in town on this errand, it occurred to him

that there was an enormous waste of power in the feet of men and animals tread-
ing the streets of London, which might be economised and made productive;
and he conceived the idea of using the streets as a grand treadmill, under which
the waste power was to be stored up by mechanical methods, and turned to
account! Another of his ingenious schemes – though then thought equally
impracticable with that last mentioned – was his proposed method of transmitting letters and packages through a tube exhausted by an air-pump. This idea
seems to have led to the projection of the Atmospheric Railway, the success
of which, so far as it went, was again due to the practical ability of Murdock's
pupil Samuel Clegg. Though the atmospheric railway was eventually abandoned, it is remarkable that Murdock's original idea has since been revived,
and practised with success, by the London Pneumatic Despatch Company.

Such is a brief sketch of the life and works of this estimable and ingenious
mechanic, for so many years the mainstay of the Soho works. Mr. Fairbairn,
who first made his friendship at Manchester in 1816, speaks of him as one
of the most distinguished veterans in mechanical engineering then living,
– "tall and well-proportioned in figure, with a most intelligent and benevolent expression of countenance." He was a man of robust constitution, and
though he sorely taxed it, he lived to an old age, surviving the elder Boulton
and Watt by many years.[35]

NOTES

1   There was a great deal of graphic vigour in Watt's correspondence about
    engines. Thus, in the case of an engine supplied to F. Scott and Co. to drive
    a hammer, it appears that instead of applying it to the hammer only, they
    applied it to also blow the bellows. The consequence was, that it worked
    both badly. They had also increased the weight of the hammer. Watt wrote,
    – "it was easy to forsee all this; and the only adequate remedy is to have
    another engine to blow the bellows. It is impossible that a regular blast can
    be had while the engine works and bellows, without a regulating belly as big
    as a church ... They have been for having a pocket bible in large print. If
    they mean to carry on their work regular, they must have a blowing engine;
    otherwise they will lose the price of one in a few months."

2   Watt to Boulton, 27th June, 1790.

3   Boulton to his son, 19th December, 1787.

4   Boulton to Matthews, 25th August, 1788. In a letter dated the preceding
    day, he wrote – "I have been exceedingly harassed last week, have many

letters before me unanswered. I cannot sleep at nights, and the room I write in is so hot by the fire-engine chimney as to relax me, and my head is distracted by the noise of the engine, by the riveting of boilers, and by a constant knocking at my door by somebody or other; but I believe and suspect that the separation of my son from me contributes more to the oppression of my spirits than anything else."

5   "I have sent my son to Mr. Wilkinson's ironworks at Bersham, in Wales, where he is to study practical book-keeping, geometry, and algebra, at his leisure hours; and three hours in the day he works in a carpenter's shop. I intend he should stay there a year; what I shall do with him next I know not, but I intend to fit him for some employment not so precarious as my own." – Watt to Mrs. Campbell, 30th May, 1784.

6   Watt, jun., to Boulton, 4th December, 1789.

7   Mr. Boulton having been absent at Bath, some time elapsed before young Watt's letter reached him. Receiving no reply, the youth became apprehensive that his letter had fallen into his father's hands, and wrote a second letter expressing his fears. Thus Boulton replied to both letters at the same time, informing his correspondent for his satisfaction that they had reached him "unopened." He proceeded –

I now send agreeable to your request, my draft for 50*l*. – payable to myself, that I might thereby conceal your name from all persons; and you may tranquillise yourself in respect of your father, as I promise you he shall know aught of the transaction.

Although I would not willingly give you pain, yet I must honestly tell you that I am not very sorry you experienced some pain and anxiety by my delay; that you may not only feel how uncomfortable it is to be in debt, but that you may experience ere long how pleasant and how cheerful is independence, which no man can possess who is in that condition.

It is possible your father's ideas may be too limited in regard to the quantum necessary for your expenses; but I think it equally probably that yours may be too diffuse, and therefore can't help wishing it in my power to expand the one and contract the other.

I know and speak from experience, that the principal articles of expenditure in the generality of young men who live in large towns are such as produce the least additions to their happiness or reputation; for which as well as for some others I know of, I cannot help urging you to cut your coat according to your cloth, as the sure means of preserving the good opinion of your father, and as most likely to induce him to open his hand more liberally to you.

Murdock's House, Sycamore Hill, Handsworth[36]

It's a subject I can't speak to him upon without raising his suspicions, but you may state to him such arguments as may seem to meet to yourself in favour of a further allowance, and if he speaks to me upon the subject, I will do the best I can for you.

I wish you to keep in view that all our great Cornish profits have died away till they are now very small, – that your father is building an expensive house, – and that he is married. For these and other reasons, I wish you to alter the scale of your expenses, as the surest means of securing your credit and your happiness, which I am desirous of promoting or I should not have expressed myself so freely and unreservedly …

I remain, dear Watt,

Your faithful and affectionate friend,

Matthew Boulton.

– Boulton to Watt, junr., 26th December, 1789. Boulton MSS.

8   Watt, junr., to Boulton, 26th March, 1789.

9   'Life of Mary Ann Schimmelpennick,' 3rd ed., 1859, pp. 125–6.

10 Ibid., p. 181.

11 "The address of the Société des Amis de la Constitution de Bourdeaux" to the Revolutionary Society in London, dated 21st May, 1791, contains the following passage: – "Le jour consacré à porter le deuil de M. Price [the Rev.

Dr. Price recently dead, – an ardent admirer of the French Revolution in
its early stages], nous avons entendu la lecture du Discours de M. l'Evêque
d'Autun sur la Liberté des Cultes: on nous a fait ensuite le rapport des
ouvrages de MM. Priestley et Payne qui ont vengé M. Price des ouvrages
de M. Burke; et c'est ainsi que nous avons fait son oraison funèbre. Peut-
être, Messieurs, apprendez vous avec quelque intérêt, que nous avons inscrit
dans la liste de nos Membres les noms de MM. Payne et Priestley; c'est
l'hommage de notre estime, et l'estime d'hommes libres a toujours son prix."

12 The representation given of Dr. Priestley's house is taken from a rare book,
entitled 'Views of the Ruins of the principal Houses destroyed during the
Riots at Birmingham, 1791.' London, 1792.

13 "At midnight," says Hutton, "I could see from my house the flames of
Bordesley Hall rise with dreadful aspect. I learned that after I quitted
Birmingham the mob attacked my house there three times. My son
bought them off repeatedly; but in the fourth, which began about nine
at night, they laboured till eight the next morning, when they had so
completely ravaged my dwelling that I write this narrative in a house
without furniture, without roof, door, chimneypiece, window, or window-
frame. – 'The life of William Hutton,' written by himself. London, 1816.

14 "Though our principles, which are well known, as friends to the
established government and enemies of republican principles, should
have been our protection from a mob whose watchword was Church and
King, yet our safety was principally owing to most of the Dissenters living
south of the town; for after the first moments they did not seem over nice
in their discrimination of religion and principles. I, among others, was
pointed out as a Presbyterian, though I never was in a meeting-house in
Birmingham, and Mr. Boulton is well known as a Churchman. We had
everything most portable packed up, fearing the worst. However, all is well
with us." – Watt to De Luc, 19th July, 1791.

15 The 'Discours' delivered by the MM. Cooper and Watt (1792) may be seen
at the British Museum.

16 'Life of Southey,' vi. 209.

17 Watt to Boulton, 16th May, 1794. Boulton MSS.

18 The Habeas Corpus Act was suspended on the 23rd May, 1794.

19 Watt to Boulton, 19th May, 1794. Boulton MSS.

20 Watt to Boulton, 23rd May, 1794. Young Watt continued to sympathise
with his political friends; as we find him, some months later, writing
Matthew R. Boulton from London as follows: – "The citizens here are all in
very high spirits since the late trials; and I had the honour of dining with

two of the *acquitted felons* on Sunday last." Watt, junr., having remained for
sometime in London on business connected with the prosecution of Bull
and others for infringement of his father's patent., Boulton, junr., kept up
an active correspondence with him on the affairs of the firm. In one letter
(19th February, 1795), after discussing various matters of detail relating to
the letter-copying machine and engine business, Boulton entreats his friend
to send him down a supply of hair-powder. "I have to intrust to your care,"
he says, "the execution of an important commission on the part of the
ladies and myself. The report of a scarcity of hair-powder has caused great
consternation amongst the beaux and belles here, and we beg of you to
preserve for us 1 cwt. of that necessary article." To which Watt, jun. replied,
– "Your new order is in train, so that I hope (whatever the poor may suffer
by the destruction of so scarce an article of nourishment) your aristocratical
vanity will be gratified, with only the additional sacrifice of one guinea per
annum to your immaculate friend Mr. Pitt, for the purpose of carrying
on this 'just and necessary war!' Under the existing circumstances, I am
doubtful whether I shall not sacrifice my aristocratical appendage [queues
being then the appendages of gentlemen], as it goes much against my
inclination to throw away my money at this moment of personal poverty,
or to contribute any sum, however small, to the support of measures which
I reprobate *in toto*. On the other hand, however, I do say that, of all the
taxes which have over been imposed within my memory, this is the most
politic and the least likely to be burdensome to the poor." – Boulton MSS.

21 Watt to Boulton, 20th March, 1796.

22 "We have won the cause hollow," Watt wrote from London. "All the
Judges have given their opinions carefully in our favour, and have passed
judgement. Some of them made better arguments in our favour than our
own counsel, for Rous's speech was too long and too divergent. I most
sincerely give you joy." – Watt to Boulton, 25th January, 1799.

23 The model was carefully preserved and exhibited with pride by his son, in
whose house at Handsworth we saw it in 1857.

24 Watt said to Robert Hart, "When Mr. Murdock introduced the slide valve,
I was very much against it, as I did not think it so good as the poppet
valve, but I gave in from its simplicity." – Hart, 'Reminiscences,' &c.

25 These several inventions were embodied by him in a patent taken out in 1799.

26 Burning springs, though by no means common in Europe, were not
unknown. They were kept burning by natural and spontaneous supplies
of carburetted hydrogen gas issuing from fissures in the earth overlying
beds of asphalte or coal. The inflammable character of fire-damp and the

explosions which it occasioned in coal mines were also familiar to most
persons living in the coal-mining districts. In 1658 Mr. Thomas Shirley
first communicated to the Royal Society the result of some experiments
which he had made on the inflammable gas issuing from a well near
Wigan in Lancashire. Some time before 1691 the Rev. Dr. Clayton, Dean
of Kildare, made some experiments on what he called the spirit of coal:
he distilled some coal in a retort, and, confining the gas produced thereby
in a bladder, he amused his friends by burning it as it issued from a pin-
hole. In 1721 Dr. Stephen Hales found it was practicable to produce elastic
inflammable air from coal and other substances, and that nearly one-third
of Newcastle coal was drawn off in vapour, gas, &c., by the action of heat.
In 1733 Sir James Lowther communicated to the Royal Society a paper
on the subject of the fire-damp issuing from the shaft of a coal mine near
Whitehaven, which had been accidentally set fire to and continued to
burn for two years. Dr. Watson, Bishop of Llandaff, and Dr. Priestley of
Birmingham, examined the properties of coal-gas, and made experiments
on its inflammable qualities, but pursued the subject no further. Lord
Dundonald also had been accustomed, for the amusement of his friends,
to set fire to the gas disengaged by the burning of coal in the process of
coke-making. The same phenomena must have been observed on a large
scale wherever coke was made. Each chamber in which coal was distilled
was in point of fact a gas resort. Oil and gas were the products of the
distillation; but strange to say, although the oil was collected and used, no
heed was taken of the gas. Nor was it until Mr. Murdock's attention was
called to the subject that lighting by gas was proved to be practicable.

27 'Philosophical Transactions,' 1808, pp. 124–132.

28 Many years later (in 1818), when Murdock was at Manchester for the
    purpose of starting one of Boulton and Watt's engines, he was invited, with
    Mr. William Fairbairn, to dine at Medlock Bank, then at some distance
    from the lighted part of the town. "It was a dark winter's night," writes
    Mr. Fairbairn, our informant, "and how to reach the house over such bad
    roads was a question not easily solved. Mr. Murdock, however, fruitful in
    resources, went to the Gas Works, (then established in Manchester), where
    he filled a bladder which he had with him, and placing it under his arm like
    a bagpipe, he discharged through the stem of an old tobacco pipe a stream
    of gas which enabled us to walk in safety to Medlock Bank."

29 Watt here alluded to the new machinery and plant erected at Soho
    under Murdock's directions, at a cost of about 5000l. for the purpose of
    manufacturing gas apparatus.

30 The invention of lighting by gas has be some writers been erroneously
attributed to Winsor. It will be observed, from the statement in the text, that
coal-gas has been in regular use long before the appearance of his scheme,
which was one of the most crude and inflated ever brought before the public.
"The Patriotic Imperial and National Light and Heat Company," proposed
amongst other things to aid and assist Government with funds in times of
emergency, to increase the Sinking-fund for reducing the National Debt, to
reward meritorious discoveries, &c. &c. Some idea of the character of the
project may be formed from Mr. [Lord] Brougham's speech in opening the
case against the Bill: – "'The neat annual profits,' says Mr. Winsor, 'agreeable
to the official experiments' (that is, the experiments of Mr. Accum ...)
'amount to 229,353,627l.' ... now Mr. Winsor says, that he will allow there
may be an error here, for the sake of argument with those who still have
their doubts; and he will admit that the sum should be taken at only one
half, or 114,845,294l.; and then giving up, to meet all possible objections,
nine-tenths of that sum, still there will remain, to be paid to the subscribers
of this company, a yearly profit of 570l. for every 5l. of deposit! So that upon
paying 5l. every subscriber is to receive 570l. a year for ever, and this to the
last farthing; it may increase but less it can never be; the clear profit is always
to be above 10,000l. per cent. Upon the capital! This is pretty well, sir, one
would think. There is here estimate and statement enough to captivate the
public; but this is not all; for Mr. Winsor has taken out a patent (of which,
indeed, he has, according to his custom, enrolled no specification, but, on
the contrary, has enrolled a surrender) for the invention of several things,
and, among others, one for rendering this gas respirable. It is not enough that
this gas (which everybody knows to be not respirable, but as poisonous to
the lungs as fixed air) should be capable of giving light; but he thinks it also
necessary to prove that it may easily be rendered respirable; in short, that there
is no way in which it may not be used, and nothing which may not be made
of it ... In another pamphlet ... Mr. Winsor endeavours to prove that this gas
is the vital principle; that in which life itself consists. If I had taken the trouble
to go through his publications, which I certainly have not done, it is hard to
say what I might not have discovered; but I should think the difficulty would
rather be, to find one quality which the gas is not stated to possess."

31 The first application of the "Gas-light and Coke Company" to Parliament
in 1809 for an Act proved unsuccessful, but the "London and Westminster
Chartered Gas-light and Coke Company" succeeded in the following year.
The Company, however, did not succeed commercially, and was on the
point of dissolution, when Mr. Clegg, a pupil of Murdock, bred at Soho,

undertook the management and introduced new and improved apparatus. Mr. Clegg first lighted with gas Mr. Ackerman's shop in the Strand in 1810, and it was regarded as a great novelty. One lady of rank was so much delighted with the brilliancy of the gas-lamp fixed on the shop counter, that she asked to be allowed to carry it home in her carriage, and offered any sum for a similar one. Mr. Winsor by his persistent advocacy of gas-lighting, did much to bring it into further notice; but it was Mr. Clegg's practical ability that mainly led to its general adoption. When Westminster Bridge was first lit up with gas in 1812, the lamplighters were so disgusted with it that they struck work, and Mr. Clegg himself had to act as lamplighter.

32 "It consisted," says Mr. Buckle, "of a piston working in a cylinder 10 feet diameter in water, with a lift of 12 feet, and raised by forcing in air from a small blowing cylinder 12 inches diameter, 18 inches stroke, which was worked by the gearing in the boring-mill." Paper read by the late William Buckle at the Institution of Mechanical Engineers at Birmingham, 23rd October, 1850.

33 Lockhart's 'Life of Scott,' one vol. edition, p. 500.

34 Mr. Buckle, in the memoir above cited, says, – "So completely was he absorbed at all times with the subject he had in hand, that he was quite regardless of everything else. When in London explaining the nature of his substitute for isinglas, he occupied handsome apartments. He, however, little respected the splendour of his drawing-room, and, fancying himself in his laboratory at Soho, he proceeded with his experiments quite careless and unconscious of the mischief he was doing. One morning his landlady calling in to receive his orders, was horrified to see her magnificent paper-hangings covered with wet fish-skins hung up to dry; and he was caught in the act of pinning up a cod's skin to undergo the same process. Whether the lady fainted or not is not on record, but the immediate ejectment of the gentleman and his fish was the consequence."

35 The young partners regarded him with a degree of affection and veneration, which often shows itself in their correspondence. Towards the later years of his life Mr. Murdock's faculties gradually decayed, and he wholly retired from the business of Soho, dying at his house at Sycamore Hill, Handsworth, on the 15th Nov., 1839, in his 85th year.

36 The first piece of iron-toothed gearing ever cast is placed on the lawn in front of Murdock's villa. The teeth are of somewhat unequal form, and the casting is rough – perhaps it has been exposed to rough usage. It bears the following inscription: – "This Pinton was cast at Carron Ironworks for John Murdock, of Bellow Mill, Ayrshire, A.D. 1760, being the first tooth-gearing ever used in millwork in Great Britain."

XXI

Application of Steam-power to Navigation – Miller and Symington – Boulton and Watt's Engine adopted by Fulton

It will be remembered that one of the early speculations of Roger Bacon related to the employment of engines of navigation without oarsmen, "so that the greatest river and sea ships, with only one man to steer them, may sail swifter than if they were fully manned," – that one of the uses to which Papin proposed to apply the steam-engine was to "propel ships against the wind and tide," in illustration of which he constructed his model steamboat, – and that, shortly after Newcomen's engine had become generally introduced as a pumping power, Jonathan Hulls took out a patent with the object of applying it to tow ships into and out of harbours. Hulls was followed, after a long interval, by Jouffroy in France and by Fitch in America, but none of their experiments proved successful; and it was not until Watt invented the condensing engine that it was found practicable to employ steam as a regular propelling power in navigation.

It was natural that the extraordinary success of Watt's invention should direct attention anew to the subject. The engine, in the powerful, compact, economical, and manageable form, into which he had brought it, was found able to effect rotary motion in the various processes of manufacture; and, in a maritime country like England, the thought that would naturally occur to many minds would be this: if the steam-engine can drive mill-wheels, why may it not in like manner be employed to drive the wheels of carriages by land and the paddle-wheels of vessels by sea? The subject was, indeed, often brought under the notice of both Boulton and Watt; but the anxiety, annoyance and expense to which they had been subjected in defending their original patent, deterred them from venturing on this new field of enterprise. Watt never made his proposed locomotive engine for running on common roads; and the model constructed by Murdcck at Redruth in 1784 remained a model still.

The subject was, however, shortly after taken up by William Symington, at Wanlockhead in Scotland, where his father was employed as engineman in superintending the working of one of Boulton and Watt's pumping-engines. The sight of this engine, and his father's employment upon it, had probably the effect of first directing his attention to steam-power and its extended uses; and having heard of Murdock's ingenious design from Boulton and Watt's men, who were constantly visiting and inspecting the pumping-engine,[1] it occurred to him to try whether he could not himself construct the model of a steam-carriage for use on common roads. He succeeded in making his model, and when it was finished, Mr. Meason, the manager of the Wanlockhead Lead Mines, was so much pleased with it that he asked the young man to accompany him to Edinburgh, to show it to the leading men of science in that city. Mr. Meason allowed it to be exhibited at his own house, Symington being in attendance to give explanations. Some of the Edinburgh professors, who came to see the model, were so much pleased with the youthful inventor (then only about twenty years of age), and the indications of mechanical genius which his machine displayed, that they strongly recommended Mr. Meason to enter him as a student at the University, which he readily assented to, and Symington accordingly matriculated at Edinburgh College in 1786, and, amongst other lectures, attended those of Dr. Black on Chemistry in the following session.

The Scotch roads were in too bad a condition at the time to admit of their being run over by a locomotive, and Symington eventually abandoned his proposed scheme. But he had also an idea that the steam-engine might be economically applied to the working of boats on canals, or ships at sea; and with that object he invented an engine specially adapted for the purpose. This clearly appears from his correspondence with Thomas Gilbert, M.P., brother to the Duke of Bridgewater's land steward. Mr. Gilbert had inspected the model of the steam-carriage while on a visit to Edinburgh, and at the same time had some conversation with Symington as to the employment of the steam-engine in hauling canal-boats, the result of which was that Symington promised to write him more fully on both topics. He proceeded to do so in a letter dated Wanlockhead, 24th September, 1786; in which, after describing the dimensions, power, mode of working, and the probable price (about 70*l.*) of a full-sized locomotive, he proceeded –

But an engine of the same power and apparatus for working boats on canals, will only coast about fifty pounds, and will only weight 110 st. Each strock of the

engine will have a force equall to 160 st. weight when applied, which undoubtedly will be able to drag a great weight upon water, when we run the proportion
between it and what a man can do in a boat with common oars, whose exertion
does not exceed more than 7 stones; but of this you will be a better judge than
me. The engine we propose for working the land-carriage is Mr. Watt's, with some
very material alterations; and before we can use it we must make an agreement
with him, which we intend to propose immediately. But the engine we propose
to work boats or skips with is an engine intirely of our own invention, and more
powerful and better adapted for the purpose than Mr. Watt's engine. This engine
of our own we have presently at worke here is a large moddle, by which we have
properly ascertained its power, and found it exceed Mr. Watt's engine nearly two
pounds upon each square inch on the piston, without any greater consumpt of
coals. Another advantage attending our engine is its being little more complicated than the old engine that works with an atmospheric pressure. We are to use
our endeavours immediately for a patent for this engine as well as our carriage;
your assistance, when we get application made, will be of great service to us, and
thankfully received by, Sir, &c. &c., William Smyington.[2]

About the same time that Symington was exhibiting his model carriage in
Edinburgh, Mr. Miller of Dalswinton was trying experiments at Leith in propelling boats by paddle-wheels worked by men at a capstan. He had a triple
vessel built, with wheels placed inside, on turning which the vessel was impelled
forward. It will be observed that this was but a repetition of the old experiment
of Blasco Garay at Barcelona, and of Savery on the Thames. The experiments
were on the whole successful, but the power employed in propelling the vessel
was felt to be defective, and the turning of the capstan was very hard work, at
which men could not be brought to work continuously for any long period.

Mr. Miller, being curious as to all mechanical novelties, went, amongst
others, to see Symington's model locomotive; and in the course of conversation with the inventor informed him of his own project, describing the
difficulty he had experienced in getting his paddles turned for lack of power.
The immediate remark of Symington was, 'Why don't you use the steam-
engine?" He proceeded to show how easily the engine might be connected
with the wheels of the boat, using the model of the steam-carriage before
him to explain his meaning. Mr. Miller appeared to have been struck by the
suggestion, and in the pamphlet which he shortly after published describing his new vessel, he referred to the probable employment of steam-power
for the purpose of driving the paddles. "I have reason to believe," he said,
"that the power of the steam-engine may be applied to work the wheels, so as

to give them a quicker motion, and consequently to increase that of the ship. In the course of this summer, I intend to make the experiment; and the result, if favourable, shall be communicated to the public."[3]

Mr. Miller subsequently contrived and constructed a double vessel, 60 feet in length, worked by a paddle-wheel placed amidships between the two halves of the ship, with a clear waterway in the middle in which the paddle was worked, propelling the vessel. An experiment with this new ship was tried in June, 1787, which was considered successful. "The vessel being put in motion by the water-wheel, wrought by five men at the capstern, was steered so as to keep the wind right ahead, and her rate of going was found by the log to be three and a half miles in the hour."[4] A sailing-match was arranged by Mr. Miller, in which he was to run his vessel from Inchcolm (a small island in the Frith of Forth) to Leith, against a Custom-house wherry which was reckoned a fast sailer. In this race the double vessel beat by a few minutes. A young man named James Taylor, who officiated in Mr. Miller's family as tutor to his two younger sons, was on board the vessel, and took his turn in working the wheels, which be found to be "very severe exercise." In consequence of this trial and its results, Taylor became persuaded that unless a more commanding power than that of men could be applied, the invention of the paddle-ship would prove of little use; and on turning the matter over in his mind, he suggested to Mr. Miller the use of the steam-engine. This, however, was no new idea, as, from what we have already stated, it is clear that it had already occurred to Symington, who had even contrived an engine for the express purpose of propelling ships. As Taylor was intimate with Symington, and a fellow-student with him at Edinburgh College in the session of 1786–7, it is probable that Taylor obtained from him his first idea of the application of the steam-engine to Mr. Miller's paddle-boat.

The result of Symington's and Taylor's suggestion was, that Mr. Miller resolved to make a further experiment; and he ordered a double boat to be built and fitted with a steam-engine for trial on Dalswinton Loch, near his country-seat in Dumfriesshire, in the course of the following summer. Syinington prepared the plans of the engine, the castings of which were executed by George Watt, an Edinburgh founder; and when the parts were ready, Symington and Taylor went together to Wanlockhead, in the summer of 1788, to have the engine erected and placed in the boat in readiness for the proposed trial.

In the mean time, other projects of a similar kind were afoot; and Boulton and Watt continued to be solicited from different quarters on the subject of engines for sailing ships. To these they continued to turn a deaf ear. They were willing to execute engines to order, but they declined to undertake them as speculations. Thus, in the spring of 1788, we find Sir John Dalrymple, one of the barons of the Court of Exchequer at Edinburgh, addressing Boulton on the subject of the proposed application of the steam-engine to the propulsion of ships, and the reply of the latter clearly shows what were then the views of the Soho firm on the subject:

Sir, – I have just received the honour of your letter of the 23rd inst., by which I observe you are intent upon applying the power of steam to the navigation of ships, boats, &c.

It is one of the applications of our engine which Mr. Watt and I have often talked of, but we were deterred from the prosecution of it more from political than mechanical difficulties, as well as from some prudential reasons; besides which, we thought we could be more useful to the public and to ourselves by confining our attention to such subjects as were within the limits of our own powers and our own country. We still continue of that opinion, and are persuaded that it would be folly in us (who have our hands and heads full of solid and important business) to engage in any set of new experiments, or, like Charles XII, go in quest of conquest in foreign kingdoms, and leave our own to be conquered.

If you or your friends want any of our steam-engines for any purpose you may think proper to apply them to, we shall be very glad to serve you upon the usual terms; although I must confess that I should be sorry to see them applied to *one* purpose which perhaps may be of as much importance to this country some time or other as Admiral Drake's fire-ship was on a former emergency.

I beg the favour of you not to consider me or Mr. Watt as schemers or projectors, but as men who are following their regular established trade and manufactures of great extent, – amongst others that of steam-engines, – and engineers, in which capacity we shall always be found attentive to your commands.[5]

Symington had many difficulties to encounter in erecting his engine at Leadhills. Though it was of very small size, being of only about two horses power, with a four-inch cylinder, it required as much skill to construct as a much larger engine would have done. The arrangement of the power was new, as well as the application; and, as in the case of every new machine, where unforeseen defects were brought to light, new expedients had to be contrived for the purpose of overcoming them. Mr. Miller became impatient for its completion, and

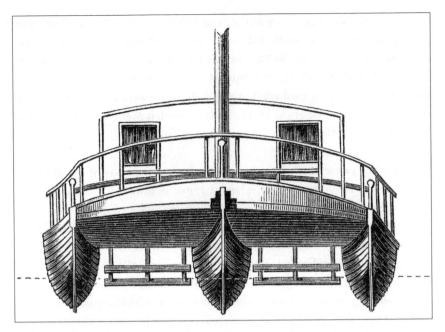

Miller's Triple Vessel

repeatedly wrote from Edinburgh urging despatch, fearing lest some other pro-jector should get the start of him in applying the steam-engine to the driving of ships. Taylor, who managed the corresponding part of the enterprise, replied, "You need be under very little apprehension as to any person getting before you in this. It is easy in conversation, but very different in execution. However, as such a circumstance would be equally unpleasant to us, to prevent it you may depend upon the greatest expedition being used."[6]

Taylor being further urged by his employer, again wrote from Leadhills on the 12th September, 1788, – "Mr. Symington and I are as busy here as we possibly can be. We work from six o'clock in the morning till dark in the eve-ning, without losing a moment; also, to forward us the more, we have called in the aid of a watchmaker here, who works along with us. We are now in great forwardness, and will not be long of finishing. I could not ascertain to a day when it will happen, but believe we shall have it at Dalswinton some time before the end of the month."[7]

The engine was shortly after finished, mounted in a strong oak frame, and taken to Dalswinton. It was then placed on the deck of Mr. Miller's double pleasure-boat, twenty-four feet long and seven broad, which had been prepared for its reception.

The engine was placed on one side of the boat, the boiler on the other side to balance it, and the paddle-wheels in the middle; the rotary motion being obtained from the engine by chains, ratchet-wheels, and catches. The first experiment was tried on the 14th of October, 1788, and proved successful, the engine being propelled at the rate of five miles an hour.[8] Among the persons present on the occasion, besides Miller, Symington, and Taylor, were Alexander Nasmyth, the landscape painter, and Robert Burns, the poet, then a tenant of Mr. Miller on the neighbouring farm of Ellisland. After a few further experiments the engine was taken out of the boat and carried into Mr. Miller's house, where it remained for many years, and was eventually deposited in the Museum of Patents at Kensington, where it is now to be seen.

The experiments made with this first steamboat were so satisfactory that Mr. Miller resolved to try one upon a larger scale. By this time Messrs. Allen and Stewart, of Leith, had built for him another double vessel, ninety feet in length; and he wrote to Symington, requesting his estimate of the cost of fitting it with a suitable steam-engine. Symington's reply was to the effect that a proper-sized engine for such a vessel would, in his opinion, be about 250*l.*, including the float-wheels. The necessary order was given, and Symington proceeded to the Carron Ironworks for the purpose of constructing it. The vessel arrived at Carron on the 24th June, and by the month of November following the engine was finished and put on board ready for trial.[9] The result was not so satisfactory as in the case of the experiment on Dalswinton Loch. The paddle-wheels were too weak; first one float and then another broke off; and the trial had to be suspended until the defects were remedied. The next trial was, however, more satisfactory. The vessel reached a speed of seven miles an hour; and this was repeated with the same result. There must, however, have been some defect in the engine performances; for, in a letter written by Miller to Taylor, who was present throughout, he expressed the opinion that Symington's engine was altogether unsuitable for giving motion to a vessel.[10] He accordingly ordered the engine to be taken out and placed in the Carron Works, and the vessel itself to be laid up at Bruce Haven.

Thus matters remained until the spring of the following year, when Mr. Miller decided on applying to Boulton and Watt for an engine of a proper construction, offering at the same time to associate them with him in his enterprise. The negotiation was opened by Robert, afterwards Lord Cullen, who addressed Watt on the subject; but his reply was not encouraging. Like his partner, Watt was averse to new speculations; and he had had too much anxiety and worry in connexion with his original enterprise to enter upon any new one. It will also be observed that he entertained doubts as to the eventual success of ocean navigation by steam. The following was his reply:

Dear Sir, – We have heard of Mr. Miller's ingenious experiments on double ships from Sir John Dalrymple, and also some vague accounts of the experiments with the steam-engine, from which we could gather nothing conclusive, except that the vessel did move with a considerable velocity.

From what we heard of Mr. Symington's engines, we were disposed to consider them as attempts to evade our exclusive privilege; but as we thought them so defective in mechanical contrivance as not to be likely to do us immediate hurt, we thought it best to leave them to be judged by Dame Nature first before we brought them to any earthly court.

We are much obliged to Mr. Miller for his favourable opinion of us and of our engines, which we hope experience would more and more justify. We are also fully sensible of his kind intentions in offering to associate us with him in his scheme; but the time of life we have both arrived at, and the multiplicity of business we are at present engaged in, must plead our excuse for entering into any new concern whatever as partners; but as engineers and engine-makers we are ready to serve him to the best of our abilities, at our customary prices, for rotative engines, and to assist in anything we can do to bring the scheme to perfection.

We conceive that there may be considerable difficulty in making a steam-engine to work in the open sea, on account of the undulating motion of the vessel affecting the *vis inertiæ* of the matter; however, this we should endeavour to obviate as far as we could.

It may not be improper to mention that Earl Stanhope has lately taken a patent for moving a vessel by steam, but not by wheels. His Lordship has also applied to us for engines; but we believe we are not likely to agree with him, as he lays too much stress upon his own ingenuity.

We cannot conclude without observing, that were we disposed to enter into any new concern whatever, there is no person we should prefer to Mr. Miller as an associate, being fully apprised of his worth and honour, and admirers of the ingenuity and industry with which he has pursued this scheme.

Permit me now, Sir, to return you my thanks for your obliging attention to me, and for the trouble you have taken in this affair, and to ask the far our of your presenting Boulton and Watt's respectful compliments to Mr. Miller. – I remain, dear Sir, &c. &c.,

James Watt.[11]

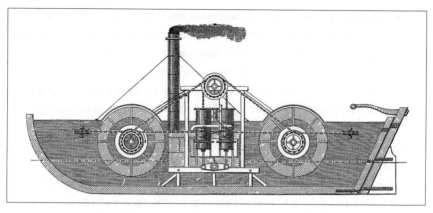

Symington's first Steamboat Engine

Mr. Miller's Experimental Steamboat

Mr. Miller proceeded no further with his experiments, on which he had already expended a large sum of money. He seems to have lost faith in the applicability of the steam-engine to the propulsion of ships, aud reverted to his original idea, as we find him taking out a patent in 1796 for a new kind of flat-bottomed ship, which he proposed to impel during calms by means of wheels worked by capstans; but he makes no mention whatever of the use of the steam-engine.

Symington was greatly disappointed with the result of his experiments. Being without the means of carrying the steamboat further, he feared that all his past labours would prove in vain, and that some more fortunate speculator would carry off the prize that seemed almost within his grasp. The subject was not, however, allowed to sleep. Fitch and Evans were pursuing the invention in America; Bumsey, another American, came over to England in 1788, with a scheme for propelling boats by steam; and Fourness and Earl Stanhope were making experiments in the same direction; but none of them had yet succeeded in constructing a practicable working steamboat. Thus ten more years passed, during which other inventors came forward, took out patents, made their trials, failed, and disappeared.

In the year 1801 Symington had another chance. Lord Dundas, Governor of the Forth and Clyde Canal Company, had been revolving in his mind whether some more expeditious and economical method than horse-power might not be contrived for hauling the boats along the canal; and, being aware of the experiments made by Miller and Symington ten years before, he determined to give Symington's engine another trial. A boat was accordingly built for the purpose of the experiment, and named the 'Charlotte Dundas,' after his Lordship's daughter. For this vessel Symington contrived a steam-engine of a greatly improved character. It was a direct-acting engine, the steam acting on each side of the piston, after the method invented by Watt, whose patent had now expired; the rotary motion of the paddle-wheels being secured by means of a connecting-rod and crank, instead of by chains and ratched-wheels, as in the first two boats.

The first trial of the vessel was perfectly satisfactory. After making a trip to Glasgow, she was employed in towing vessels along the canal. She was also occasionally sent down the Frith to bring up ships detained by contrary winds to the canal entrance at Grangemouth.[12]

Fortune at length seemed to smile on poor Symington, and his spirits were proportionately elate at the result of these important experiments. He had, in fact, achieved a decided success in the 'Charlotte Dundas,' – in which he combined together, for the first time, those improvements which constitute the present system of Steam Navigation. Indeed Mr. Woodcroft, a competent judge, says that "the vessel might, from the simplicity of its machinery, have been at work at this day with such ordinary repairs as are now occasionally required to all steamboats."[13]

Lord Dundas was so well satisfied with the performances of the vessel that he proposed to introduce the inventor to the Duke of Bridgewater, the great canal proprietor, who had expressed to him his wish to employ some method of hauling his boats more effective than horse-power. His Lordship accordingly directed Symington to have a model of his steamboat constructed for the purpose of showing it to the Duke. Symington went up to London himself to explain its mechanical arrangements, and the Duke was so much pleased with it that he ordered eight boats of the same construction to be made as speedily as possible for use upon his canal. Symington returned to Scotland to proceed with the execution of this important order.

But in the moment of his apparent triumph fate again proved hostile to the inventor. Though Lord Dundas was fully satisfied with the performances of the 'Charlotte Dundas,' and hailed the use of steam as the beginning of a new era in navigation, the proprietors of the canal became seriously alarmed lest the banks should be washed away by the waves which the steamboat raised in its wake, and they came to the resolution of prohibiting all further experiments. To add to Symington's vexation, the very same day on which this adverse decision of the canal managers reached him, he received intelligence of the death of the Duke of Bridgewater, and an order to suspend the erection of the eight steamboats until fresh instructions had been given. By this time Lord Dundas had expended about 7000*l.* on his experiments, and was not disposed to proceed any further with them. The 'Charlotte Dundas,' the first successful steamboat, was accordingly laid up at Bainsford, in a creek of the canal; and the attempt to introduce steam navigation on canals was from that time suspended.[14]

Symington's experiments, though they proved most unfortunate as respected himself, nevertheless led to the adoption of the system of navigation by steam both in America and Scotland. Among the many visitors who inspected the 'Charlotte Dundas ' were Fulton the American artist, and Andrew Bell the engineer, of Glasgow. Fulton was on board the first vessel in the month of July, 1801, when she made a run of eight miles on the Forth and Clyde Canal in an hour and twenty minutes; on which occasion he narrowly inquired into the action of the engine and paddle-wheels, and made careful sketches of the vessel and her machinery.[15] Andrew Bell also made frequent visits to the 'Charlotte Dundas,' as well as to the pattern shop where the models of the machinery were kept; and there is little doubt that, like Fulton, he obtained his ideas of steam navigation principally from what Symington had accomplished. Fulton and Bell were well acquainted with each other, and kept up a correspondence on the subject of steamboats. Bell, according to his own account, supplied Fulton with information and drawings of steamboat machinery; and it was by his recommendation that Fulton ordered the engine for his first successful steamboat from Boulton and Watt.

With the information obtained at Grangemouth, Fulton proceeded to Paris, where we shortly find him in communication with Mr. Livingstone, the United States' envoy, who, like Fulton, took much interest in the sub-

ject of steam navigation. They had a model steamboat built for trial on
the Seine; but when on the point of making the first experiment, the
weight of the machinery broke the boat in two, and the whole went
down together. Fulton's greatest difficulty, as was to be expected, consisted in finding a suitable engine to propel his proposed boat, and he
wrote to his friends in England on the subject. In March, 1802, we find
him addressing Dr. Cartwright, who had invented an improvement in the
steam-engine, which he thought would render it more suitable for driving
vessels, requesting to be informed of the cost of one of six horse power,
with particulars of its size and weight. Fulton communicated to his correspondent that, besides his proposed steamboat, he was experimenting
on his 'Nautilus' or diving-boat for navigating under water; the object of
this invention being to blow up the English ships of war which were then
blockading the French ports. The experiments with the 'Nautilus' under
water were said to have proved tolerably successful, though it had not yet
succeeded in blowing up any of the English ships.

Not being able to obtain any satisfactory information from Dr. Cartwright,
Fulton addressed a letter to James Watt, jun., of Soho, requesting to be
informed of the price of a light and compact engine for his proposed vessel.
"The object of my investigation," he said, "is to find whether it is possible to
apply the engine to working boats up our long rivers in America. The persons
who have made such attempts have commenced by what they call improving
Watt's engine, but without having an idea of the physics which he hid in it
from common observers; but such improvements have appeared to me like
the improvements of the preceptor of Alcibiades, who corrected Homer for
the use of his scholars. Their ill success, and their never having found a good
mode of taking a purchase in the water, are the reasons why they have all
failed. Having, during the course of my experiments on submersive navigation, found an excellent mode of taking a purchase on the water, I wish to
apply the engine to the movement. The only thing wanting is to arrange the
engine as light and compact as possible."[16]

The information asked for was duly communicated to Fulton, and
a few months later he sent Boulton and Watt the drawings of parts of
an engine which he requested them to make for him. By this time the
rumour had gone abroad of the destructive powers of the 'Nautilus,' and
Lord Stanhope publicly called attention to the subject in the House of
Lords, representing the dangerous character of the invention. On Fulton's
order reaching Soho, Boulton suspected that it might really be intended
for the 'Nautilus,' and he at once communicated with Government on the

Machinery of the 'Charlotte Dundas'

subject. To Lord Hawkesbury he wrote, –

> I presume your Lordship is not unacquainted with the name of Fulton. I mean Fulton the engineer and pretended inventor of an infernal machine for destroying the British Navy. He is the same person whom Lord Stanhope alluded to in some of his speeches in the House of Peers.
>
> I never had any transaction or acquaintance with him. However, he has written to my house (Boulton and Watt) from Paris; and has transmitted drawings of sundry parts of a steam-engine. The remainder, he says, is to be executed under his own directions, and though he orders them to be shipped for America, it is not impossible but they may be transhipped before they reach there.
>
> The drawings and letter were delivered to my house in London-street by a Mr. Barlow; and as he refers to Sir Francis Baring for payment, I directed my agent (Mr. John Woodward) to call upon Sir Francis, and in consequence thereof he wrote to my house a letter, of which I enclose a correct copy as well as of Mr. Fulton's.
>
> Whatever doubts we may have of his project, we have none respecting the propriety of acquainting your Lordship with every particular as to this matter that has come to our knowledge.[17]

Boulton concluded by requesting instructions how to act; but all necessity for further caution was shortly after removed by Fulton coming over to England and imparting his secret to the British Government. An old Danish brig was placed at his disposal in Walmer Roads, and after two days' effort, during which he was assisted by Sir Home Popham, he eventually succeeded in blowing up the vessel; but he accomplished his purpose with so much difficulty, that from that time no further fears were entertained of the much dreaded 'Nautilus.'

In the following year the steam-engine ordered by Fulton for his proposed boat was proceeded with at Soho. It was of about nineteen horse power. The cylinder was 24 inches in diameter, and the stroke four feet. The dimensions were as nearly as possible the same as those of Symington's 'Charlotte Dundas' engine; and Mr. Woodcroft pertinently remarks that "such similarity in the dimensions cannot easily be imagined to have been accidental." The engine, when finished, was sent to America early in 1805. She was there fitted on board the vessel which had been prepared for her reception; and the first voyage of Fulton and Livingstone's 'Clermont' was made in August, 1807, when a speed of nearly four miles an hour was attained. This was the first vessel that ran regularly for commercial purposes and for the benefit of her owners; and though Fulton neither invented the ship, nor the engine by which she was driven, nor the combination of the two, he was entitled to every merit for the perseverance and ability with which he carried his important enterprise to a successful issue.

A few years later Henry Bell, in like manner, introduced steam navigation on the Clyde. He had at an early period pressed the subject on the consideration of the Government, but failed to induce them to take up the scheme.[18] He then resolved himself to start a steamboat, as the best and most practical method of exhibiting its powers; and the 'Comet,' of thirty tons burthen, was built to his order by Messrs. John Wood and Company, of Port Glasgow. The vessel began to ply regularly between Glasgow and Greenock in August, 1812;[19] and before long Clyde steamers were known all over the world.

It will thus be observed how very gradual has been the invention of the steamboat. It has been made step by step, by many men living in many ages. First, we have Blasco Garay making experiments with paddle-wheels in the harbour of Barcelona three hundred years ago, the revival probably of some old and half-forgotten method of propelling ships; then the repetition of the experiment by Prince Rupert and Savery in the Thames more than a hundred and fifty years later; next Savery's invention of his steam-engine, followed by Papin's idea of combining the engine with the paddles, and his construction of a model to illustrate its practicability. Later, we have Jonathan Hulls's patent for his steamboat, in which the engine was worked by atmospheric pressure, followed by numerous experiments with a like object, in England, France, and America. The invention of the condensing engine of Watt, and its application to rotary motions, was the next great step. Miller's revival of the experiments with paddle-wheels led to the application by Symington of Papin's idea of combining the steam-engine with the paddles, which he at length successfully worked out in the 'Charlotte Dundas.' And finally the invention was applied to practical purposes by Fulton and Livingstone in America, and by Bell in Scotland.

And thus became established, in the eloquent words of George Canning, "the new and mighty power, new at least in the application of its might, which walks the waters like a giant rejoicing in its course, stemming alike the tempest and the tide, accelerating intercourse, shortening distances, creating, as it were, unexpected neighbourhoods, and new combinations of social and commercial relations, and giving to the fickleness of winds and the faithlessness of waves the certainty and steadiness of a highway upon the land." But it is a noteworthy fact, that it was not until the invention of James Watt was applied to the purposes of steam navigation that its prcoticability was established and its success secured. Until then, all the experiments which had been made were regarded as comparatively fruitless, though they were leading step by step to the great result; and to this day the engines constructed after Watt's principle continue to be the great motive power alike of river and ocean navigation.

The 'Comet' passing Dumbarton (by R. P. Leitch)

NOTES

1   The Symingtons, father and son, began at an early period to design
     improvements on Watt's pumping-engine, and took out a patent for
     a fire-engine on a new principle as early as the year 1785. Watt heard
     of its progress from time to time; but he had no great opinion of the
     Symingtons, and treated their alleged invention with indifference. On
     the 28th September, 1787, he wrote Boulton, – "Isaac Perrins [a fitter] is
     returned from Scotland. He says Symington has invented a new engine,
     which is to work under 12½ lbs. on the inch and has got a patent for it,
     which Mr. M[eason] has paid for. By his account it seems to be on the
     same principle as the Trumpeters. As soon as they can rely fully on the
     new engine, the old one is to be pulled down, and Symington is to put up
     one of his in the house, and, on that answering, ours is to be stopped!"

2   This interesting letter, so important as regards the early history of
     the invention of the steamboat, appeared for the first time in the
     supplementary volume to the 'Official Description and Illustrated
     Catalogue of the Great Exhibition of 1851,' to which it was contributed by
     Mr. W. C. Aitkin of Birmingham.

3   'The Elevation, Section, Plans, and Views, of a Triple Vessel, and of
     Wheels, with Explanations of the Figures in the Engraving, and a short
     Account of the Properties and Advantages of the Invention.' By Patrick
     Miller, Esq., of Dalswinton, Edinburgh, 1787.

4   Mr. Miller's statement to the Royal Society, 20th December, 1787.

5   Boulton to Sir John Dalrymple, 26th March, 1788. The "one purpose"
     alluded to by Boulton is supposed to have been the Torpedo, then a
     favourite scheme with French inventors for blowing up English ships.

6   Taylor to Miller, 20th August, 1788. 'Supplementary Vol. to Official
     Description and illustrated Catalogue of the Exhibition of 1851,' p. 1473.

7   Ibid.

8   The following contemporary account of the trial appeared in the 'Scots
     Magazine' for November, 1788: – "On October 14th, a boat was put in
     motion by a steam-engine upon Mr. Miller of Dalswinton's piece of water
     at that place. That gentleman's improvements in naval affairs are well
     known to the public. For some time past his attention has been turned to
     the application of the steam-engine to the purposes of navigation. He has
     now accomplished, and evidently shown to the world, the practicability
     of this, by executing it upon a small scale. A vessel, 25 feet long and 7

broad, was, on the above date, driven with two wheels by a small engine. It answered Mr. Miller's expectations fully, and afforded great pleasure to the spectators. The success of this experiment is no small accession to the public. Its utility in canals, and all inland navigation, points out to be of the greatest advantage, not only to this island, but to many other nations of the world. The engine used is Mr. Symington's new patent engine."

9 From a memorandum found amongst Mr. Boulton's papers, we learn that the following were the details of Symington's engine – "Engine hath two cylinders of 18 inches diameter each and 2 feet stroke. The rods of each piston are connected to a circular barrel of cast iron by means of chains, so that whilst one piston moves down the other ascends, and so gives the barrel a reciprocating motion. Upon the axis of the barrel is an arm or lever which works the plug and working gear. Each of the cylinders hath 2 pistons, one at top and the other at bottom; the 2 bottom pistons have their rods moving in stuffing-boxes and are connected together by a beam. The steam is admitted into the cylinder at its side, between the 2 pistons, and moves the one up and the other down; but the motion of the upper is greater than the under. When the upper piston is got to the top and the under one to the bottom, the steam valve is shut and the exhaustion one opened; by which the steam is admitted into the bottom of the cylinder, and is in its way met by a jet of cold water, which condenses it, and then it is squeezed out by the under piston, which in fact makes the bottom of the cylinder an air-pump. Whilst this condensation is going forward in the one cylinder, the steam is operating in the other, and *vice versâ*."

10 "I am now satisfied," he said, that Mr. Symington's steam-engine is the most improper of all steam-engines for giving motion to a vessel, and that he does not know how to calculate frictions or mechanical powers. By means of a new well-constructed valve-wheel, and the pinion being doubled in diameter, I doubt not that the velocity of the vessel's motion will be increased; but, do as you will, a great deal of power of the engine must be lost in friction. I remember well that when the small engine was wrought in the boat at Dalswinton, I had formed the same idea, and that I told you so; but not having studied the subject, I gave up my own common sense. This is now past remedy. As the engine cannot be of use to me now, I hope, with the aid of Mr. Tibbets and Mr. Stainton, you will get it sold before you leave Carron." – Miller to Taylor, 7th December, 1789.

11 J. Watt to R. Cullen, 24th April, 1790, 'Supplementary Volume to Official Descriptive and Illustrated Catalogue of the Exhibition of 1851,' p.1475.

12   One day in March, 1802, on the occasion of a strong west wind blowing, when the canal-boats could with difficulty be moved to windward, the steamer took in tow two laden sloops, the 'Active' and 'Euphemia,' of seventy tons each, from Lock 20 to Port Dundas, Glasgow, a distance of 19½ miles, in six hours.

13   'A sketch of the Origin and Progress of Steam Navigation.' By Bennet Woodcroft. London, 1848.

14   Symington continued to struggle for many years under the burden of debt which he had incurred by his experiments; and though a sum of 100*l.* was granted him from the Privy Purse in 1824, and 50*l.* a year or two afterwards, he remained in a state of poverty during the rest of his life. He died on the 22nd March, 1831, and was buried in the churchyard of St. Botolph, Aldgate, London.

15   The following deposition was made on oath by Robert Weir of Kincardine, before Robert Dundas J. P. for the county of Perth, at Blair Castle, on the 23rd October, 1824: – "That, in the year 1801, he remembers of Mr. Symington erecting a boat, and fitting a steam-engine into it, and dragging two vessels along the Forth and Clyde Canal by means of the said steamboat. That the deponent was employed as engine-fireman on board of the said boat. Deposes that the following persons, now living, were also on board, viz., Alexander Hart and John Allen, ship-builders, Grangemouth, and John Esplin and William Gow, shipmasters there. That some time after the first experiment, while the boat was lying upon the canal at Lock 16, it was visited by a stranger, who requested to see the boat worked. That the said William Symington desired the deponent to light the furnace, which was done, and the stranger was carried about four miles along the canal, and brought back. That this stranger made inquiries both as to the mode of constructing and of working the boat, and took notes of the information given him by the said William Symington. That the deponent heard the stranger say his name was Fulton, and that he was a native of the United States of America. That the deponent remembers Mr. Symington remarking that the progress of the boat was much impeded by the narrowness of the canal, to which Mr. Fulton answered that the objection would not apply to the large rivers of North America, where he thought the boat might be used to great advantage." – From copies of affidavits in the 'Biography of William Symington.' By J. and W. R. Rankin, Engineers, Falkirk, 1862.

16   In one of his letters, Bell says – "Fulton came at different times to the country and stopped with me for some time." – 'Life of Henry Bell,' p. 74.

17 Cited in Muirhead's 'Life of James Watt,' 2nd ed. p. 426

18 Boulton to Lord Hawkesbury, 22nd August, 1803. Boulton MSS

19 It is stated in the 'Life of Henry Bell,' that he applied to Mr. Watt in the year 1801, for his advice as to a suitable engine for a steamboat; but Watt gave him no encouragement to proceed with his design. "How many noblemen, gentlemen, and engineers," he wrote to Bell, "have puzzled their brains, and spent thousands of pounds, and none of these, nor yourself, have been able to bring the power of steam in navigation to a successful issue." – 'Life of Bell.' By E. Morris, Glasgow, 1844, p. 30.

20 The starting of the 'Comet' naturally excited great interest along the Clyde. In the evenings, thousands of spectators lined the banks as far as Govan to see her pass up from Greenock. The masters of the old sailing craft, however, regarded the 'Comet' with apprehension and dismay. The old Highland gabert men were especially hostile, denouncing the new vessel as being impelled by the "teevil's wun" (devil's wind). The story is told of the steamer one day coming up with a fly boat tacking against the tide, when the crew began to jeer the skipper of the fly, calling upon him to come along with his lazy craft. "Get oot o' my sight," he cried, in reply, "I'm just gaun as it pleases the breath o' the Almichty, and I'll ne'er fash my thumb how fast ye gang wi' your blasted deevil's reek."

Watt's House, Heathfield (by Percival Skelton)

XXII

Declining Years of Boulton and Watt – Bereavements – Gregory Watt – Death of Boulton

On the dissolution of the original partnership between Boulton and Watt at the expiry of the patent in 1800, Boulton was seventy-two years old, and Watt sixty-four. The great work of their life had been done, and the time was approaching when they must needs resign into other hands the great branches of industry which they had created. Watt, though the younger of the two, was the first to withdraw from an active share in the concerns of Soho. He could scarcely be said to taste the happiness of life until he had cast business altogether behind him.

It was far different with Boulton, to whom active occupation had become a second nature. For several years, indeed, his constitution had been show-ing signs of giving way, and nature was repeating her warnings, at shorter recurring intervals, that it was time to retire. But in the case of men such as Boulton, with whom business has become a habit and necessity, as well as a pleasure and recreation, to retire is often to die. He himself was accustomed to say that he must either "rub or rust;" and as the latter was contrary to his nature, he rubbed on to the end, continuing to take an active interest in the working of the great manufactory which it had been the ambition of his life to build up.

The department of business that most interested him in his later years was the coinage. His chief pleasure consisted in seeing his new and beautiful pieces following each other in quick succession from the Soho Mint. Nor did he cease occupying himself with new inventions; for we find him as late as 1797 taking out a patent for raising water by impulse, somewhat after the manner of Montgolier's Hydraulic Ram, to which he added many ingenious improve-ments. His house at Soho continued to be the resort of distinguished visitors;

and his splendid hospitality never failed. But, as years advanced and his infirmities increased, we find him occasionally expressing a desire for quiet. He would then retire to Cheltenham for the benefit of the waters, requesting his young partners to keep him advised from time to time of the proceedings at Soho. Thus we find young Watt writing him during his absence on one occasion, – "Everything is going on well here: the Mint works six presses at present with ease; but, unless you have secured a supply of copper, I fear they will soon work out the present stock." In the same letter his young friend advised him that he had duly depatched the chemical apparatus; for even at Cheltenham Boulton could not be idle, but undertook a careful analysis of all the waters of the place, the results of which he entered, in minute detail, in his memorandum-books.

An alarming incident occurred at Soho towards the end of 1800, which is worthy of passing notice, as illustrative of Boulton's vigour and courage even at this advanced period of his life. A large gang of Birmingham housebreakers, knowing the treasures accumulated in the silver-plate house, determined to break into it and carry off the silver, as well as the large sum of money usually accumulated in the counting-house for the purpose of paying the wages of the workmen, upwards of 600 in number, on Christmas Eve. They had provided false keys for most of the doors, and bribed the watchman, who communicated the plot to Boulton, to admit them within the gates. He took his steps accordingly, arming a number of men, and stationing them in different parts of the building.

The robbers made the attempt on three several occasions. On the first night they tried their keys on the counting-house door, but failed to open it, on which they shut their dark lantern and retired. Boulton sent an account of the proceedings each night to his daughter in London. On the first attempt being made, he wrote, – "The best news I can send you is that we are all alive; but I have lost my voice and found a troublesome cough by the agreeable employment of thief-watching." Two nights after, the burglars came again, with altered keys, but still they could not open the counting-house door. The third night they determined to waive art, and break in by force. They were allowed to break in and seize their booty, and were making off with 150 guineas and a load of silver, when Boulton gave the word to seize them. A quantity of tow soaked with turpentine was instantly set fire to, numerous lights were turned on, and the robbers found themselves surrounded on all sides by armed men. Four of them were taken after a desperate struggle; but the fifth, though severely wounded, contrived to escape over the tops of the houses in Brook-row.

Writing to his friend Dumergue, in London, of the exploit, Boulton said, – "You know I seldom do things by halves; so I have sent the four desperate wolves to Stafford Gaol, and I believe the fifth is much wounded. If I had made my attack with a less powerful army than I did, we should probably have had a greater list of killed and wounded."[1] It was in allusion to this exploit that Sir Walter Scott said of Boulton to Allan Cunningham, "I like Boulton; he is a brave man, and who can dislike the brave?"[2] The incident, when communicated to Scott during one of his visits to Soho, is said to have suggested the scene in 'Guy Mannering,' in which the attack is made on Dirk Hatterick in the smuggler's cave.

With Watt, occupation in business was not the necessity that it was to Boulton; and he was only too glad to get rid of it and engage in those quiet pursuits in which he found most pleasure. In the year 1790, he removed from the house he had so long occupied on Harper's Hill, to a new and comfortable house which he had built for himself at Heathfield in the parish of Handsworth, where he continued to live until the close of his life. The land surrounding the place was, until then, common, and he continued to purchase the lots as they were offered for sale, until, by the year 1794, he had enclosed about forty acres. He took pleasure in laying out the grounds, planting many of the trees with his own hands; and in course of time, as the trees reached maturity, the formerly barren heath became converted into a retreat of great rural beauty.

Annexed to the house, in the back yard, he built a forge, and upstairs, in his "Garret," he fitted up a workshop, in which he continued to pursue his mechanical studies and experiments for many years. While Watt was settling himself for the remainder of his life in the house at Heathfield, Boulton was erecting his large new Mint at Soho, which was completed and ready for use in 1791.

When the lawsuits, which had given Watt so much anxiety, were satisfactorily disposed of, an immense load was removed from his mind; and he indulged in the anticipation of at last enjoying the fruits of his labour in peace. Being of frugal habits, he had already begun to save money, and indeed accumulated as much as he desired. But when the heavy arrears of Cornish dues were collected, about the period of expiry of the patent, a considerable sum of money necessarily fell to Watt's share; and then he began to occupy himself in the pleasant recreation of looking out for an investment of it in land. He was, however, hard to please, and made many journeys before he succeeded in buying his estate.

"I have yet met with nothing to my mind," he wrote from Somerton; "Lord Oxford has some very considerable estates to sell near Abergavenny, but the

roads to them are execrable, and it seemed that it would be a sort of banish-
ment to live at them, though the parts I saw are in themselves pleasant. I am
to-day informed of one with a house near Dorchester, which I have sent to
inquire about, though I have my doubts that it will prove like the rest. I propose, if nothing hinders, to be at Taunton to-morrow night, and shall then visit
the Wedgwoods, who at present live at Upcot, near that place. Afterwards, I
propose making a tour through the eastern part of Devonshire, and returning
by Dorsetshire to Bath; but my resolves may be altered by the attractions of
various magnets, so that I cannot tell you where to write to mo till I get some
fixed residence."[3]

A fortnight later he was at Exmouth, but still undecided.

"In respect to estates," he writes, – "I have seen nothing that pleases me. Most
of them, as you know by experience, are surrounded with bad roads, beggarly
villages, or some other nuisance, and one need not purchase plagues. On the
whole, something nearer home seems more suitable to me than anything in
these western counties, which, though they have more luxuriant vegetation,
and perhaps a milder climate, are not exempt from cold, as I experience here
colder weather than we had last autumn in Scotland. But the greatest drawback
is the absence of such society as one is used to, and their abominably hilly
roads, as they never flinch, but go straight up any hill which comes in their way,
and Nature has bestowed plenty upon them."[4]

Eventually Watt made several purchases of land at Doldowlod, on the
banks of the Wye, between Rhayader and Newbridge, in Radnorshire. There
was a pleasant farmhouse on the property, in which he occasionally spent
some pleasant months in summer time amidst beautiful scenery; but he had
by this time grown too old to root himself kindly, in a new place; and his
affections speedily drew him back again to the neighbourhood of Soho, and
to his comfortable home at Heathfield.

During the short peace of Amiens in the following year, he made the lon-
gest journey in his life. Accompanied by Mrs. Watt, he travelled through
Belgium, up the banks of the Rhine to Frankfort, and home by Strasburg and
Paris. While absent, Boulton wrote him many pleasant letters, telling him of
what was going on at Soho. The brave old man was still at the helm there, and
wrote in as enthusiastic terms as ever of the coins and medals he was striking
at his Mint. Though strong in mind, he was, however, growing feebler in
body, and suffered much from attacks of his old disease. "It is necessary for

me," he wrote, "to pass a great part of my time, in or upon the bed; nevertheless, I go down to the manufactory or the Mint once or twice a day, without injuring myself as heretofore; but not without some fatigue. However, as I am now taking bark twice a day, I find a daily increase of strength, and flatter myself with the pleasure of taking a journey to Paris in April or May next."[5]

On Watt's arrival in London, a letter of hearty welcome from Boulton met him; but it conveyed at the same time, the sad intelligence of the death of Mrs. Keir, a lady beloved by all who knew her, and a frequent inmate at Soho and Heathfield. One by one the members of the circle were departing, leaving wide gaps, which new friends could never fill up. The pleasant associations which are the charm of old friendships, were becoming mingled with sadness and regret. The grave was closing over one after another of the Soho group; and the survivors were beginning to live for the most part upon the memories of the past. But it is one of the penalties of old age to suffer a continuous succession of such bereavements; and that state would be intolerable but for the comparative deadening of the feelings which mercifully accompanies the advance of years. "We cannot help feeling with deep regret," wrote Watt, "the circle of our old friends gradually diminishing, while our ability to increase it by new ones is equally diminished; but perhaps it is a wise dispensation of Providence so to diminish our enjoyments in this world that when our turn comes we may leave it without regret."[6]

One of the deaths most lamented by Watt was that of Dr. Black of Edinburgh, which occurred in 1799. Black had watched to the last with tender interest the advancing reputation and prosperity of his early protégé. They had kept up a continuous and confidential correspondence on subjects of mutual interest for a period of about thirty years. Watt, though reserved to others, never feared unbosoming himself to his old friend, telling him of the new schemes he had on foot, and freely imparting to him his hopes and fears, his failures and successes. When Watt visited Scotland he rarely failed to take Edinburgh on his way, for the purpose of spending a few days with Black and Robison. The latter went express to London, for the purpose of giving evidence in the suit of Watt against the Hornblowers, and his testimony proved of essential service. "Our friend Robison," Watt wrote to Black, "exerted himself much; and, considering his situation, did wonders." When Robison returned to Edinburgh, his Natural Philosophy class received him with three cheers. He proceeded to give them a short account of the trial, which he characterised as "not more the cause of Watt *versus* Hornblower, than of science against ignorance." "When I had finished," said he, "I got another plaudit, that Mrs. Siddons would have relished."[7]

No one was more gratified at the issue of the trial than Dr. Black, who, when Robison told him of it, was moved even to tears. "It's very foolish," he said, "but I can't help it when I hear of anything good to Jamie Watt." The Doctor had long been in declining health, but was still able to work. He was busy writing another large volume, and had engaged the engraver to come to him for orders on the day after that on which he died. His departure was singularly peaceful. His servant had delivered to him a basin of milk, which was to serve for his dinner, and retired from the room. In less than a minute he returned, and found his master sitting where he had left him, but dead, with the basin of milk unspilled in his hand. Without a struggle, the spirit had fled. As the servant expressed it, "his poor master had given over living." He had twice before said to his doctor that "he had caught himself forgetting to breathe." On hearing of the good old man's death, Watt wrote to Robison, – "I may say that to him I owe, in a great measure, what I am; he taught me to reason and experiment in natural philosophy, and was a true friend and philosopher, whose loss will always be lamented while I live. We may all pray that our latter end may be like his; he has truly gone to sleep in the arms of his Creator, and been spared all the regrets attendant on a more lingering exit.

I could dwell longer on this subject; but regrets are unavailing, and only tend to enfeeble our own minds, and make them less able to bear the ills we cannot avoid. Let us cherish the friends we have left, and do as much good as we can in our day!"[8]

Lord Cockburn, in his 'Memorials,' gives the following graphic portrait of the father of modern chemistry – "Dr. Black was a striking and beautiful person; tall, very thin, and cadaverously pale; his hair carefully powdered, though there was little of it except what was collected into a long thin queue; his eyes dark, clear, and large, like deep pools of pure water. He wore black speckless clothes, silk stockings, silver buckles, and either a slim green silk umbrella, or a genteel brown cane. His general frame and air was feeble and slender. The wildest boy respected Black. No lad could be irreverent towards a man so pale, so gentle, so elegant, and so illustrious. So he glided, like a spirit, through our rather mischievous sportiveness, unharmed."[9]

Of the famous Lunar Society, Boulton and Watt now remained almost the only surviving members. Day was killed by a fall from his horse in 1789. Josiah Wedgwood closed his noble career at Etruria in 1795, in the sixty-fifth year of his age. Dr. Withering, distinguished alike in botany and medicine, died in 1799, of a lingering consumption. Dr. Darwin was seized by his last attack of angina pectoris in 1802, and, being unable to bleed himself, as he had done before, he called upon his daughter to apply the lancet to his arm; but, before she could do so, he fell back in his chair and expired. Dr. Priestley, driven forth into exile,[10] closed his long and illustrious career at Northumberland in Pennsylvania in 1803. The Lunar Society was thus all but extinguished by death; the vacant seats remained unfilled; and the meetings were no longer held.

But the bereavements which Watt naturally felt the most, were the deaths of his own children. He had two by his second wife, a son and a daughter, both full of promise, who had nearly grown up to adult age, when they died. Jessie was of a fragile constitution from her childhood, but her health seemed to become re-established as she grew in years. But before she had entered womanhood, the symptoms of an old pulmonary affection made their appearance, and she was carried off by consumption. Mr. Watt was much distressed by the event, confessing that he felt as if one of the strongest ties that bound him to life was broken, and that the acquisition of riches availed him nothing when unable to give them to those he loved. In a letter to a friend, he thus touchingly alluded to one of the most sorrowful associations connected with the deaths of children: – "Mrs. Watt continues to be much affected whenever anything recalls to her mind the amiable child we have parted with; and these remembrances occur but too frequently, – her little works of ingenuity, her books and other objects of study, serve as mementoes of her who was always to the best of her power usefully employed even to the last day of her life. With me, whom age has rendered incapable of the *passion* of grief; the feeling is a deep regret; and, did nature permit, my tears would flow as fast as her mother's."

To divert and relieve his mind, as was his wont, he betook himself to fresh studies and new inquiries. It is not improbable that the disease of which his daughter had died, as well as his own occasional sufferings from asthma, gave a direction to his thoughts, which turned on the inhalation of gas as a remedial agent in pulmonary and other diseases. Dr. Beddoes of Bristol had started the idea, which Watt now took up and prosecuted with his usual zeal. He contrived an apparatus for extracting, washing, and collecting gases, as well as for administering them by inhalation. He professed that he had taken up the subject not because he understood it, but because nobody else did, and that he could not withhold anything which might be of use in prompting others to do better. The result of his investigations was published at Bristol under the title of 'Considerations on the Medicinal use of Fictitious Airs,' the first part of which was written by Dr. Beddoes, and the second part by Watt.

But a still heavier blow than the loss of his only daughter, was the death of his son Gregory a few years later. He was a young man of the highest promise, and resembled Watt himself in many respects – in mind, character, and temperament. Those who knew him while a student at Glasgow College, spoke of him long after in terms of the most glowing enthusiasm. Among his fellow-students were Francis, afterwards Lord Jeffrey, and the poet Campbell. Both were captivated not less by the brilliancy of his talents than by the charming graces of his person. Campbell spoke of him as "a splendid stripling – literally the most beautiful youth I ever saw. When be was only twenty-two, an eminent English artist – Howard, I think – made his head the model of a picture of Adam." Campbell, Thomson, and Gregory Watt, were class-fellows in Greek, and avowed rivals; but the rivalry only served to cement their friendship. In the session of 1793–4, after a brilliant competition which excited unusual interest, the prize was awarded to Thomson; but, with the exception of the victor himself, Gregory was the most delighted student in the class. "He was," says the biographer of Campbell, "a generous, liberal, and open-hearted youth; so attached to his friend, and so sensible of his merit, that the honours conferred on Thomson obliterated all recollections of personal failure."[11] Francis Jeffrey was present at the commemoration of the first of May, two years later, and was especially struck with the eloquence of young Watt, "who obtained by far the greatest number of prizes, and degraded the prize-readers most inhumanly by reading a short composition of his own, a translation of the Chorus of the Medea, with so much energy and grace, that the verses seemed to me better perhaps than they were in reality. He is a young man of very eminent capacity, and seems to have all the genius of his father, with a great deal of animation and ardour which is all his own."[12]

Campbell thought him born to be a great orator, and anticipated for him the greatest success in Parliament or at the Bar. His father had, however, already destined him to follow his own business. Indeed, Gregory was introduced a partner into the Soho concern about the same time as Mr. Boulton, jun., and his elder brother James. But he never gave much attention to the business. Scarcely had he left college, before symptoms of pulmonary affection showed themselves; and, a physician having been consulted, Mr. Watt was recommended to send his son to reside in the south of England. He accordingly went to Penzance for the benefit of its mild climate, and, by a curious coincidence, he took up his abode as boarder and lodger in the house of Humphry Davy's mother. The afterwards brilliant chemist was then a boy some years younger than Gregory. He had already made experiments in chemistry, with sundry phials and kitchen utensils, assisted by an old glyster apparatus presented to him by the surgeon of a French vessel wrecked on the coast. Although Gregory possessed great warmth of heart,

there was a degree of coldness in his manner to strangers, which repelled
any approach to familiarity. When his landlady's son, therefore, began talking to him of metaphysics and poetry, he was rather disposed to turn a
deaf ear; but when Davy touched upon the subject of chemistry, and made
the rather daring boast for a boy, that he would undertake to demolish
the French theory in half an hour, Gregory's curiosity was roused. The barrier of ice between them was at once removed; and from thenceforward
they became attached friends.[13] Young Davy was encouraged to prosecute
his experiments, which the other watched with daily increasing interest;
and in the course of the following year, Gregory communicated to Dr.
Beddoes, of Bristol, then engaged in establishing his Pneumatic Institution,
an account of Davy's experiments on light and heat, the result of which was
his appointment as superintendent of the experiments at the Institution,
and the subsequent direction of his studies and investigations.

Gregory's health having been partially re-established by his residence at
Penzance, he shortly after returned to his father's house at Birmingham,
whither Davy frequently went, and kept up the flame of his ambition by
intercourse with congenial minds. Gregory heartily co-operated with his
father in his investigations on air, besides inquiring and experimenting on
original subjects of his own selection. Among these may be mentioned his
inquiries into the gradual refrigeration of basalt, his paper on which, read
before the Royal Society, would alone entitle him to a distinguished rank
among experimentalists.[14]

By the kindness of his elder brother James, Gregory Watt was relieved of
his share of the work at Soho, and was thereby enabled to spend much of his
time in travelling about for the benefit of his health. Early in 1801, we find him
making excursions in the western counties in company with Mr. Murdock,
jun.; and looking forward with still greater anticipations of pleasure to the
tour which he subsequently made through France, Germany, and Austria. We
find him afterwards writing his father from Freiburg, to the effect that he was
gradually growing stronger, and was free from pulmonary affection. From
Leipzig he sent an equally favourable account of himself, and gave his father
every hope that on his return he would find him strong and sound.

These anticipations, however, proved delusive, for the canker was already
gnawing at poor Gregory's vitals. Returned home, he busied himself with his
books, his experiments, and his speculations; assisting his father in recording
observations on the effects of nitrous oxide and other gases. But it was shortly
found necessary to send him again to the south of England for the benefit of
a milder climate. In the beginning of 1804, his father and mother went with

him to Clifton, where he had an attack of intermittent fever, which left him
very weak. From thence they removed to Bath, and remained there for about
a month, the invalid being carefully attended by Dr. Beddoes. During their
stay at Bath, Gregory's brother paid him a visit, and was struck by his altered
appearance. The fever had left him, but his cough and difficulty of breathing
were very distressing to witness. As usual in such complaints, his mind was
altogether unaffected. "Indeed," wrote his brother, "he is as bright, clear, and
vigorous, upon every subject as I ever knew him to be. His voice, too, is firm
and good, and when he enters into conversation I should lose the recollection
of his complaint if his appearance did not so forcibly remind me of it. It is
fortunate that he does not suffer much bodily pain, or, so far as I can discover,
any mental anxiety as to the issue of his complaint."[15]

When Gregory was sufficiently recovered from the debilitating effects of
his fever, he was moved to Sidmouth, where he appeared to improve; but he
himself believed the sea air to be injurious to him, and insisted on being again
removed inland. During all this time his father's anxiety may be imagined,
though he bore up with as much equanimity as was practicable under circumstances so distressing. "Ever since we left Bath," he wrote to Mr. Boulton
at Soho, "ours has been a state of anxiety very distressing to us, and the communication of which would not have been pleasing to our friends. To add to
this, I have myself been exceedingly unwell, though I am now much better.
Gregory suffered very much from the journey, which was augmented by his
own impatience; and though he seemed to recover a little from his fatigue
during the first week, his breath became daily worse, until we were obliged
to remove him, on Thursday last, to the neighbourhood of Exeter, where he
now is with his aunt."[16] The invalid became rapidly worse, and survived his
removal only a few days. "This day," wrote the sorrowing father to Boulton,
"the remains of poor Gregory were deposited in a decent, though private
manner, in the north aisle of the cathedral here, neat the transept ... I mean
to erect a tablet to his memory on the adjoining wall; but his virtues and
merits will be best recorded in the breasts of his friends ... As soon as we can
settle our accounts, we shall all return homewards, with heavy hearts."[17]

Davy was deeply affected by Gregory Watt's death; and in the freshness of
his grief he thus unbosomed himself to his friend Clayfield:

Poor Watt! He ought not to have died. I could not persuade myself that he
would die; and until the very moment when I was assured of his fate, I would
not believe he was in any danger. His letters to me, only three or four months
ago, were full of spirit, and spoke not of any infirmity of body, but of an

increased strength of mind. Why is this in the order of Nature, – that there is such a difference in the duration and destruction of his works? If the mere stone decays it is to produce a soil which is capable of nourishing the moss and the lichen; when the moss and the lichen die and decompose, they produce a mould which becomes the bed of life to grass, and to a more exalted species of vegetables. Vegetables are the food of animals, – the less perfect animals of the more perfect; but in man, the faculties and intellect are perfected, – he rises, exists for a little while in disease and misery, and then would seem to disappear, without, an end, and without producing any effect.

We are deceived, my dear Clayfield, if we suppose that the human being who has formed himself for action, but who has been unable to act, is lost in the mass of being; there is some arrangement of things which we can never comprehend, but in which his faculties will be applied ... We know very little; but, in my opinion, we know enough to hope for the immortality, the individual immortality of the better part of man. I have been led into all this speculation, which you may well think wild, in reflecting upon the fate of Gregory! My feeling has given wings to my mind. He was a noble fellow, and would have been a great man. Oh! there was no reason for his dying – he ought not to have died.[18]

More deaths! A few years later, and Watt lost his oldest friend, Professor Robison of Edinburgh, his companion and fellow-worker at Glasgow College nearly fifty years before. Since then, their friendship had remained unchanged, though their respective pursuits kept them apart. Robison continued busily and usefully occupied to the last. He had finished the editing of his friend Black's lectures, and was occupied in writing his own 'Elements of Mechanical Philosophy,' when death came and kindly released him from a lingering disorder which had long oppressed his body, though it did not enervate his mind. A few years before his death he wrote Watt, informing him that he had got an addition to his family in a fine little boy, a grandchild, healthy and cheerful, who promised to be a source of much amusement to him. "I find this a great acquisition," said he, "notwithstanding a serious thought sometimes stealing into my mind. I am infinitely delighted with observing the growth of its little soul; and particularly with the numberless instincts, which formerly passed unheeded. I thank the French theorists for more forcibly directing my attention to the finger of God, which I discover in every awkward movement and every wayward whim. They are all guardians of his life, and growth, and powers. I regret that I have not time to make infancy, and the development of its powers, my sole study."[19] In 1805 he was taken from his little playfellow, and from the pursuit of his many ingenious speculations.[20] Watt said of him, "he was a man of the clearest head and the most science of anybody I have ever known, and his friendship to me ended only with his life, after having continued for nearly half a century ... His religion and piety, which made him patiently submit without even a fretful or repining word in nineteen years of unremitting pain, – his humility, in his modest opinion of himself – his kindness, in labouring with such industry for his family during all this affliction, – his moderation for himself, while indulging an unbounded generosity to all about him, – joined to his talents, form a character so uncommon and so noble, as can with difficulty be conceived by those who have not, like me, had the contemplation of it."

Little more remains to be recorded of the business life of Boulton and Watt. The former, notwithstanding his declining health and the frequent return of his malady, continued to take an active interest in the Soho coinage. Watt often expostulated with him, but in vain, urging that it was time for him to retire wholly from the anxieties of business. On Boulton bringing out his Bank of England silver dollar, with which he was himself greatly pleased, he sent some specimens to Watt, then staying at Clifton, for his inspection. Watt replied, – "Your dollar is universally admired by all to whom we have shown it, though your friends fear much that your necessary attention to the operation of the coinage may injure your health."[21] And again he wrote from Sidmouth, – "We are all glad to hear of your amendment, which we hope will be progressive, and possibly it might be better if you could summon up resolution enough to rid yourself of some of those plagues you complain of; but while you suffer yourself to be intruded upon in the manner you do, you can never enjoy that quiet which is now so necessary to your health and comfort."[22] Mrs. Watt joined her entreaties to those of her husband, expressing the wish that, for Mr. Boulton's sake, it might rain every day, to prevent his fatiguing himself by walking to and from the works, and there occupying himself with the turmoils of business. Why should he not do as Mr. Watt had done, and give up Soho altogether, leaving business and its anxieties to younger and stronger men? But business, as we have already explained, was Boulton's habit, and pleasure, and necessity. Moreover, occupation of some sort served to divert his attention from the ever-present pain within him; and, so long as his limbs were able to support him, he tottered down the hill to see what was going forward at Soho.

As for Watt, we find that he had at last learnt the art of taking things easy, and that he was trying to make life as agreeable as possible in his old age. Thus at Cheltenham, from which place Mrs. Watt addressed Boulton in the letter of advice above referred to, we find the aged pair making pleasant excursions in the neighbourhood during the day, and reading novels and going to the theatre occasionally in the evening. "As it is the fashion," wrote Mrs. Watt, – "and wishing to be very fashionable people, we subscribe to the library. Our first book was Mrs. Opie's 'Mother and Daughter,' a tale so mournful as to make both Mr. Watt and myself cry like schoolboys that had been whipped; … and to dispel the gloom that poor Adeline hung over us, we went to the theatre last night to see the 'Honeymoon,' and were highly pleased."

Towards the end of 1807 Boulton had a serious attack of his old disease, which fairly confined him to his bed; and his friends feared lest it should prove his last illness. He was verging upon his eightieth year, and his constitution, though originally strong, was gradually succumbing to confinement and pain. He nevertheless rallied once more, and was again able to make occasional visits to the works as before. He had promised to send a box of medals to the Queen, and went down to the Mint to see them packed. The box duly reached Windsor Castle, and De Luc acknowledged its reception:

"As no words of mine," he said, "could have conveyed your sentiments to Her Majesty so well as those addressed to me in your name, I contented myself with putting the letter into her hands. Her Majesty expressed her sensibility for the sufferings you had undergone during the period of your silence, and at your plentiful gift, for which she has charged me to thank you; and as, at the same time that you have placed the whole at her own disposal, you have mentioned the Princesses, Her Majesty will make them partakers in the present.

De Luc concluded by urging Mr. Boulton to abstain from further work and anxiety, and reminded him that after a life of such activity as his had been, both body and mind required complete rest.

"Life," said he, "in this world is a state of trial, and as long as God gives us strength we are not to shun even painful employments which are duties. But in the decline of life, when the strength fails, we ought to drop all thought of objects to which we are no longer equal, in order to preserve the serenity and liberty of mind with which we are to consider our exit from this world to a better. May God prolong your life without pain for the good you do constantly, is the sincere wish of your very affectionate friends (father and daughter), De Luc."[23]

Boulton's life was, indeed, drawing to a close. 'He had for many years been suffering from an agonising and incurable disease – stone in the kidneys and bladder – and waited for death as for a friend. The strong man was laid low;

Boulton's Monument in Handsworth Church[24]

and, the night had at length come when he could work no more. The last letter which he wrote was to his daughter, in March, 1809; but the characters are so flickering and indistinct as to be scarcely legible. "If you wish to see me living," he wrote, "pray come soon, for I am very ill." Nevertheless, he suffered on for several months longer. At last he was released from his pain, and peacefully expired on the 17th of August, 1809, at the age of eighty-one. Though he fell like a shock of corn in full season, his death was lamented by a wide circle of relatives and friends. A man of strong affections, with an almost insatiable appetite for love and sympathy, he inspired others with like feelings towards himself; and when he died, they felt as if a brother had gone. He was alike admired and beloved by his workmen; and when he was carried to his last resting-place in Handsworth Church, six hundred of them followed the hearse, and there was scarcely a dry eye among them.[25]

Matthew Boulton was, indeed, a man of truly noble nature. Watt, than whom none knew him better, was accustomed to speak of him as "the princely Boulton." He was generous and high-souled, a lover of truth, honour, and uprightness. His graces were embodied in a manly and noble person. We are informed through Dr. Guest that on one occasion, when Mr. Boulton's name was mentioned in his father's presence, he observed, "*the ablest man* I ever knew." On the remark being repeated to Dr. Edward Johnson, a courtly man, he said,

– "As to his ability, other persons can better judge. But I can say that he was *the best mannered man* I ever knew." The appreciation of both was alike just and characteristic, and has since been confirmed by Mrs. Schimmelpenninck. She describes with admiration his genial manner, his fine radiant countenance, and his superb munificence: "He was in person tall, and of a noble appearance; his temperament was sanguine, with that slight mixture of the phlegmatic which gives calmness and dignity; his manners were eminently open and cordial; he took the lead in conversation; and, with a social heart, had a grandiose manner, like that arising from position, wealth, and habitual command. He went about among his people like a monarch bestowing largesse."

Boswell was equally struck by Boulton's personal qualities when he visited Soho in 1776, shortly after the manufacture of steam-engines had been begun there. "I shall never forget," he says, "Mr. Boulton's expression to me when surveying the works. 'I sell here; sir, what all the world desires to have, POWER.' He had," continues Boswell, "about seven hundred people at work. I contemplated him as an iron chieftain, and he seemed to be a father of his tribe. One of the men came to him complaining grievously of his landlord for having distrained his goods. "Your landlord is in the right, Smith," said Boulton; "but I'll tell you what – find a friend who will lay down one half of your rent, and I'll lay down the other, and you shall have your goods again."

It would be a mistake to suppose that there was any affectation in Boulton's manner, or that his dignified bearing in society was anything but natural to him. He was frank, cheerful, and affectionate, as his letters to his wife, his children, and his friends, amply demonstrate. None knew better than he how to win hearts, whether of workmen, mining adventurers, or philosophers. "I have thought it but respectful," he wrote Watt from Cornwall, "to give our folks a dinner at a public-house near Wheal Virgin to-day. There were present William Murdock, Lawson, Pearson, Perkins, Malcolm, Robert Muir, all Scotchmen, and John Bull, with self and Wilson, – for the engines are all now finished, and the men have behaved well, and are attached to us." At Soho he gave an entertainment on a much larger scale upon his son coming of age in 1791, when seven hundred persons sat down to dinner. Boswell's description of him as the father of his tribe is peculiarly appropriate. No well-behaved workman was ever turned adrift. On the contrary, fathers introduced their sons into the factory, and brought them up under their own eye, watching over their conduct and their mechanical training. Thus generation after generation of workmen followed in each other's footsteps at Soho.

There was, no doubt, good business policy in this; for Boulton knew that by attaching the workmen to him, and inspiring them with pride in the concern, he was maintaining that prestige which, before the days of machine tools, would not have been possible without the aid of a staff of carefully-trained and highly-skilled mechanics. Yet he had many scapegraces amongst them – hard drinkers, pugilists,[26] cock-fighters, and scamps. Watt often got wholly out of patience with them, and urged their dismissal, whatever might be the consequence. But though none knew so well as Watt how to manage mathines, none knew so ill how to manage men. Boulton's practical wisdom usually came to the rescue. He would tolerate any moral shortcoming save treachery and dishonesty. But he knew that most of the men had been brought up in a bad school, often in no school at all. "Have pity on them, bear with them, give them another trial," he would say; "our works must not be brought to a standstill because perfect men are not yet to be had." "True wisdom," he observed on another occasion, "directs us, when we can, to turn even evils into good. We must take men as we find them, and try to make the best of them."

Still further to increase the attachment of the workmen to Soho, and keep together his school of skilled industry, as he called it, Boulton instituted a Mutual Assurance Society in connexion with the works; the first of the kind, so far as we are aware, established by any large manufacturer for the benefit of his workmen. Every person employed in the manufactory, in whatsoever condition, was required to be a member. Boys receiving 2s. 6d. a week paid a halfpenny weekly to the box; those receiving 5s. paid a penny a week, and so on, up to men receiving 20s. a week, who contributed 4d.; payments being made to them out of the fund during sickness and disablement, in proportion to their contributions during health. The effects of the Society were most salutary; it cultivated habits of providence and thoughtfulness amongst the men; bound them together by ties of common interest; and it was only in the cases of irreclaimable drunkards that any members of the Soho Friendly Society ever came upon the parish.

But this was only a small item in the constitution of the Soho manufactory. Before its establishment, comparatively little attention had been given to the organisation of labour on a large scale. Workshops were so small that everything went on immediately under the master's eye, and workmen got accustomed to ply at their work diligently, being well watched. But when manufacturing was carried on upon so large a scale as at Soho, and separate processes were conducted in different rooms and workshops, it was impossible that the master's eye should be over all his workers, or over even any considerable portion of them at the same time. It was therefore necessary to introduce a new system. Hence the practice of inspection by deputy, and the appointment of skilled and trustworthy foremen for the purpose of enforcing strict discipline in the various shops, and at the same time economising labour and ensuring excellence of workmanship. In carrying out this arrangement, Boulton proved remarkably successful: and Soho came to be regarded as a model establishment. Men came from all parts to see and admire its organisation; and when Wedgwood proceeded to erect his great pottery works at Etruria, he paid many preliminary visits to Soho for the purpose of ascertaining how the difficulties occasioned by the irregular habits of the workpeople had been so successfully overcome by his friend, and applying the results of his experience in the organisation of his own manufactory.

Though Boulton could not keep his eye directly on the proceedings in the shops, he was quick to discern when anything was going wrong. While sitting in the midst of his factory, surrounded by the clang of hammers and the noise of engines, he could usually detect when any stoppage occurred, or when the machinery was going too fast or too slow, and issue his orders accordingly. The sound of the tools going, and the hammers clanging, which to strangers was merely an intolerable noise, was an intelligible music in his ears; and, like the leader of an orchestra, who casts his eye at once in the direction of the player of a wrong note, so Boulton was at once conscious of the slightest dissonance in the performances of his manufactory, and took the necessary steps immediately to correct it.

From what we have already said, it will be sufficiently clear that Boulton was a first-rate man of business. He had a hearty enthusiasm for his calling, and took a just pride in it. In conducting it, he was guided by fine tact, great knowledge of character, and sound practical wisdom. When fully satisfied as to the course he should pursue, he acted with remarkable vigour and promptitude, bending his whole mind to the enterprise which he had taken in hand. It was natural that he should admire in others the qualities he himself desired to possess. "I can't say," he wrote to Watt, "but that I admire John Wilkinson for his decisive, clear, and distinct character, which is, I think, a first-rate one of its kind." Like Wilkinson, Boulton was also distinguished for his indomitable pluck; and in no respect was this more strikingly displayed than in his prosecution of the steam-engine enterprise.

Playfair has truly said, that had Watt searched all Europe over, he could not have found another person so fitted to bring his invention before the public in a manner worthy of its merits and importance. Yet Boulton was by no means eager to engage in the scheme. Watt could with difficulty persuade him to take it up; and it was only in exchange for a bad debt that he at length became a partner in it. But when once fairly committed, he threw himself into the enterprise with an extraordiny degree of vigour. He clearly recognised in the steam-engine a power destined to revolutionise the industrial operations of the world. To M. Argand, the famous French lamp inventor, he described it as "the most certain, the most regular, the most durable, and the most effective machine in Nature, so far as her powers have yet been revealed to mortal knowledge;" and he declared to him that, finding he could be of more use to manufactures and to mankind in general by employing all his powers in the capacity of an engineer, than in fabricating any kind of clincaillerie whatsoever, he would thenceforward devote himself wholly to his new enterprise.

But it was no easy work he had undertaken. He had to struggle against prejudices, opposition, detraction, and difficulties of all kinds. Not the least difficulty he had to strive against was the timidity and faintheartedness of his partner. For years Watt was on the brink of despair. He kept imploring Boulton to relieve him from his troubles; he wished to die and be at rest; he "cursed his inventions;" indeed he was the most miserable of men. But Boulton never lost heart. He was hopeful, courageous, and strong – Watt's very backbone. He felt convinced that the invention must eventually succeed, and he never for a moment lost faith in it. He braved and risked everything to "carry the thing through." He mortgaged his lands to the last farthing; borrowed from his personal friends; raised money by annuities; obtained advances from bankers; and had invested upwards of 40,000*l.* in the enterprise before it began to pay.

During this terrible struggle he was more than once on the brink of insolvency, but continued as before to cheer and encourage his fainting partner. "Keep your mind and your heart pleasant if possible," he wrote to Watt, "for the way to go through life sweetly is not to regard rubs." To those about Watt he wrote, "Do not disturb Mr. Watt, but keep him as free from anxiety as you can." He himself took the main share of the burden, – pushing the engine amongst the Cornish miners, bringing it under the notice of London brewers and water companies, and finding money to meet the heavy liabilities of the firm.

So much honest endeavour could not fail. And at last the tide seemed to turn. The engine became recognised as a grand working power, and there was almost a run upon Soho for engines. Then pirates sprang up in all directions, and started new schemes with the object of evading Watt's patent. And now a new battle had to be fought against "the illiberal, sordid, unjust, ungenerous, and inventionless misers, who prey upon the vitals of the ingenious, and make haste to seize upon what their laborious and often costly application has produced."[27] At length this struggle, too, was conclusively settled in Boulton and Watt's favour, and they were left at last to enjoy the fruits of their labour in peace.

Watt never could have fought such a series of battles alone. He would have been a thousand times crushed; and, but for Boulton's unswerving courage and resolute determination, he could neither have brought his engine into general use, nor derived any adequate reward for his great invention. Though his specification lodged in the Patent Office might clearly establish his extraordinary mechanical genius, it is most probable that he himself would have broken his heart over his scheme, and added only another to the long list of great martyr inventors.

None was more ready to acknowledge the immense services of Boulton in introducing the steam-engine to general use as a working power, than Watt himself. In the MS. memoir of his lately deceased friend deposited among the Soho papers, dated Glasgow, 17th September, 1809, Watt says, – "Through the whole of this business Mr. Boulton's active and sanguine disposition served to counterbalance the despondency and diffidence which were natural to me; and every assistance which Soho or Birmingham could afford was procured. Mr. Boulton's amiable and friendly character, together with his fame as an engineer and active manufacturer, procured us many and very active friends in both Houses of Parliament ... Suffice it to say, that to his generous patronage, the active part he took in the management of the business, his judicious advice, and his assistance in contriving and arranging many of the applications of the steam-engine to various machines, the public are indebted for great part of the benefits they now derive from that machine. Without him, or some similar partner (could such a one have been found), the invention could never have been carried by in to the length that it has been.

"Mr. Boulton was not only an ingenious mechanic, well skilled in all the arts of the Birmingham manfacturers, but he possessed in a high degree the faculty of rendering any new invention of his own or of others useful to the public, by organising and arranging the processes by which it could be carried on, as well as of promoting the sale by his own exertions and those of his numerous friends and correspondents. His conception of the nature of any invention was quick, and he was not less quick in perceiving the uses to which it might be applied, and the profits which might accrue from it. When he took any scheme in hand, he was rapid in executing it, and on those occasions spared neither trouble nor expense. He was a liberal encourager of merit in others, and to him the country is indebted for various improvements which have been brought forward under his auspices ...

In respect to myself, I can with great sincerity say that be was a most affectionate and steady friend and patron, with whom, during a close connexion of
thirty-five years, I have never had any serious difference.

As to his improvements and erections at Soho – his turning a barren heath
into a delightful garden, and the population and riches he has introduced into
the parish of Handsworth, I must leave such subjects to those whose pens are
better adapted to the purpose, and whose ideas are less benumbed with age
than mine now are.[28]

We have spoken of Boulton's generosity, which was in keeping with his
whole character. At a time when he was himself threatened with bankruptcy,
we have seen him concerting a scheme with his friend Wedgwood to enable
Dr. Priestley to pursue his chemical investigations free from pecuniary anxiety.
To Watt he was most liberal, voluntarily conceding to him at different times
profits derived from certain parts of the steam-engine business, beyond the
proportions stipulated in the deed of partnership. In the course of his correspondence we find numerous illustrations of his generosity to partners as well
as to workmen; making up the losses they had sustained, and which at the time
perhaps he could ill afford. His conduct to Widow Swellengrebel illustrates
this fine feature in his character. She had lent money to Fothergill, his partner
in the hardware business, and the money was never repaid. The consequence
was, that the widow and her family were seriously impoverished, and on their
return to their friends in Holland, Boulton, though under no obligation to do
so, remitted her an annuity of fifty pounds a year, which he continued to the
close of her life. "I must own," he wrote, "I am impelled to act as I do from
pity, as well as from something in my own disposition that I cannot resist."[29]

In fine, Matthew Boulton was a noble, manly man, and a true leader of
men. Lofty-minded, intelligent, energetic, and liberal, he was one of those
who constitute the life blood of a nation, and give force and dignity to the
national character. Working in conjunction with Watt, he was in no small
degree instrumental in introducing and establishing the great new working
power of steam which has exercised so extraordinary an influence upon all the
operations of industry.

NOTES

1   Boulton to Dumergue, 25th December, 1800.
2   Lockhart's 'Life of Scott.' 8vo. ed. p. 457. One of Scott's visits to Soho

was made in company with his wife in the spring of 1803. Boulton was so
pleased with the visit, that he urged Scott, or at least his wife, to repeat it,
which produced the following letter, dated London, 13th May, 1803:
My dear Sir, – He was a wise man who said 'Trust not thy wife with
a man of fair tongue.' Now so I have very little wisdom of any own, I
am content to gather all I can get at second hand, and therefore, upon
the faith of the sage whom I have quoted, I should be guilty of great
imprudence were I to permit Charlotte to wait upon you on her return,
or even to answer your kind letter to Mr. Dumergue. That task I therefore
take upon myself; and you must receive my thanks along with hers, for
your very kind and flattering invitation to Soho. But independent of
my just suspicion of a beau who writes such flattering love-letters to my
wife, our time here (owing to the sitting of our Courts of Justice, which
I must necessarily attend), lays us under an indispensable necessity of
returning to Scotland as speedily as possible, and by the nearest road. We
can therefore only express our joint and most sincere regret that we cannot
upon this occasion have the honour and satisfaction of visiting Soho and
its hospitable inhabitants. Mrs. Nicolson, Mr. and Miss Dumergue join
Charlotte and me in the most sincere good wishes to Miss Boulton, to
you, and to all your friends; and I suspect so foolish a letter will make you
believe you have escaped a very idle visitor in,

Dear Sir,
Your very faithful servant,
Walter Scott.

3   Watt to M. Robinson Boulton, 9th September, 1799.
4   Watt to M. Robinson Boulton, 26th September, 1799.
5   Boulton to Watt, 10th October, 1802. One of Boulton's objects in making
his contemplated journey to Paris, was to undertake the erection of
coining machinery for the French Government, who were about to recoin
the whole of their gold, silver, and copper money. With their imperfect
machinery, he calculated that it would take them nearly twenty years to
accomplish this; whereas with his new machinery he could undertake to
turn out a thousand million of pieces in three years. He communicated
to Watt, that he had been making experiments as to the maximum speed
of his coining machines, worked by the steam-engine, and found that he
could regularly strike fifty-three of his copper pieces or fifty-six English
crown-pieces per minute, while he could with one press in collars also
regularly strike India copper pieces of half the diameter at the rate of 106
to 112 per minute, or from 6360 to 6720 pieces per hour; but when pieces

of half an inch diameter were wanted he had recourse to his new small press, with which he could strike from 150 to 200 pieces per minute! "My presses," said he, "are far more exact and more durable, and my means of working them are now infinitely beyond anything they (the French coiners) have ever thought of, and my mint is now in far better order than ever."

6   Watt to Boulton, 23rd November, 1802.

7   Robison to Watt, 3rd February, 1797.

8   Cited in Muirhead's 'Origin and Progress of the Mechanical Inventions of James Watt,' ii. 264.

9   Lord Cockburn's 'Memorials,' 51.

10 It is a remarkable fact that Dr. Priestley was regarded with as much suspicion in America as he had been in England. The American government looked upon him as a spy in the interest of France; and he had great difficulty in forming a Unitarian congregation. The horror of the French Revolution, which had extended to America, was the cause of the hostile feeling displayed towards him. "The change that has taken place," he said, in a letter dated 6th September, 1798, "is indeed hardly credible, as I have done nothing to provoke resentment; but, being a citizen of France, and a friend to the Revolution, is sufficient. I asked one of the more moderate of the party whether he thought, if Dr. Price, the great friend of their own revolution, were alive, he would now be allowed to come into this country. He said, he believed he would not!" – In 1801 Dr. Priestley, by deed of trust, appointed Matthew Boulton, Samuel Galton, and Wm. Vaughan, Esqrs., trustees for Mrs. Finch (his daughter) and her children, in respect of 1200*l.* invested for their benefit in public securities.

11 Beattie's 'Life of Campbell,' i. 112.

12 Letter to M. R. Morehead, 7th May, 1796.

13 Paris's 'Life of Davy,' i. 48–9.

14 'Philosophical Transactions,' xcix. 279.

15 J. Watt, Jun., to M. F. Boulton, 8th June, 1804.

16 Watt to Boulton, Sidmouth, 14th October, 1804.

17 Watt to Boulton, Exeter, 22nd October, 1804.

18 Paris's 'Life of Davy,' i. 198–200.

19 Cited in Muirhead's 'Mechanical Inventions of James Watt, – Correspondence,' ii. 269.

20 One of these, thrown out in a letter to Watt, may be mentioned – a speculation since revived by the late Dr. S. Brown of Edinburgh, – the transmutation of bodies. "These are wonderful steps," said he, "which

are every day making in chemical analysis. The analysis of the alkalis and alkaline earths by Guyton, by Henry, and others, will presently lead, I think, to the doctrine *of a reciprocal convertability of all things into all.* It brings to mind a minister lecturing on the first chapter of one of the Gospels, when, after reading, 'Adam begat Abel, and Abel begat,' &c., – to save himself the trouble of so many cramp names, he said, 'and so they all begat one another to the 15th verse.' I expect to see alchemy revive, and be as universally studied as ever."

21 Watt to Boulton, 13th May, 1804.

22 Watt to Boulton, 14th October, 1804.

23 De Luc to Boulton, Windsor Castle, 25th January, 1807. It had been arranged that George III, the Queen, and the Princesses, should pay a visit to Soho in 1805, though the King had by that time become quite blind. When told of Boulton's illness, and that he was confined to bed, his Majesty replied, "Then I will visit Mr. Boulton in his sick-chamber" (MS. Memoir by Mr. Keir). The royal visit was eventually put off, the Council advising that the King should go direct to Weymouth and nowwhere else.

24 The monument to Boulton is on the left hand of the altar in the illustration; that of Murdock is opposite to it, on the right

25 The following is the inscription on the mural monument erected to his memory in the side aisle of Handsworth church, in the composition of which James Watt assisted:

Sacred to the Memory of
Matthew Boulton, F. R. S.
By the skilful exertion of a mind turned to Philosophy and Mechanics,
The application of a taste correct and refined,
And, an ardent spirit of enterprise, he improved, embellished, and
extended
The Arts and Manufactures of his country,
Leaving his Establishment of Soho a noble monument of his
Genius, industry, and success.
The character his talents had raised, his virtues adorned and exalted.
Active to discern merit, and prompt to relieve distress,
His encouragement was liberal, his benevolence unwearied.
Honoured and admired at home and abroad,
He closed a life eminently useful, the 17th of August, 1509, Aged 81,
Esteemed, loved, and lamented.

26 Isaac Perrins was one of the most noted among the fighters of Soho. Mr. Scale, a partner in the hardware business, wrote to Mr. Boulton,

then at Cosgarne (15th October, 1782), – "Perrins has had a battle with the famous Jemmy Sargent for a hundred guineas, in which Perrins came off conqueror without a fall or hurt: in 13 rounds he knocked down his antagonist 13 times. They had it out at Colemore on our Wake Monday. The Sohoites all returned with blue cockades." Mrs. Watt, in a gossipy letter to Mr. Boulton of the same date, says "1500*l*. was betted against Perrins at Birmingham, and lost." Perrins's success led him to turn "professional bruiser" for a time, and he left his place in the smith's shop. But either not succeeding in his new business, or finding the work harder than that of the smithy, he came back to Soho, and, being a good workman, he was taken on again and remained in Boulton's employment till the close of his life, leaving sons to succeed him in the same department.

27 Boulton to De Luc, 20th October, 1787.

28 The MS. Memoir is dated Glasgow the 17th September, 1809, at which period Watt was in his 73rd year. It had evidently been written at the request of M. Robinson Boulton, Esq., shortly after his father's death. We find various testimony to the same effect as the above in the Soho papers. Thus Mr. Peter Ewart, C. E., speaks of Mr. Boulton's remarkable quickness in selecting objects to which machinery might be applied with advantage, and of his great promptitude and determination in carrying his plans into effect. He also describes the contagiousness of his example, which strengthened the weak and inspired the timid. "He possessed," says Mr. Ewart, "above all other men I have ever known, the faculty of inspiring others with a portion of that ardent zeal with which he himself pursued every important object he had in view; and it was impossible to be near him without becoming warmly interested in the success of his enterprises. The urbanity of his manners, and his great kindness to young people in particular, never failed to leave the most agreeable impression on the minds of all around him; and most truly may it be said that he reigned in the hearts of those that were in his employment." – Boulton MSS.

29 Boulton to M. Vanlinder, Rotterdam, 24th April, 1788.

XXIII

Closing Years of James Watt – His Death – Conclusion

The fragile and sickly Watt outlived the most robust of his contemporaries. He was residing at Glenarbach, near Dumbarton, with relatives, when the intelligence reached him of the death of his partner. To his son James he wrote at once, expressing his deep sorrow at the loss of his "very worthy and beloved friend."[1] To Mr. Boulton's son and successor he wrote, – "However we may lament our own loss, we must consider, on the other side, the torturing pain he has so long endured, and console ourselves with the remembrance of his virtues and eminent qualifications. Few men have possessed his abilities, and still fewer have exerted them as he has done; and if to these we add his urbanity, his generosity, and his affection to his friends, we shall make up a character rarely to be equalled. Such was the friend we have lost, and of whose affection we have reason to be proud, as you have to be the son of such a father."[2]

The deaths of his friends, one by one, reminded Watt of his own mortality, and frequent references to the subject occur in his letters about this time. He felt as if he were in danger of being left in the world alone. But he did not give himself up to melancholy, as he had been prone to do at the earlier periods of his life. Shortly after his son Gregory died, he wrote to a relative, – "I know that all men must die, and I submit to the decrees of Nature, I hope with due reverence to the Disposer of events. Yet one stimulus to exertion is taken away, and, somehow or other, I have lost my relish for my usual occupations. Perhaps time may remedy that in some measure; meanwhile I do not neglect the means of amusement which are in my power."

Watt was at no loss for occupation to relieve the tedium of old age. He possessed ample resources in himself; and found pleasure alike in quiet meditation and in active work. His thirst for knowledge was still unslaked, and he sought to allay it by reading. His love of investigation was as keen as ever, and he gratified it by proceeding with experiments on air, on light, and on electricity. His inventive faculty was still potent, and he occasionally varied his occupation by labouring to produce a new machine or to improve an old one. At other times, when the weather allowed, he would take a turn at planting in his grounds and gardens; and occasionally vary his pleasure by a visit to Scotland, to London, or to his estate in Wales. Strange to say, his health improved with advancing age, and though occasionally dyspeptic, he was now comparatively free from the racking headaches which had been the torment of his earlier years. Unlike Boulton, who found pleasure in the active pursuit of business, Watt had always regarded it as a worry, and he was now glad to have cast it altogether behind him. His mind was free from harassing cares; his ambition in life was satisfied; he was no more distressed by fears of Cornish pirates; and he was content to enjoy at last the fruits of his labour in peace. And thus it was that Watt's later years may be pronounced to have been the happiest of his life.

He had, indeed, lost nearly all his old friends, and often thought of them with a melancholy regret, not, however, unmingled with pleasure. But other young friends gathered about him, sat at his feet, and looked up to him with an almost reverential admiration. Among these we find Rennie and Telford the engineers, Campbell the poet, Humphry Davy, Henry Brougham, Francis Horner, and other rising men of the new generation. Lord Brougham bears testimony to Watt's habitual cheerfulness, and his enjoyment of the pleasures of society during the later years of his life. "I can speak on the point," he says, "with absolute certainty, for my own acquaintance with him commenced after my friend Gregory's decease. A few months after that event, he calmly and with his wonted acuteness discussed with me the composition of an epitaph to be inscribed on his son's tomb. In the autmnn and winter of 1805 he was a constant attendant at our Friday Club, and in all our private circles, and was the life of them all."[3]

To the close of his life Watt continued to take great pleasure in inventing. It had been the pursuit of his life, and in old age it became his hobby. "Without a hobby-horse," said he, "what is life?" He proceeded to verify his old experiments, and to live over again the history of his inventions. When Mr. Kennedy of Manchester asked him, at one of his last visits to Heathfield, if he had been able, since his retirement from business, to discover anything new in the steam-engine, he replied, "No; I am devoting the remainder of my life to perfect its details, and to ascertain whether in any respect I have been wrong."

But he did not merely confine himself to verifying his old inventions. He also contrived new ones. One of the machines that occupied his leisure hours for many years, was his machine for copying statuary. We find him busy with it in 1810, and he was still working upon it in the year of his death, nearly ten years later. The principle of the machine was to make a cutting tool or drill travel over the work to be executed, in like ratio with the motion of a guide-point placed upon the bust to be copied. It worked, as it were, with two hands; the one feeling the pattern, the other cutting the material into the required form. The object could be copied either of the full size, or reduced with the most perfect accuracy to any less size that might be required.[4] In preparing the necessary tools, Watt had the able assistance of his friend Murdock, who was always ready with his kindly suggestions and criticisms. In January, 1813, Watt wrote him, – "I have done a little figure of a boy lying down and holding out one arm, very successfully; and another boy, about six inches high, naked, and holding out both his hands, his legs also being separate. But I have been principally employed in making drawings for a complete machine, all in iron, which has been a very serious job, as invention goes on very slowly with me now. When you come home, I shall thank you for your criticisms and assistance."[5]

The material in which Watt executed his copies of statuary were various, – marble, jet, alabaster, ivory, plaster of Paris, and mahogany. Some of the specimens we have seen at Heathfield are of exquisite accuracy and finish, and show that he must have brought his copying-machine to a remarkable degree of perfection before he died. There are numerous copies of medallions of his friends, – of Dr. Black, De Luc, and Dr. Priestley; but the finest of all is a reduced bust of himself, being an exact copy of Chantrey's original plaster-cast. The head and neck are beautifully finished, but there the work has stopped, for the upper part of the chest is still in the rough. Another exquisite work, than which Watt never executed a finer, is a medallion of Locke in ivory, marked "January, 1812." There are numerous other busts, statuettes, medallions, – some finished, others half executed, and apparently thrown aside, as if the workman had been dissatisfied with his work, and waited, perhaps, until he had introduced some new improvement in his machine.

Watt took out no patent for the invention, which he pursued, as he said, merely as "a mental and bodily exercise." Neither did he publish it, – but went on working at it for several years before his intentions to construct such a machine had become known. When he had made considerable progress with it,

he learned, to his surprise, that a Mr. Hawkins, an ingenious person in his neighbourhood, had been long occupied in the same pursuit. The proposal was then
made to him that the two inventors should combine their talents and secure the
invention by taking out a joint patent. But Watt had already been too much
worried by patents to venture on taking out another at his advanced age. He
preferred prosecuting the invention at his leisure merely as an amusement; and
the project of taking out a patent for it was accordingly abandoned. It may not
be generally known that this ingenious invention of Watt has since been revived
and applied with sundry modifications by our cousins across the Atlantic, in
fashioning wood and iron in various forms; and powerful copying-machines
are now in regular use in the Government works at Enfield, where they are
employed in rapidly, accurately, and cheaply manufacturing gun-stocks!

Watt carried on the operations connected with this invention for the most
part in his Garret, a room immnediately under the roof at the kitchen end of
the house at Heathfield, and approached by a narrow staircase. It is a small
room, low in the ceiling, and lighted by a low broad window, looking into
the shrubbery. The ceiling, though low, inclines with the slope of the roof on
three sides of the room, and, being close to the slates, the place must necessarily have been very hot in summer, and very cold in winter. A stove was
placed close to the door, for the purpose of warming the apartment, as well
as enabling the occupant to pursue his experiments, being fitted with a sand-
bath and other conveniences. But the stove must have been insufficient for
heating the garret in very cold weather, and hence we find him occasionally informing his correspondents that he could not proceed further with his
machine until the weather had become milder.

His foot-lathe was fixed close to the window, fitted with all the appliances
for turning in wood and metal fifty years since; while a case of drawers fitted
into the recess on the left-hand side of the room, contained a large assortment
of screws, punches, cutters, taps, and dies. Here were neatly arranged and
stowed away many of the tools with which he worked in the early part of his
life, one of the drawers being devoted to his old "flute tools." In other divi-
sions were placed his compasses, dividers, scales, decimal weights, quadrant
glasses, and a large assortment of instrument-making tools. A ladle for melting lead, and a soldering-iron were hung ready for use near the stove.

Crucibles of metal and stone were ranged on the shelves along the opposite
side of the room, which also contained a large assortment of bottles filled with
chemicals, boxes of fossils and minerals, jars, gallipots, blowpipes, retorts, and
the various articles used in chemical analysis. In one corner of the room was a
potter's lathe. A writing-desk was placed as close to the window, for the sake

Watt's garret at Heathfield (by Percival Skelton)

of the light, as the turning-lathe would allow; and in the corner was the letter-copying machine, conveniently at hand.

In this garret Watt spent much of his time during the later period of his life, only retiring from it when it was too hot in summer, or too cold in winter to enable him to prosecute his work. For days together he would confine himself here, without even descending to his meals. He had accordingly provided himself, in addition to his various other tools, with sundry kitchen utensils, – amongst others, with a frying-pan and Dutch oven – with which he cooked his meals. For it must be explained that Mrs. Watt was a thorough martinet in household affairs, and, above all things, detested "dirt." Mrs. Schimmelpenninck says she taught her two pug-dogs never to cross the hall without first wiping their feet on the mat. She hated the sight of her husband's leather apron and soiled hands while he was engaged in his garret-work, so he kept himself out of her sight at such times as much as possible. Some notion of the rigidity of her rule may be inferred from the fact of her having had a window made in the kitchen wall, through which she could watch the servants, and observe how they were getting on with their work. Her passion for cleanliness was carried to a pitch which often fretted those about her by the restraints it imposed; but her husband, like a wise man, gently submitted to her rule. He was fond of a pinch of snuff, which Mrs. Watt detested, regarding it only as so much "dirt;" and Mr. Muirhead says she would seize and lock up the offending snuff-box whenever she could lay hands upon it. He adds that at night, when she retired from the dining-room, if Mr. Watt did not follow at the time fixed by her, a servant would enter and put out the lights, even when a friend was present, on which he would slowly rise and meekly say, "We must go." One can easily understand how, under such circumstances, Watt would enjoy the perfect liberty of his garret, where he was king, and could enjoy his pinch of snuff in peace, and make as much "dirt" with his turning-lathe, his crucibles, and his chemicals, as he chose, without dread of interruption.

One of the fears which haunted Watt as old age advanced upon him was, that his mental faculties, in the exercise of which he took so much pleasure, were deserting him. To Dr. Darwin he said, many years before, – "Of all the evils of age, the loss of the few mental faculties one possessed in youth is most grievous." To test his memory, he again began the study of German, which he had allowed himself to forget; and he speedily acquired such profioiency as enabled him to read the language with comparative ease. But he gave still stronger evidence of the integrity of his powers. When in his seventy-fifth year, he was consulted by the Glasgow Waterworks Company as to the best mode of conveying water from a peninsula across the Clyde to the Company's engines at Dalmarnock, – a difficulty which appeared to them almost insurmountable; for it was necessary to fit the pipes, through which the water passed, to the uneven and shifting bed of the river. Watt, on turning over the subject in his mind, shortly hit upon a plan, which showed that his inventive powers were unimpaired by age. Taking the tail of the lobster for his model, he devised a tube of iron similarly articulated, of which he forwarded a drawing to the Waterworks Company; and, acting upon his recommendation, they had the tube forthwith executed and laid down with complete success. Watt declined to be paid for the essential service he had thus rendered to the Waterworks Company; but the directors made handsome acknowledgment of it by presenting him with a piece of plate of the value of a hundred guineas, accompanied by the cordial expression of their thanks and esteem.

Watt did not, however, confine himself to mechanical recreations at home. In summer-time he would proceed to Cheltenham, the air of which agreed with him, and make a short stay there; or he would visit his friends in London, Glasgow, or Edinburgh. While in London, his great delight was in looking in at the shop-windows, – the best of all industrial exhibitions, – for there he saw the progress of manufacture in all articles in common use amongst the people. To a country person, the sight of the streets and shop-windows of London alone, with their display of objects of art and articles of utility, is always worth a visit. To Watt it was more interesting than passing along the finest gallery of pictures.

At Glasgow, where he stayed with his relatives the Macgregors, he took pleasure in revisiting his old haunts, dined with the College Professors,[6] and noted with lively interest the industrial progress of the place. The growth of Glasgow in the course of his lifetime had, indeed, been extraordinary, and it was in no small degree the result of his own industrial labours. The steam-engine was everywhere at work; factories had sprung up in all directions; the Broomielaw was silent no longer; the Clyde was navigable from thence to the sea, and its waters were plashed by the paddles of a thousand steamers. The old city of the tobacco lords had become a great centre of manufacturing industry; it was rich, busy, and prosperous; and the main source of its prosperity was the steam-engine. A long time had passed since Watt had first taken in hand the repair of the little Newcomen engine in Glasgow College, and afterwards laboured in the throes of his invention in his shop in the back court in King Street. There were no skilled mechanics in Glasgow then, and the death of the "old white-iron man" who helped him had been one of his sorest vexatious. Things were entirely changed now. Glasgow had already become famous for its engine-work, and its factories contained among the most skilled mechanics in the kingdom. Watt's early notion that Scotchmen were incapable of becoming first-rate mechanics, like Englishmen, was confuted by the experience of hundreds of workshops; and to none did the practical contradiction of his theory give greater pleasure than to himself. He delighted to visit the artisans at their work, and to see with his own eyes the improvements that were going forward; and when he heard of any new and ingenious arrangement of engine-power, he would hasten to call upon the mechanic who had contrived it, and make his acquaintance.

One of such calls, which Watt made during a visit to Glasgow, in 1814, has been pleasantly related by Mr. Robert Hart, who, with his brother, then carried on a small steam-engine factory in the town. "One forenoon," he says, "while we were at work, Miss Macgregor and a tall elderly gentleman came into the shop. She, without saying who he was, asked if we would show the gentleman our small engine. It was not going at the time, and was covered up. My brother uncovered it. The gentleman examined it very minutely, and put a few pointed questions, asking the reason for making her in that form. My brother, seeing he understood the subject, said that she had been so made to try what we thought was an improvement; and for this experiment we required another cistern and air-pump. He was beginning to show what was properly Mr. Watt's engine, and what was not; when, at this observation,

Miss Macgregor stopped him, saying, – 'Oh, he understands it; *this is Mr. Watt.*' I never at any time saw my brother so much excited as he was at that moment. He called on me to join them, saying, – 'This is Mr. Watt!' Up to this time I had continued to work at what I was doing when they came; and, although I had heard all that was said, I had not joined the party till I learned who he was. Our supposed improvement was to save condensing water, and was on the principle introduced by Sir John Leslie, to produce cold by evaporation in a vacuum. Mr. Watt took much interest in this experiment, and said he had tried the same thing on a larger scale, but without the vacuum, as that invention of Professor Leslie's was not known at the time. He tried it exposed to the air, and also kept wet; and at one of the large porter-breweries in London he had fitted up an apparatus of the same nature. The pipes forming his condenser were laid in the water of the Thames, but he could not keep them tight, from the expansion and contraction of the metal, as they were exposed to various temperatures." The conversation then diverged to the subject of his early experiments with the Newcomen engine, the difficulties he had encountered in finding a proper material for steam-pipes, the best method of making steam-joints, and the various means of overcoming obstacles which occur in the prosecution of mechanical experiments, in the course of which he reverted to the many temporary expedients which he had himself, adopted in his early days.

Watt was so much pleased with the intelligence of the brothers Hart, that he invited them to call upon him that evening at Miss Macgregor's, where they found him alone with the ladies. " In the course of conversation," continues Mr. Hart, "which embraced all that was new at the time, the expansion and the slow contraction of metals were touched on. This led to a discussion on iron in engine-making," in which Watt explained the practice which experience had led him to adopt as the best. The conversation then turned upon the early scene of his inventions, the room in the College, the shop in King Street, the place on Glasgow Green near the Herd's house where the first idea of a separate condenser flashed upon his mind, and the various steps by which he had worked out his invention. He went on to speak of his experience at Kinneil and Boroughstoness, of the Newcomen engine he had erected and worked, there for the purpose of gaining experience, and incidentally to many of the other interesting events in his past career. At a late hour the brothers took their leave, delighted, as they well might be, with the affability and conversableness of "the great Mr. Watt."

But it was not mechanics alone that Watt fascinated by his powers of conversation and his stores of knowledge relating to the special business of his life: he was equally at home amongst philosophers, women, and children. When close upon his eighty-second year, he formed one of a distinguished party assembled in Edinburgh, at which Sir Walter Scott, Francis Jeffrey, and others were present. He delighted the northern literati with his kindly cheerfulness, not less than he astonished them by the extent and profundity of his information. "This potent commander of the elements," says: Scott, – "this abridger of time and space, this magician, whose cloudy machinery has produced a change in the world, the effects of which, extraordinary as they are, are perhaps only now beginning to be felt, – was not only the most profound man of science, the most successful combiner of powers, and combiner of numbers, as adapted to practical purposes, – was not only one of the most generally well-informed, but one of the best and kindest of human beings. There he stood, surrounded by the little band of Northern literati, men not less tenacious, generally speaking, of their own opinions, than the national regiments are supposed to be jealous of the high character they have won upon service. Methinks I yet see and hear what I shall never see or hear again. The alert, kind, benevolent old man had his attention alive to every one's question, his information at every one's command. His talents and fancy overflowed on every subject. One gentleman was a deep philologist, he talked with him on the origin of the alphabet as if he had been coeval with Cadmus; another, a celebrated critic, you would have said the old man had studied political economy and belles-lettres all his life; of science it is unnecessary to speak, it was his own distinguished walk."[7]

Indeed, the extent of his knowledge was the wonder of all who came in contact with him. "It seemed," said Jeffrey, "as if every subject that was casually started had been that which he had been occupied in studying." Yet, though no man was more ready to communicate knowledge, none could be less ambitious of displaying it. In company, when not spoken to, he sat as if tranquilly pursuing his own meditations, with his head bent forward or leaning on his hand. But as he could not fail to be a prominent feature in any society that he entered, it was seldom that he was left outside the circle of social talk. Men of letters, men of science, artists, ladies and children, thronged about him. Once when on a visit to his friend Rennie in London, he accompanied him to an evening party at Sir George Warrender's. At first he sat by himself, quiet and abstracted, until some young ladies engaged him in conversation, which gradually turned upon the mystery of the fabrics they wore, the insignificant materials out of which they were formed, and the beauty and value given to them by the industry and ingenuity of man; and, other auditors being attracted by his descriptions, he shortly found himself the centre of a group of fair and admiring listeners."

He seemed to be alike at home on all subjects, the most recondite and the most common, the most special and the most general. Mrs. Schimmelpenninck[8] relates how he took her upon his knee when a little girl, and explained to her the principles of the hurdy-gurdy, the piano, the Pan's-pipe, and the organ; teaching her how to make a dulcimer and improve a Jew's-harp. To a Swedish artist he communicated the information that the most pliant and elastic painting-brush was to be made out of rats' whiskers. He advised ladies how to cure smoky chimneys, how to warm and ventilate dwellings, and how to obtain fast colours, while he would willingly instruct a maid-servant as to the best way of cleaning a grate.[9] A lady still living, who remembers Watt, informs us that he used to carry a carpenter's foot-rule in the side pocket of his breeches, and would occasionally bring it out in after-dinner conversation or elsewhere, to illustrate the subject under discussion.

He was full of anecdotes relating to all manner of subjects; which he was accustomed to tell in a very effective way.[10] He spoke in a low grave tone, with a broad Scottish accent. The late Mr. Murdock mentioned to us one of his favourite stories relating to two smugglers pursued by excise-men. The two smugglers had reached the mouth of a coal-pit and got into the corve-cage with their apparatus, the excisemen only coming up in time to see them descending the shaft, where they were soon out of sight. On the ascending corves coming up to the settle-board, the excise-men asked to be sent down after the smugglers, and they were sent down accordingly. Halfway down the shaft they met the smugglers in the other cage *coming up!* And so the relator kept them ascending and descending, passing and repassing each other, – his auditors being in convulsions of laughter, while he himself seemed wholly unmoved. Campbell, the poet, who paid Watt a visit in February, 1819, only six months before his death, describes him as so full of anecdote that he spent one of the most amusing days he had ever enjoyed with a man of science and a stranger to his own pursuits. To the last he was a great reader of novels; and Mrs. Watt and he had many a hearty cry over the imaginary woes of love-lorn heroes and heroines. Scott says no novel of the least celebrity escaped his perusal, and that this gifted man of science was as much addicted to productions of this sort as if he had been a very milliner's apprentice of eighteen. A lady, still living,[11] informs us that she remembers the admiration which Watt expressed for the Waverley novels, then making their appearance in rapid succession, and used to quote his opinion as a great authority for her own devotion to such works, – forgetting that, as the old frame requires the arm-chair after the heat and burden of the day, so the taxed mind needs rest and recreation after long years of study, anxiety, and labour.

Mr. Stockdale, of Carke, gives the following account of a visit which his sister, a cousin of Mr. Boulton's, paid to Heathfield in 1818, shortly before Mr. Watt's death: – "When tea was announced to Mr. Watt, he came from his 'garret,' and on being told who my sister was, he asked after her relations in the kindest way, and then sat down in his arm-chair. A cup of tea was handed to him, and alongside of it was placed a small cup containing a yellow powder, of which he took a spoonful and put it into his tea, observing that he had long been plagued with a stomach complaint, for which he had found this powder of mastich a sovereign remedy. He talked more than my sister expected. Sometimes he fell into a reverie, appearing absorbed in thought, his eyes fixed on space, and his head leaning over his chest. After a while, he retired to his study, and my sister returned to Soho." Mr. Rollins, of Birmingham, sculptor, supplies the following further reminiscence. When a youth in a local architect's office, he was sent out to Heathfield one afternoon, to submit to Mr. Watt the plans of certain proposed alterations in the parish church of Handsworth. The church stood a few fields off, and its spire rose above the trees within sight of the drawing-room windows. It was his parish church, in which his friend Boulton had been buried, and where he himself was to lie. When the young man mentioned his errand, Mr. Watt said he was just about to take his afternoon's nap. "But you can sit down there and read that newspaper, and when I have got my nap I will look at the plans." So saying he composed himself to rest in his arm-chair; the youth scarce daring to turn the page for fear of disturbing him. At length, after a short sleep, he woke full up and said, "Now let me see them." He looked over the plans, examined them in detail, and criticised them keenly. He thought the proposed alterations of a paltry character, unworthy of the wealth and importance of the parish; "Why," said he, "if these plans be carried out, preaching at Handsworth will be like pitching the word of God out of a keyhole!" When Mr. Watt's decided views as to the insufficiency of the design was reported to the committee, steps were taken greatly to enlarge it, and Handsworth Church was thus indebted to his suggestions for much of its present beauty.

He proceeded with the completion of his sculpture-copying machine until nearly the close of his life. When the weather was suitable, he would go up stairs to his garret, don his woollen surtout and leather apron, and proceed with his work. He was as fastidious as ever, and was constantly introducing new improvements. It was a hobby and a pursuit, and served him as well as any other. To M. Berthollet he wrote, – "Whatever may be its success, it has at least had the good effect of making me avoid many hours of ennui, by employing my hands when I could not employ my head, and given me some exercise when I could not go out." it also pleased him to see the invention growing under his hands as of old, though it is possible that during his later years he added but little to the machine. Indeed, it seems to have been as nearly as possible complete by the year 1817, if we may judge by the numerous exquisitely-finished specimens of reduced sculpture – busts, medallions, and statuary – laid away in the drawers of the garret at Heathfield. He took pleasure in presenting copies to his more intimate friends, jocularly describing them as "the productions of a young artist just entering his eighty-third year." Shortly after, the hand of the cunning workman was stopped by death. The machine remained unfinished, according to its author's intentions; and it is a singular testimony to the skill and perseverance of a man who had accomplished so much, that it is almost his only unfinished work.

In the autumn of 1819 he was seized by his last illness. It could scarcely be called a seizure, for he suffered little, and continued calm and tranquil, in the full possession of his faculties, almost to the last. He was conscious of his approaching end, and expressed from time to time his sincere gratitude to Divine Providence for the worldly blessings he had been permitted to enjoy, for his length of days, and his exemption from the infirmities of age. "I am very sensible," said he to the mourning friends who assembled round his deathbed, "of the attachment you show me, and I hasten to thank you for it, as I feel that I am now come to my last illness." He parted with life quietly and peacefully, on the 19th of August, 1819, in the eighty-third year of his age. He was buried near his deceased friend and partner Mr. Boulton, in Handsworth Church. Over his remains, which lie in a side aisle, was placed a monument by Chantrey, perhaps his finest work, justifying the compliment paid to the sculptor that he "cut breath;" for when first uncovered before the old servants assembled round it at Soho, it so powerfully reminded them of their old master, that they "lifted up their voices and wept."

Watt has been fortunate in his monumental honours. The colossal statue of him in Westminster Abbey, also from the chisel of Chantrey, bears upon it an epitaph from the pen of Lord Brougham, which is beyond comparison the finest lapidary inscription in the English language; and among its other signal merits, it has one which appertains rather to its subject than its author, that, lofty as is the eulogy, every word of it is true.[12] The monument was raised by public subscriptions, initiated at a meeting in London presided over by the Prime Minister, and attended by the most illustrious statesmen, men of science, men of letters, and men of art, of the time, who met for the purpose of commemorating in some suitable manner the genius of Watt. "It has ever been reckoned one of the chief honours of my life," says Lord Brougham, "that I was called upon to pen the inscription upon the noble monument thus nobly reared.

Watt was also honoured during his lifetime. Learned Societies were proud to enrol him amongst their members. He was a Fellow of the Royal Societies of London and Edinburgh, a Foreign Associate of the Institute of France, and a Member of the Batavian Society. The University of Glasgow conferred on him the degree of Doctor of Law. Lord Liverpool offered him a baronetcy; but, consistent with the simplicity of his character, he declined the honour. He was invited to serve as Sheriff on two occasions, for Staffordshire and for Radnorshire; but he strongly pleaded to be excused undertaking the office. He was "a timid old man," and hoped that he "should not have a duty imposed upon him that he was totally unfit for, nor have his grey hairs weighed down with a load of vexatious cares. My inventions," he said, "are giving employment to the best part of a million of people, and having added many millions to the national riches, I have a natural right to rest in my extreme age." His pleas were in both cases regarded as sufficient, and he was excused the office.

It is altogether unnecessary to pronounce a panegyric on the character and achievements of James Watt. This has already been done by Lord Jeffrey in language that cannot be surpassed. Sir James Macintosh placed him "at the head of all inventors in all ages and nations;" and Wordsworth the poet, twenty years after his death, said, "I look upon him, considering both the magnitude and the universality of his genius, as perhaps the most extraordinary man that this country ever produced: he never sought display, but was content to work in that quietness and humility, both of spirit and of outward circumstances, in which alone all that is truly great and good was ever done."

Watt was himself accustomned to speak of his inventions with the modesty of true genius. To a nobleman who expressed to him his wonder at the greatness of his achievements, he said, "the public only look at my success, and not on the intermediate failures and uncouth constructions which have served as steps to enable me to climb to the top of the ladder." Watt looked back upon his twenty long years of anxiety and labour before the engine succeeded, and heaved a sigh. "Without affecting any maidenly coyness," he wrote to Dr. Darwin, who proposed to eulogise him in his 'Botanic Garden,' "you really make me appear contemptible in my own eyes by considering how far short my pretensions, or those of the invention, were of the climax of human intellect, – I that know myself to be inferior to the greatest part of enlightened men in most things. If I have excelled, I think now it has been by chance, and by the neglects of others. Preserve the dignity of a philosopher and historian; relate the facts, and leave posterity to judge. If I merit it, some of my countrymen, inspired by the *amor patriæ*, may say, 'Hoc a Scoto factum fuit.'"

Although the true inventor, like the true poet, is born, not made, – and although Watt pursued his inventions because he found his highest pleasure in inventing, – his greatest achievements were accomplished by unremitting application and industry. He was a keen observer and an incessant experimenter. "Observare" was the motto he deliberately adopted; and it expresses the principle and success of his life. He was always on the watch for facts, noting and comparing them. He took nothing for granted; and accepted no conclusions save on experimental evidence. "Nature can be conquered," he said, "if we can but find out her weak side." His patience was inexhaustible. He was never baffled by failure, from which he declared that he learnt more than from success. "It is a great thing," he once observed to Murdock, "to find out what will not do: it leads to one finding out what *will* do."

"Give me facts," he once said to Boulton, "I am sick of theory: give me actual facts." Yet, indispensable though facts are, theory is scarcely less so in invention; and it was probably because Watt was a great theorist, that he was a great inventor. His invention of the separate condenser was itself the result of a theory, the soundness of which he proved by experiment. So with the composition of water, the theory of which he at once divined from the experiments of Priestley. He continued theorising during the whole progress of his invention of the steam-engine. New facts suggested new arrangements and the application of entirely new principles, until in course of time the engine of Newcomen became completely transformed.

Watt's engine was not an invention merely – it might almost be called a creation. "The part which he played," says M. Bataille, "in the mechanical application of the force of steam, can only be compared to that of Newton in astronomy, and of Shakspeare in poetry. And is not invention the poetry of science? It is only when we compare Watt with other mechanicians that we are struck by his immense superiority, we compare him, for example, with Smeaton, who was, perhaps, after him, the man who had advanced the farthest in industrial mechanism. Smeaton began, about the same time as Watt, his inquiries as to the best means of improving the steam-engine. He worked long and patiently, but in an entirely technical spirit. While he was working out his improvements, Watt had drawn forth from his fertile imagination all those brilliant inventions to which we owe the effective working steam-engine. In a word, Smeaton knew how to improve, but Watt knew how to create."[13]

As for the uses of the steam-engine, they are too widely known to stand in need of illustration. Had Watt, at the outset of his career, announced to mankind that he would invent a power that should drain their mines, blow their furnaces, roll and hammer their metals, thrash and grind their corn, saw their timber, drive their looms and spindles, print their books, impel ships across the ocean, and perform the thousand offices in which steam is now regularly employed, he would have been regarded as an enthusiast, if not as a madman. Yet all this the steam-engine has done and is now doing. It has widely extended the dominion of man over inanimate nature, and given him an almost unbounded supremacy over the materials which enter into his daily use. It has increased his power, his resources, and his enjoyments. It is the most universal and untiring of labourers, – the steam-power of Great Britain alone being estimated as equal to the manual labour of upwards of four hundred millions of men, or more than double the number of males supposed to inhabit the globe.[14] It is, indeed, no exaggeration to say that the steam-engine of Watt is without exception, the greatest invention of modern times; and that it has been instrumental in effecting the most remarkable revolution in all departments of industry that the world has ever seen.

Some months since, we visited the little garret at Heathfield in which Watt pursued the investigations of his later years. The room had been carefully locked up since his death, and had only once been swept out. Every thing lay very much as he left it. The piece of iron he was last employed in turning lay on the lathe. The ashes of the last fire were in the grate, the last bit of coal was in the scuttle. The Dutch oven was in its place over the stove, and the frying-pan in which he cooked his meal was hanging by its accustomed nail. Many objects lay about or in the drawers, indicating the pursuits which had been interrupted by death, – busts, medallions, and figures, waiting to be copied by the sculpture-machine, – many medallion moulds, a store of plaster of Paris, and a box of plaster casts from London, the contents of which do not seem to have been disturbed. Here are Watt's ladles for melting lead, his foot-rule, his glue-pot, his hammer. Reflecting mirrors, an extemporised camera with the lenses mounted on pasteboard, and many camera-glasses laid about, indicate interrupted experiments in optics. There are quadrant-glasses, compasses, scales, weights, and sundry boxes of mathematical instruments, once doubtless highly prized. In one place a model of the governor, in another of the parallel motion, and in a

little box, fitted with wooden cylinders mounted with paper and covered
with figures, is what we suppose to be a model of his proposed calculating
machine. On the shelves are minerals and chemicals in pots and jars, on
which the dust of nearly half a century has settled. The moist substances
have long since dried up, the putty has been turned to stone, and the paste
to dust. On one shelf we come upon a dish in which lies a withered bunch
of grapes. On the floor, in a corner, near to where Watt sat and worked,
is a hair-trunk – a touching memorial of a long past love and a long dead
sorrow. It contains all poor Gregory's school-books, – his first attempts
at writing, his boy's drawings of battles, his first school exercises down
to his College themes, his delectuses, his grammars, his dictionaries, and
his class books, – brought into this retired room, where the father's eye
could rest upon them. Near at hand is the sculpture-machine, on which
he continued working to the last. Its wooden framing is worm-eaten and
dropping into dust, like the hands which made it. But though the great
workman has gone to rest, with all his griefs and cares, and his handiwork

Watt's statue in
Handsworth Church

is fast crumbling to decay, the spirit of his work, the thought which he put into his inventions, still survives, and will probably continue to influence the destinies of his race for all time to come.

NOTES

1 "Though I was in some measure prepared," he wrote, "yet I had hoped that he might have recovered from this fit, as he had done from other severe ones. Such wishes, however, were selfish; for in respect to himself, none of his friends could rationally have desired the prolongation in torture, without hope of relief. May he therefore rest in peace; and when our end approaches us, may we have as little to reproach us and as much to console us as he had." – Mr. Watt to his son, 22nd August, 1809. Boulton MSS.

2 Watt to M. Robinson Boulton, 23rd August, 1809.

3 Lord Brougham's 'Lives of Philosophers of the Time of George III'. The Friday Club of Edinburgh was so called because of the evening of the week on which it met and supped. It numbered amongst its members Professor Playfair, Walter Scott, Henry Brougham, Francis Jeffrey, Leonard Horner, Lord Corehouse, Sir W. Drummond, and others known to fame. Watt was a regular attender of the Club during his Edinburgh visits.

4 In March, 1811, he wrote Dr. P. Wilson as follows: – "For want of other news I must now say a little upon my late invention, with which Dr. Herschel seemed much pleased. It continues to succeed, and I have realised some more of my ideas on the subject. I have executed several small busts in alabaster, not being strong enough to work in marble. I had a difficulty in getting the several segments which form the surface of the bust to meet, but have now accomplished it. It requires a very accurate construction of the machine, and a very accurate adjustment of the tools, so that their axes may be always equally distant from each other, as the axes of the pattern and that of the stone to be out are. I have also made some improvements in the tools for cutting marble and other hard stones. The things you saw were done by the tool and the guide-point, moving in parallel lines, straight or circular, and very near one another; (an illustration of Euclid's position, that the motion of a point generates a line, and the motion of a line generates a surface). I have now contrived, though not executed, that the two points, the guide and the cutting point, may move in any line, whether straight or crooked, square or diagonal, so that an inscription might be cut in stone from a drawing on paper." – Cited in Muirhead's 'Mechanical inventions of James Watt,' ii. 329–30.

5   Cited in Muirhead's 'Mechanical Inventions,1 &c., ii. 340–1. These
    drawings must be in existence, and of great interest, as showing the vigour
    of Watt's inventive faculty at this late period of his life.

6   In 1808 Mr. Watt made over 300*l.* to the College by Deed of Gift, for
    the purpose of founding a prize for students in Natural Science, as some
    acknowledgment of "the many favours" which the College had conferred
    upon him. – In 1818 he gave to the Town of Greenock 100*l.* for the
    purpose of purchasing books for the Mathematical School. "My intention
    in this donation," he observed in his letter to Mr. Anderson of Greonock,
    "is to form the beginning of a scientific library, for the instruction of
    the youth of Greenock; and I hope it will prompt others to add to it,
    and to render my townsmen as eminent for their knowledge as they are
    for their spirit of enterprise." Watt's idea has since been carried out by
    his townsmen, and the Watt Library is now one of the most valuable
    institutions of Greenock. It ought to be added, that the erection of the
    building was mainly due to the munificence of Mr. Watt's son, the late
    James Watt, Esq., of Aston Hall, near Birmingham. A marble statue of
    Watt, by Chantrey, is placed in the Library, with an inscription from the
    pen of Lord Jeffrey.

7   Answer by the author of 'Waverley' to the Epistle Dedicatory of 'The
    Monastery.'

8   'Autobiography of Mrs. Schimmelpenninck,' 3rd ed. 35.

9   The following anecdote is told by Mrs. Schimmelpenninck – "During
    the peace of Amiens, Mr. Watt visited Paris. It so happened that while
    going through one of the palaces, I believe the Tuileries, a French
    housemaid appeared much perplexed concerning some bright English
    stoves which had just been received, and which she did not know how to
    clean. An English gentleman was standing by, to whom she appealed for
    information. This was Charles James Fox. He could give no help; "But,"
    said he, "here is a fellow-countryman of mine who will tell you all about
    it." This was Mr. Watt, to whom he was at the moment talking; and who
    proceeded to give the housemaid full instructions as to the best mode of
    cleaning her grate. This anecdote I have often heard Mrs. Watt tell with
    great diversion."

10 Lord Brougham says, "His voice was deep and low, and if somewhat
    monotonous, it yet seemed in harmony with the weight and the beauty of
    his discourse, through which, however, there also ran a current of a lighter
    kind; for he was mirthful, temperately jocular, nor could anything to more
    advantage set off the living anecdotes of men and things, with which the

grave texture of his talk was interwoven, than his sly and quiet humour, both of mind and look, in recounting them." – 'Lives of Philosophers of the Time of George III.'

11 "I remember, as a young girl," she says, "the pleasant dinners and people I have seen at Soho. I remember being present one day when Bertrand de Moleville, the exiled minister of Louis XVI, left the dinner-table to make an omelette, which was, of course, pronounced 'excellent.' That man then gave me a lifelong lesson, – of the power of enjoyment and of giving pleasure by his cheerful bright manner and conversation, under such sad circumstances as exile and poverty. I looked at him with great admiration, and I have his face distinct before me now, though I saw him only that once."

12 The following is the inscription:

Not to perpetuate a name
Which must endure while the peaceful arts flourish,
but to show
That mankind have learned to honour those
who best deserve their gratitude,
the King,
his ministers, and many of the nobles
and commoners of the realm,
raised this monument to
James Watt,
who directing the force of an original genius
early exercised in philosophic research
to the improvement of the steam-engine,
enlarged the resources of this country,
increased the power of man,
and rose to an eminent place
among the most illustrious followers of science,
and the real benefactors of the world.
Born at Greenock, 1736.
Died at Heathfield, in Staffordshire, 1819.

13 E. M. Bataille, 'Traité des Machines à Vapeur.' Paris, 1847–9.

14 What the steam-engine has done for the West is well known. What is yet expected from it in the East may be gathered from the few pregnant words lately uttered by Hassan Ali Khan, Persian Ambassador at the Court of France, at the recent celebration in Paris of a national festival instituted nineteen centuries before the birth of Christ. Having recalled the minds

of his hearers to the early fire worship of his country, which sprang from
the primeval idolatry, he proceeded to say that it was still to Fire that he
fondly looked for the regeneration of Persia. Fire had changed the face of
Europe. In the steam-engine, the railroad, the electric spark, the screw or
paddle ship, far more than in gunpowder or rifled canon, fire was the great
benefactor that would bless one day the land of his forefathers, who had
instinctively worshipped that element in secret anticipation of what was to
come.

Handsworth Church, the burial-place of Boulton, Watt and Murdock
(by Percival Skelton)

Also available from Nonsuch Publishing

For forthcoming titles and sales information see

www.nonsuch-publishing.com